Chemistry
Problems and Solutions

At Stride, Inc. (NYSE: LRN)—formerly K12 Inc.—we are reimagining lifelong learning as a rich, deeply personal experience that prepares learners for tomorrow. Since its inception, Stride has been committed to removing barriers that impact academic equity and to providing high-quality education for anyone—particularly those in underserved communities. The company has transformed the teaching and learning experience for millions of people by providing innovative, high-quality, tech-enabled education solutions, curriculum, and programs directly to students, schools, the military, and enterprises in primary, secondary, and post-secondary settings. Stride is a premier provider of K-12 education for students, schools, and districts, including career learning services through middle and high school curriculum. Providing a solution to the widening skills gap in the workplace and student loan crisis, Stride equips students with real world skills for in-demand jobs with career learning. For adult learners, Stride delivers professional skills training in healthcare and technology, as well as staffing and talent development for Fortune 500 companies. Stride has delivered millions of courses over the past decade and serves learners in all 50 states and more than 100 countries. The company is a proud sponsor of the Future of School, a nonprofit organization dedicated to closing the gap between the pace of technology and the pace of change in education. More information can be found at stridelearning.com, K12.com, destinationsacademy.com, galvanize.com, techelevator.com, and medcerts.com.

Book Staff and Contributors

Daniel Franck
Senior Content Specialist

Jane Willan
Content Specialist

Suzanne Montazer
Art Director

Jayoung Cho
Print Designer

Christopher Yates
Cover Designer

Patrick Keeney
Instructional Designer

Susan Raley
Quality Control Specialist

Jim Miller
Designer

Elia Ben-Ari
Text Editor

Alexandra E. Haase
Project Manager

Bror Saxberg
Chief Learning Officer

John Holdren
Senior Vice President for Content and Curriculum

Maria Szalay
Senior Vice President for Product Development

Tom DiGiovanni
Senior Director, Product Development

Kim Barcas
Creative Director

Jeff Burridge
Managing Editor

Sally Russell
Senior Manager, Media

Chris Frescholtz
Senior Project Manager, High School

Corey Maender
Program Manager, High School

Lisa Dimaio Iekel
Production Manager

John G. Agnone
Director of Publications

Illustration Credits

All illustrations © Stride, Inc. unless otherwise noted

Front cover: (chair) © Berlinfoto/Dreamstime; (welding) © Inger Anne Hulbækdal/Dreamstime; (knee) © James Group Studios/iStockphoto.com; (smelting) © Oleg Fedorenko/Dreamstime; (stormy weather) © Michal Koziarski/iStockphoto.com; (fireworks) © Scott Cooley Photography/iStockphoto.com; (VW car) © Anne Clark/iStockphoto.com; (periodic table) © Thinkstock/Jupiterimages; (test tube) © Photos.com/Jupiterimages

Contents: iv (chemistry) © mrloz/iStockphoto.com; (smelting) © Mikhail Olykainen/BigStockPhoto.com

978-1-60153-029-5

Printed by Sheridan KY, Versailles, KY, USA, May 2022.

Contents

How to Use This Book   vi

1 Chemistry and Society   2

2 Matter and Energy   4

3 Pure Substances   6

4 Mixtures   8

5 Properties of Substances   10

6 Problem Solving in Chemistry   12

7 Metric System: Base Units   14

8 Metric System: Derived Units   16

9 Graphing   18

10 Scientific Methods in Chemistry   20

11 Early Theories of the Atom   22

12 The Nuclear Atom   24

13 Atomic Number and Mass Number   26

14 Ions   28

15 Isotopes and Atomic Mass   30

16 The Bohr Atom   32

17 Electron Orbitals   34

18 The Quantum Atom and Atomic Spectra   36

19 Atomic Number and the Periodic Law   38

20 The Periodic Table   40

21 Electron Arrangement Patterns   42

22 Trends Within the Periodic Table   44

23 Metals   48

24 Nonmetals   50

25 Metalloids   52

26 Inner Transition Metals   54

27 Monatomic Ions   56

28 Polyatomic Ions   58

29 The Ionic Bond and Salts   60

30 Properties of Ionic Compounds   62

31 Naming Ionic Compounds   64

32 Bonding in Metals   66

33 The Covalent Bond and Molecules   **68**

34 Lewis Dot Structures   **72**

35 Molecular Shapes   **74**

36 Van der Waals Forces   **78**

37 The Conservation of Mass   **80**

38 Balancing Chemical Equations   **82**

39 Combustion Reactions   **84**

40 Synthesis Reactions   **86**

41 Decomposition Reactions   **88**

42 Single-Displacement Reactions   **90**

43 Double-Displacement Reactions   **92**

44 Oxidation-Reduction Reactions   **94**

45 Stoichiometry and Its Uses   **98**

46 Mole-Number Relationships   **100**

47 Mole-Mass Relationships   **102**

48 Mole-Volume Relationships   **104**

49 Moles and Chemical Equations   **106**

50 Calculating Yields of Reactions   **108**

51 Percent Yield   **112**

52 The Behavior of Gases   **114**

53 Boyle's Law   **116**

54 Charles's Law   **118**

55 Gay-Lussac's Law   **120**

56 The Ideal Gas Law   **122**

57 Absolute Zero   **126**

58 Dalton's Law of Partial Pressures   **128**

59 Graham's Law of Effusion   **130**

60 Phase Diagrams   **132**

61 Some Properties of Liquids   **134**

62 Some Properties of Solids   **136**

63 Solutions   **138**

64 The Dissolving Process   **140**

65 Molarity and Mole Fraction   **142**

66 Molality and Mass Percent   **146**

67 Colligative Properties   **148**

68 Separating Solutions   **152**

69 Properties of Acids and Bases   **154**

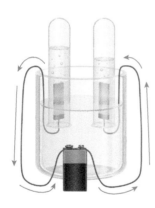

70 Arrhenius Acids and Bases **156**

71 Brønsted-Lowry and Lewis Acids and Bases **158**

72 Measuring Acids and Bases **160**

73 Titration **164**

74 Strengths of Acids and Bases **166**

75 The Conservation of Energy **168**

76 Measuring the Flow of Heat **170**

77 Specific Heat **172**

78 Changes in Enthalpy **174**

79 Writing Thermochemical Equations **176**

80 Heat During Changes of State **178**

81 Hess's Law **180**

82 Reaction Rates and Energy of Activation **184**

83 Factors Affecting Reaction Rates **186**

84 Collision Theory **188**

85 Equilibrium **190**

86 Le Châtelier's Principle **194**

87 Spontaneous Reactions **198**

88 Entropy and Free Energy **200**

89 Electrochemical Processes **202**

90 Voltaic Cells **204**

91 Dry Cells **206**

92 Electrolytic Cells **208**

93 Hydrocarbons and Other Organic Chemicals **210**

94 Polymers **216**

95 Carbohydrates and Fats **218**

96 Proteins and Nucleic Acids **222**

97 Forces Within the Nucleus **226**

98 Radioactivity and Half-Life **228**

99 Transmutation of Elements **232**

100 Nuclear Fission and Fusion **234**

General Information **236**

Problem-Set Information **238**

Answer Key **244**

Periodic Table **256**

How to Use This Book

This book has been designed so that you can practice solving chemistry problems in a systematic, step-by-step manner. Each problem set follows the same format.

Take a minute to study these two pages; they offer you a chance to see the format of each problem set. Read the numbered text in order. You will then be able to understand the best way to approach each problem set. When doing a problem set, be sure to do each task one after the other, because all of the information on a page contributes to your success in solving chemistry problems.

6 These items remind you of some of the basic knowledge to keep in mind when solving each problem. They are reminders of important information, so be sure you understand each one before proceeding.

5 This box lists the objectives you are to master when doing the problems. Read them carefully, because they state the challenge that is set out for you.

1 This green tab shows the problem set number. Use it for easy reference.

Problem Set 47

2 The problem set title tells you the subject matter of the problems.

Mole-Mass Relationships

3 This bold text gives you the primary content of the page. It summarizes the most important concept of this set of problems.

You can use the mole to relate the mass of an individual atom or molecule to the mass of a sample of a substance made up of that atom or molecule.

Chemists must often compare quantities of different substances. The same mass of different substances may contain very different numbers of atoms or molecules. Therefore, it is more accurate to use the mole to compare macroscopic quantities of substances. We can calculate the molar mass of a substance—the mass of one mole of the substance—from its chemical formula and the average atomic masses of the elements in it. If we know a substance's molar mass, we can determine the number of moles of the substance in a given sample.

4 This text further explains important concepts to keep in mind when doing the problems.

OBJECTIVE

- Use the mole to solve molar mass and sample mass problems.

EXAMPLE 1

Calculate the Molar Mass of a Compound

Oseltamivir ($C_{16}H_{28}N_2O_4$) is a drug for the treatment of influenza infections ("flu"). What is the molar mass of oseltamivir?

Solution

1 **Collect** List the molar masses of the elements in the compound.

Element	Average Atomic Mass (amu)
Carbon	12.011
Hydrogen	1.0079
Nitrogen	14.007
Oxygen	15.999

2 **Strategize and Calculate** Multiply the average atomic mass of each element by the number of atoms of that element in one molecule of oseltamivir. The mass of the compound is the sum of the total masses.

Total mass of carbon in the molecule $= 16 \times 12.011 = 192.18$ amu
Total mass of hydrogen in the molecule $= 28 \times 1.0079 = 28.221$ amu
Total mass of nitrogen in the molecule $= 2 \times 14.007 = 28.014$ amu
Total mass of oxygen in the molecule $= 4 \times 15.999 = 63.996$ amu

Total mass of one molecule of oseltamivir $= 312.41$ amu

3 **Solve** The mass of one molecule of oseltamivir is 312.41 amu, so the molar mass of oseltamivir is 312.41 g/mol.

REMEMBER

THE MOLE

- The mass of one mole of a substance in grams is the same as the mass of one atom or molecule of the substance in atomic mass units.

- One mole of a substance contains 6.023×10^{23} atoms or molecules of that substance.

- The molar mass of a substance is the mass of one mole of the substance. It is given in grams per mole, or g/mol.

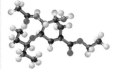

In this model of the chemical structure of oseltamivir, carbon atoms are black, hydrogen atoms are white, nitrogen atoms are blue, and oxygen atoms are red.

8 Don't forget to read the example's title. It will focus your mind on exactly what you are attempting to do.

7 Before you attempt to do any assigned problems, work through each example. Use a pencil and paper, and write out each solution as you go. Reading the example is not enough; for best results, work out the example on the page as you read.

9 Each chemisty problem in each example follows a series of steps that must be performed in sequence.

Read each step carefully.

Write all work on your own paper as you go.

If necessary, go back and do the example again until you understand each step.

Each example prepares you to solve problems in the problem set, and each one examines a different type of problem. You will achieve the best results if you do each example slowly and carefully and *write* each example as you proceed.

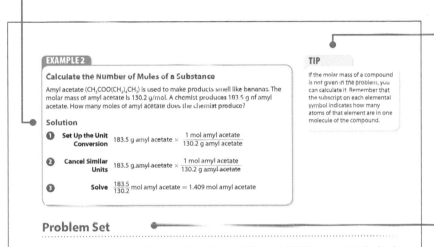

EXAMPLE 2

Calculate the Number of Moles of a Substance

Amyl acetate ($CH_3COO(CH_2)_4CH_3$) is used to make products smell like bananas. The molar mass of amyl acetate is 130.2 g/mol. A chemist produces 183.5 g of amyl acetate. How many moles of amyl acetate does the chemist produce?

Solution

❶ Set Up the Unit Conversion 183.5 g amyl acetate $\times \dfrac{1 \text{ mol amyl acetate}}{130.2 \text{ g amyl acetate}}$

❷ Cancel Similar Units 183.5 g amyl acetate $\times \dfrac{1 \text{ mol amyl acetate}}{130.2 \text{ g amyl acetate}}$

❸ Solve $\dfrac{183.5}{130.2}$ mol amyl acetate = 1.409 mol amyl acetate

TIP

If the molar mass of a compound is not given in the problem, you can calculate it. Remember that the subscript on each elemental symbol indicates how many atoms of that element are in one molecule of the compound.

10 The tips will guide you as you work through each problem. If you get stuck, the tip can get you moving again.

11 These are the problems you will be asked to solve. There are six problems in some problem sets and nine in others. They are arranged from least to most challenging; as a rule, problem 1 is easier than problem 6. The problems labeled **Challenge** are the most difficult, and often require a longer time to complete.

Problem Set

1. The formula for sucrose is $C_{12}H_{22}O_{11}$. What is the molar mass of sucrose?

2. A chemical reaction produces 56.2 g of iron sulfide (molar mass 87.92 g/mol). How many moles of iron sulfide does the reaction produce?

3. A student needs 1.52 mol of sodium hydroxide (molar mass 40.00 g/mol). How many grams of sodium hydroxide are required?

4. Chlorophyll allows plants to carry out photosynthesis. There are two forms of chlorophyll: chlorophyll *a* ($C_{55}H_{72}O_5N_4Mg$) and chlorophyll *b* ($C_{55}H_{70}O_6N_4Mg$). What is the difference in molar mass between these two forms?

5. A chemical engineer needs 52.4 mol of acetone (C_3H_6O). How many grams of acetone are needed?

6. A chemist needs 0.035 mol of copper(II) sulfate ($CuSO_4$). The chemist has 785 mg of copper(II) sulfate. How many more grams of copper(II) sulfate does the chemist need?

7. **Challenge** A biologist grows a turmeric plant in an atmosphere containing $^{14}CO_2$, so all the carbon-containing compounds in the plant contain only carbon-14 (^{14}C). What would be the difference in mass between one mole of curcumin ($C_{21}H_{20}O_6$) produced by this plant and one mole of curcumin produced by a plant grown in a normal atmosphere? (Hint: The molar mass of carbon-14 is 14.003 g/mol.)

8. **Challenge** In rocks, the mineral albite ($NaAlSi_3O_8$) can react with carbon dioxide and water to form the mineral kaolinite ($Al_2Si_2O_5(OH)_4$) as well as several other products. Two molecules of albite are required to form each molecule of kaolinite. If 1.49 kg of albite completely reacts with carbon dioxide and water, how many grams of kaolinite will form?

9. **Challenge** One mole of $Pb(NO_3)_2$ can react with two moles of KI to produce one mole of PbI_2 and two moles of KNO_3. How many grams of KI are required to completely react with 45.3 mg of $Pb(NO_3)_2$?

Note Many problems involve numeric calculations. Have a calculator handy when doing the problems. Most problems can be solved with a simple calculator that can do arithmetic. Some problem sets, such as those involving pH, require a scientific calculator that can do logarithmic calculations.

Answers You can find the answers to all odd-numbered problems on pages 244–255 of this book. Students using the K12 Inc.'s High School Chemistry program can find full, worked-out answers to all problems in the online Solution Key for each problem set.

Chemistry and Society

Since the study of chemistry began centuries ago, this science has branched into several different specialties that help us understand our world and better our lives.

Chemistry is the study of the materials around us. Chemists strive to understand the matter that these materials are made of, how matter is structured, and how different types of matter interact. Modern chemistry probably got its start around the eighteenth century, when scientists began to characterize elements and categorize the chemical reactions they observed. Since then, chemistry has branched into five main specialties: organic chemistry, the study of carbon-containing compounds; inorganic chemistry, the study of compounds that don't contain carbon; biochemistry, the study of the chemistry of living things; physical chemistry, the study of the physics of chemistry; and analytical chemistry, the study of the physical and chemical properties of matter, including its composition and structure. Each of these branches of chemistry has given new insight into the materials that make up our world and given us new ways to use the materials around us.

OBJECTIVES

- Define the study of chemistry.
- Identify the main branches of chemistry.
- Explain how chemistry has contributed to society and our way of life.

EXAMPLE 1

Identify the Branches of Chemistry

A chemist is developing a tool to measure the weight and structure of different types of salt. What kind of chemist is she?

Solution

1 Recall Relevant Information The chemist wants to measure weight and structure, which are physical and chemical properties of a material. Remember what chemists in the different branches of chemistry study: organic chemists study carbon-containing compounds; inorganic chemists study compounds that do not contain carbon; biochemists study the chemistry of living things; physical chemists study the physical basis of chemical behavior; and analytical chemists study the physical and chemical properties of matter.

2 Solve This chemist is developing a tool to measure the properties of a chemical, so she is probably an analytical chemist.

REMEMBER

BRANCHES OF CHEMISTRY

- Organic chemists study carbon-containing compounds.
- Inorganic chemists study compounds that don't contain carbon.
- Biochemists study the chemistry of living things.
- Physical chemists study the physics of chemistry.
- Analytical chemists study matter's physical and chemical properties.

EXAMPLE 2

Identify How Chemistry Benefits Other Sciences

Doctors have complicated jobs that bring together many areas of science, including chemistry. Which branches of chemistry might a doctor use?

Solution

1 **Identify Connections**   Think of the parts of a doctor's job and how those parts might relate to chemistry. A doctor analyzes the content of bodily fluids, including blood and urine, and analyzing chemical composition is a part of analytical chemistry. The human body is a living thing, and studying the chemistry of living things is biochemistry. Almost all the molecules that make up the human body contain carbon, so a doctor needs to understand organic chemistry. Some medicines that a doctor prescribes don't contain carbon, so a doctor may also need to learn inorganic chemistry.

2 **Solve**   On any given day at the job, a doctor might use analytical chemistry, biochemistry, organic chemistry, and inorganic chemistry.

TIP

The sciences are very interconnected. Many different kinds of scientists use chemistry in their jobs. In addition, chemists often use other kinds of science in their jobs.

Problem Set

1. A chemist is studying the compounds in blood. What branch or branches of chemistry may the chemist use? Explain your answer.

2. What type of chemist studies how materials conduct electricity?

3. What branches of chemistry might a chemist who designs new types of makeup use?

4. What branches of chemistry do scientists use to design cell phones?

5. **Challenge**   How has chemistry contributed to what we eat?

6. **Challenge**   Chemistry has many subspecialties, such as geochemistry and astrochemistry. If the prefix *astro-* means star, what do astrochemists study?

Matter and Energy

Matter exists in different physical states. The addition or removal of different types of energy can produce physical or chemical changes in matter.

Matter as we experience it in our daily lives exists in one of three physical states: solid, liquid, or gas. Each state has specific properties. Solids are rigid and have fixed shapes and volumes. Liquids have fixed volumes, but not fixed shapes. They take the shapes of their containers. Gases have neither fixed shapes nor fixed volumes. They expand to fill their containers. When changes in energy affect matter, it can change its form. Most physical and chemical changes require the addition or release of energy, such as heat energy or electrical energy. Changes in matter are either physical changes or chemical changes. A physical change does not affect the identity of a substance. Physical changes include changes of state. In contrast, a chemical change transforms a substance into a different substance.

OBJECTIVES

- Define the states of matter.
- Give examples of solids, liquids, and gases.
- Compare and contrast physical and chemical changes.
- Identify the role of energy in physical and chemical changes.

REMEMBER

STATES OF MATTER

- Another way to say that a gas takes the shape of its container is to say that it is compressible—that is, its volume will decrease when pressure is put on it. Solids and liquids are not compressible.

- A fourth state of matter, plasma, also exists. It consists of charged particles at extremely high temperatures. Plasmas are rare on earth.

- Changing from one state to another is a physical change because the material in question does not change into another material.

- Changing to a different state of matter requires a material to absorb or release energy. Changing a material from solid to liquid or from liquid to gas requires the material to absorb energy. Changing a material from gas to liquid or from liquid to solid requires the material to lose energy.

EXAMPLE 1

Describe States of Matter

A scientist is studying three samples of matter. The table shows the scientist's observations about the samples. Identify the most likely state of each sample.

Sample	Shape	Volume (mL)
1	Takes the shape of its container	15.0
2	Spherical	25.0
3	Takes the shape of its container	Fills the full volume of its container

Solution

1 Recall Relevant Information Remember the properties of solids, liquids, and gases. A solid has a definite shape and volume. A liquid has a definite volume, but not a definite shape. A gas has neither a definite shape nor a definite volume.

2 Solve Sample 1 has a definite volume, but not a definite shape, so it must be a liquid. Sample 2 has a definite shape and a definite volume, so it is a solid. Sample 3 has neither a definite volume nor a definite shape, so it is a gas.

EXAMPLE 2

Decide Whether a Change Is Physical or Chemical

When sucrose ($C_{12}H_{22}O_{11}$) dissolves in water, it gives the water a sweet taste. If you allow the water to evaporate, the sucrose is left behind. When sucrose burns, it becomes black and crumbly and loses its sweet taste. Which of these changes is physical, and which is chemical?

Like physical changes, chemical changes involve the absorption or release of energy. Unlike most physical changes, most chemical changes are difficult to undo.

Solution

1 **Recall Relevant Information** A physical change is one that alters a material's form but not the molecules that make it up. A chemical change alters the molecules that make up a material. When sugar dissolves in water, its molecules do not change—they become suspended in the liquid. Dissolved sugar can be recovered easily by evaporating the water. When sugar burns, it undergoes a chemical reaction with air that changes its molecular properties. It is difficult to return burned sugar to its previous form.

2 **Solve** Because dissolving sucrose in water does not change the chemical composition of either the sucrose or the water, it is a physical change. Because burning sucrose changes the sucrose into different substances, it is a chemical change.

Problem Set

1. What is the normal state of matter for common kitchen baking soda ($NaHCO_3$)?

2. When rubbing alcohol (C_3H_8O) changes from a liquid to a gas, must the liquid rubbing alcohol absorb or release energy for the process to occur?

3. A student wants to determine whether a certain substance is a liquid or a gas. What property of the substance should the student examine? Explain your answer.

4. A scientist melts solid iron into a liquid, then shapes it into a block and lets it cool. After several weeks, the iron block rusts. Identify the physical and chemical changes that took place.

5. **Challenge** The state of a substance is determined by the arrangement of the particles (atoms, ions, or molecules) that make up the substance. In some substances, the particles cannot move very much. In other substances, the particles can move past one another but they cannot move too far from one another. In yet other substances, the particles are so far apart that they do not interact very much. Which state of matter is associated with each of these particle arrangements? Explain your answer.

6. **Challenge** Sweat is liquid water that your skin secretes. As the sweat on your skin evaporates, it helps cool your body. Use what you know about heat transfer during state changes to explain why the evaporation of sweat cools your body.

Pure Substances

Compounds and elements are pure substances.

Scientists refer to elements and compounds as *pure substances*. Pure substances are made of only one type of atom, molecule, or formula unit. A molecule is composed of two or more atoms that are bonded together by sharing electrons. Elements are made of only one kind of atom and cannot be broken down into simpler substances by chemical processes. Compounds are made of atoms of more than one element. They can be broken down into elements by chemical processes.

OBJECTIVE

- Use chemical formulas to distinguish between elements and compounds.

EXAMPLE 1

Identify Elements, Compounds, Atoms, and Molecules

The following are chemical formulas of four pure substances: Co (cobalt), CO_2 (carbon dioxide), O_3 (ozone), and H_2O (water). Which substances are compounds? Which substances are elements? Which formula(s) represent single atoms, and which represent molecules? Explain your answers.

Solution

1 Define Recall the definitions of elements, compounds, atoms, and molecules. Compounds contain atoms of more than one element. Elements contain only one kind of atom. An atom is the smallest unit of an element that has all the properties of that element. Molecules contain more than one atom.

2 Apply Definitions Compare the pure substances in the question with the definitions you've recalled.

Substance	Number of Atoms	More Than One Kind of Atom?
Co	1	No
CO_2	3	Yes
O_3	3	No
H_2O	3	Yes

3 Solve CO_2 and H_2O are both made of different kinds of atoms, so they are compounds. Co and O_3 are both made of a single kind of atom, so they are both elements. Co represents a single atom. CO_2, H_2O, and O_3 all represent molecules, because they contain more than one atom.

REMEMBER

PURE SUBSTANCES

- Elements and compounds are pure substances.

- An atom is the smallest unit of an element that still has the properties of that element.

- Compounds can be separated into their component elements only by chemical processes.

TIP

The word *molecule* refers to two or more atoms that are bound together in a specific way: by sharing electrons. In many compounds, however, atoms form bonds in a different way: by exchanging electrons. Scientists use the term *formula unit*, instead of *molecule*, to refer to the smallest unit of these types of compounds.

EXAMPLE 2

Write Chemical Formulas for Elements and Compounds

Sodium chloride, or table salt, is a compound made of the elements sodium and chlorine. Each formula unit of sodium chloride is made of one atom of sodium and one atom of chlorine. (These atoms are not joined together by a covalent bond, and thus sodium chloride is not a molecule.) The two elements can be separated by running an electric current through a solution of sodium chloride in water. Chlorine gas bubbles out of the solution at one electrode, and sodium metal is deposited at the other electrode. Chlorine gas exists as molecules made of two atoms of chlorine. Sodium metal exists as atoms. Write the chemical formulas for sodium chloride, chlorine gas, and sodium metal.

Solution

1 Identify   Using the periodic table at the back of the book, identify the chemical symbols for atoms of sodium and chlorine. Sodium's chemical symbol is Na. Chlorine's chemical symbol is Cl.

2 Solve   A formula unit of sodium chloride is made of one atom of sodium and one atom of chlorine, so its chemical formula is NaCl. A molecule of chlorine gas is made of two atoms of chlorine, so its chemical formula is Cl_2. Sodium metal exists as atoms, so its chemical formula is Na.

REMEMBER

CHEMICAL FORMULAS

- Symbols in a chemical formula represent atoms of elements.

- Chemical symbols for elements can be either one capital letter (for example, H) or a capital letter and a lowercase letter (for example, He). Refer to the periodic table for the chemical symbols of the various elements.

- A subscript on a chemical symbol in a chemical formula indicates how many atoms of that element are in one molecule of the compound. If there is no subscript on a chemical symbol, there is one atom of that element in one molecule of the compound. The subscripts 0 and 1 are never used.

Problem Set

1. Each molecule of a compound contains one atom of nitrogen (N) and three atoms of hydrogen (H). Write the chemical formula for this compound.

2. The main substances in air are N_2 (nitrogen), O_2 (oxygen), CO_2 (carbon dioxide), H_2O (water), and Ar (argon). Which of these substances are elements? Which are compounds? Which are molecules?

3. Ancient philosophers classified water as an element. Why do modern scientists not classify water as an element?

4. Of the chemical formulas MgO, Br_2, Ne, and CO_2, which represents both an element and a molecule? Explain your answer.

5. **Challenge**   A formula unit of aluminum oxide consists of two aluminum atoms and three oxygen atoms. What is the chemical formula of aluminum oxide?

6. **Challenge**   Complete the table below by indicating how many elements and how many atoms are present in one molecule or formula unit of each substance.

Formula	Number of Elements	Number of Atoms
CCl_4		
Fe_2O_3		
$(NH_4)_2SO_4$		

Mixtures

Most mixtures can be separated by understanding and utilizing the physical or chemical properties of the substances in the mixture.

A mixture is a physical blend of two or more pure substances. Chemists must often recognize and separate mixtures. A mixture forms when pure substances (elements or compounds) are combined physically, but not chemically. That is, the substances do not change into new substances when they are mixed. It is easy to identify some mixtures, such as soil, because you can see the different substances that make them up. Other mixtures, such as tea or air, may appear to be pure substances. A mixture such as soil or vegetable soup, in which the different components are not evenly distributed throughout the mixture, is a heterogeneous mixture. A mixture such as tea, in which the different components are evenly distributed, is a homogeneous mixture. A homogeneous mixture can be, and often is, called a *solution*.

OBJECTIVES

- Describe types of mixtures.
- Describe ways to separate mixtures.

EXAMPLE 1

Identifying Mixtures

Is ocean water a homogeneous or heterogeneous mixture? How can you tell? Name two components of the mixture we call ocean water. Is fog a homogeneous or heterogeneous mixture? How can you tell? Name two components of this mixture.

Solution

1 Recall Definitions In a homogeneous mixture, the particles of the substances in the mixture are evenly distributed. In a heterogeneous mixture, the particles in the mixture are unevenly distributed.

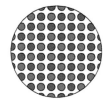 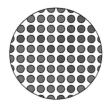

homogeneous mixture   heterogeneous mixture

2 Solve Consider the composition of ocean water and fog. Ocean water is a solution of various salts in water. The salt particles are evenly mixed with the water molecules. Therefore, ocean water is a homogeneous mixture. Fog is a suspension of water droplets in air. That is, the water droplets are floating in the air. The air and water droplets together are a mixture. The water droplets are not evenly mixed with the air, at least not over a very large area. Therefore, fog is a heterogeneous mixture.

REMEMBER

MIXTURES

- Mixtures can be solid, liquid, or gas, or any combination of states.
- In a solution, the more plentiful component is called the *solvent*, and the less plentiful one is called the *solute*.
- Heterogeneous mixtures can sometimes be identified as mixtures by visual observation alone, but homogeneous mixtures cannot.

TIP

Note that one component of the fog mixture is itself a mixture: air is a homogeneous mixture of gases.

EXAMPLE 2

Separating Mixtures

When table salt, sand, and sawdust are stirred together, they form a heterogeneous mixture. Briefly describe how you could separate the components of this mixture.

Separation procedures can be based on differences in physical properties, such as solubility, boiling point, size, density, and magnetism.

Solution

1 List Properties   Mixtures are generally separated based on the properties of their components. These properties include solubility in water, particle size, density, and attraction to magnets.

2 Compare Properties   None of the materials is attracted to magnets. Salt is soluble in water, but sand and sawdust are not. Sawdust will float in water, but sand and salt will not. The sizes of the particles in sand, salt, and sawdust are similar.

3 Solve   The procedure below will allow the three components of the mixture to be separated based on their properties:

1. Mix the mixture with water. The salt will dissolve, the sand will sink to the bottom, and the sawdust will float.

2. Skim off the sawdust, leaving a mixture of salt, water, and sand.

3. Filter the solution to remove the sand.

4. Allow the water to evaporate. The salt will be left behind.

Problem Set

1. Which of these is a heterogeneous mixture?
    A. tap water
    B. black coffee
    C. sports drink
    D. chunky chicken soup

2. Describe a procedure to separate a heterogeneous mixture of steel pins and wooden toothpicks.

3. Explain why chemical properties, such as flammability, are not as useful for separating mixtures as physical properties are.

4. Crude oil is a mixture of different liquid hydrocarbons that must be separated before they can be made into useful products. The liquids are all soluble in one another. Suggest a process for separating this mixture of liquids.

5. **Challenge** Identify a homogeneous mixture of a gas dissolved in a liquid. Identify the components of the mixture. Do not answer carbonated water. (Hint: Most gases will dissolve to a certain extent in any liquid they are in contact with.)

6. **Challenge** Describe a two-step process for separating a heterogeneous mixture of sand, marbles, and iron filings (small particles of iron). Identify the property on which each step is based.

Properties of Substances

The chemical properties of a substance describe how the substance can react to form new substances. The physical properties of a substance are properties that you can observe without changing the chemical identity of the substance.

Chemical and physical changes happen all around us. Cooking, burning, and other chemical reactions are examples of chemical changes. Melting, freezing, and boiling are examples of physical changes. The physical and chemical properties of a substance can change during chemical and physical changes. Mass, volume, color, density, hardness, and magnetism are examples of physical properties. Flammability and reactivity are examples of chemical properties. Scientists often use physical and chemical properties to identify unknown substances and predict the results of chemical reactions.

OBJECTIVES
- Distinguish chemical properties from physical properties.
- Distinguish chemical changes from physical changes.
- Describe the distinctions between chemical changes and physical changes at the molecular level.

EXAMPLE 1

Describe a Chemical Change

The diagram below shows what happens when hydrogen and oxygen molecules react.

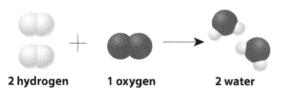

2 hydrogen   1 oxygen   2 water

Explain why this is a chemical change in terms of changes taking place at the molecular level.

Solution

1 Recall Definitions   Remember that during a chemical change, new substances form. Therefore, bonds between atoms must be broken and new ones formed during a chemical change.

2 Apply   Examine the diagram to identify the bonds that exist on each side. The left-hand side of the diagram shows oxygen gas and hydrogen gas. In oxygen gas, two oxygen atoms are bound together. In hydrogen gas, two hydrogen atoms are bound together. The right-hand side of the diagram shows water molecules. In a water molecule, two hydrogen atoms are bound to one oxygen atom.

3 Solve   This must be a chemical change because bonds are both formed and broken. During the reaction, bonds between oxygen atoms in oxygen gas and between hydrogen atoms in hydrogen gas break. In addition, bonds between hydrogen and oxygen atoms form, producing water.

REMEMBER

PROPERTIES OF SUBSTANCES
- Chemical changes generally produce changes in both chemical and physical properties. Physical changes generally produce changes in only physical properties.
- All chemical properties (for example, flammability) are related to chemical changes.
- Changes of state are physical changes.
- Some physical properties, such as boiling point, are related to physical changes, and some, such as density, are not.
- Some physical properties, such as mass, depend on the amount of a substance present, and some, such as density, do not.

EXAMPLE 2

Describe Physical Changes

Most liquids expand when they are heated. Describe the change (if any) in each of these properties of a liquid when it is heated:

- volume
- mass
- density

Solution

1 **Recall Definitions**   Volume is the 3-D space occupied by a substance. Mass is the amount of matter in a substance and is proportional to the number of particles of that substance. Density is the ratio of a substance's mass to its volume $\left(D = \frac{m}{V}\right)$. It is a measure of how tightly the particles of a substance are packed together.

2 **Solve**   The volume will increase, because the substance will expand. The mass will not change, because the number of particles does not change. The substance's density will decrease, because the same mass will be divided by a larger volume.

Problem Set

1. Which of these changes is a chemical change?
   A. iron rusting
   B. water boiling
   C. glass breaking
   D. a balloon popping

2. Some properties of liquid water are very different from those of solid water (ice). Explain why freezing is considered a physical change, even though the properties of water change when it freezes.

3. Identify two physical properties of matter that depend on the amount of material in an object. Identify two physical properties that do **not** depend on the amount of material in an object.

4. Is forming a mixture a physical change or a chemical change? Is forming a compound a physical change or a chemical change? Give examples to support your answers.

5. **Challenge**   A scientist has a sample of a substance that could be steel, sodium, silver, or aluminum. Name two properties the scientist could use to identify the substance, and explain why the scientist could use each property to identify the substance.

6. **Challenge**   Steel has a density of 7.9 g/cm³. What is the mass of a steel sphere with a diameter of 5.00 cm? Show your work.

Problem Solving in Chemistry

Measurements expressed in English units can be converted to SI units and should be written with the correct number of significant figures.

- **Convert between SI and English units of measurement.**
- **Express measurements with the correct number of significant figures.**

All countries now accept the International System of Units, known as the SI system. The SI system is the modern form of the original metric system, and so the terms *SI* and *metric* are often used interchangeably. In the United States and some other countries, people still use other measurement systems for everyday, nonscientific measurements. The most common is known as the English system and includes familiar units such as feet, miles, and degrees Fahrenheit. In science, SI units are most commonly used, so it is important to know how to convert between one system and another. It is also important for scientists to use the correct number of significant figures in measurements and calculations. If they use an incorrect number of significant figures, calculations based on their data will be imprecise, and their conclusions may be wrong. The data could also mislead other scientists.

EXAMPLE 1

Convert Between SI Units and English Units

A researcher recorded that a chemical reaction required 2.90 gal water and raised the temperature of the reaction vessel by 57°F. Convert the researcher's measurements to the SI units of liters and degrees Celsius.

Solution

1 **Collect** First, identify the necessary conversion factors. There are 3.785 L in 1 gal. The equation below shows how to convert from degrees Fahrenheit (F) to degrees Celsius (C):

$$C = \left(\frac{5}{9}\right)(F - 32)$$

2 **Set Up Unit Conversions and Equations**

$$2.90 \text{ gal} \times \frac{3.785 \text{ L}}{1 \text{ gal}}$$

$$C = \left(\frac{5}{9}\right)(57°F - 32)$$

3 **Solve**

$$2.90 \text{ gal} \times \frac{3.785 \text{ L}}{1 \text{ gal}} = 11.0 \text{ L}$$

$$C = \left(\frac{5}{9}\right)(57°F - 32) = 14°C$$

REMEMBER

SIGNIFICANT FIGURES

- All nonzero digits are significant.
- Zeros between two nonzero digits are significant.
- Zeros to the right of a decimal point, but with no nonzero digit to the right of them, are significant.
- Zeros that show the order of magnitude of a number are not significant.
- The number of significant figures in an exact conversion factor, such as 1,000 mg/g, does not affect the number of significant figures in a calculation.
- The number of significant figures in an exactly counted number, such as 45 beakers, does not affect the number of significant figures in a calculation.

EXAMPLE 2

Perform Calculations with the Correct Number of Significant Figures

A sample of sodium chloride (NaCl) has a mass of 1.86 g. A scientist removes a 0.62 g portion of the sample. If NaCl is 40.02% sodium (Na) by mass, what is the mass of Na in the remaining sample? Express the answer with the correct number of significant figures.

Solution

1 Set Up the Calculations First, calculate the mass of NaCl remaining in the sample. Then, multiply the mass by the percentage of Na in NaCl to determine the mass of Na in the remaining sample.

mass of NaCl remaining = initial mass − mass removed
mass of Na in sample = percentage of Na × mass of NaCl remaining

2 Recall Rules for Significant Figures The result of an addition or subtraction has the same number of decimal places as the input with the smallest number of decimal places. The result of a multiplication or division has the same number of significant figures as the input with the smallest number of significant figures.

3 Solve Both 1.86 g and 0.62 g have two significant figures to the right of the decimal point, so the result of subtracting them should also have two significant figures to the right of the decimal point

1.86 g − 0.62 g = 1.24 g

1.24 g has three significant figures, and 40.02% has four. Therefore, the result of multiplying them together should have three significant figures.

(1.24 g)(40.02%) = 0.496 g

TIP

In addition and subtraction, significant figures are determined by the factor with the smallest number of decimal places; in multiplication and division, significant figures are determined by the factor with the fewest digits.

TIP

Writing numbers in scientific notation can make it easier to see how many significant digits they contain. Scientific notation is also useful for writing very large or very small numbers in a more readable form.

Problem Set

1. Which English unit is closest in length to the SI unit of a meter?

2. Give the number of significant figures in each of the following measurements: 1.200×10^8 s, 101.010 kg, 0.00004 m.

3. A scientist reacts 5.5847 g of iron and 3.206 g of sulfur in a sealed reaction vessel. If no matter enters or leaves the reaction vessel, what will be the mass of the products if both reactants are entirely used up? Give the answer with the correct number of significant figures.

4. One fluid ounce is equal to 29.57 mL. How many fluid ounces are in 3.5 L of water? Give your answer with the correct number of significant figures.

5. Absolute zero temperature is defined to be 0 K. Express absolute zero in degrees Celsius and degrees Fahrenheit. Use the conversion formulas in the back of this book.

6. How many centimeters are in 1.456 mi? Express your answer in scientific notation.

7. **Challenge** A dilute acid solution contains 2.0×10^{-4} g acid in a volume of 20.0 mL. A student adds 20.0 mL of water to the solution. What is the new concentration in grams per milliliter? Calculate the concentration by dividing mass by volume.

8. **Challenge** A scientist determines the density of a liquid to be 1.35 g/cm³. What is the density of the liquid in grams per cubic inch (g/in³)?

9. **Challenge** How many milliliters are in 1 ft³ of water? Give your answer in scientific notation with four significant figures.

Metric System: Base Units

Metric units used to express measured quantities may be either base units or derived units, and their magnitudes are indicated by standard prefixes.

There are seven SI base units. All other metric units are derived from these seven units. All but one of the seven SI base units are defined based on stable properties of the universe, such as the speed of light. Only the unit for mass is defined by an actual physical object. For convenience and clarity, scientists use standard prefixes to indicate larger or smaller units. Each prefix indicates a specific power of ten.

OBJECTIVE

- Distinguish between metric base units and derived units.

EXAMPLE 1

Identify Metric Base Units

A student measured the length, mass, and temperature of an object. She also measured the amount of electric current flowing through the object over time. Which of these sets of measurements could be the student's measurements?

    A. 0.5 K, 195.2 A, 350 m, 30 s, 15 cd

    B. 0.5 m, 195.2 kg, 350 K, 30 A, 15 s

    C. 0.5 kg, 195.2 mol, 350 cd, 30 K, 15 s

    D. 0.5 cd, 195.2 K, 350 A, 30 mol, 15 m

Solution

1 Recall The seven metric base units are the meter (m), the kilogram (kg), the kelvin (K), the second (s), the mole (mol), the candela (cd), and the ampere (A). The meter describes length, the kilogram describes mass, the kelvin describes temperature, the second describes time, the mole describes the amount of a substance present, the candela describes luminous intensity (brightness of light), and the ampere describes electric current.

2 Solve The student measured length, mass, temperature, electric current, and time. Therefore, she must have recorded measurements with units of m, kg, K, A, and s. Choice B is the only option that includes all of these units, so choice B must be the correct answer.

REMEMBER

UNITS

- Units raised to powers are indicated by superscripts— for example, cm^3 for cubic centimeters.

- Units with negative exponents appear in the denominator when the units are written as fractions—for example, $m \cdot s^{-1}$ is the same as m/s.

- The seven SI base units are the meter (m), the kilogram (kg), the kelvin (K), the second (s), the mole (mol), the candela (cd), and the ampere (A). All other SI units are derived from these seven base units.

TIP

The prefixes used with SI units indicate different powers of ten. For example, the prefix *kilo-*, indicated by the letter *k*, indicates 1,000 (10^3) units; so, 1 km = 1,000 m.

EXAMPLE 2

Convert Between Metric Base Units

One property that scientists commonly use in identifying substances is density. The density of an object is equal to the mass of the object divided by its volume. A scientist determines that the mass of a sample of a material is 367.2 mg, and that its volume is 823.8 cm³. What is the material's density in kilograms per cubic meter (kg/m³)?

TIP

When you perform unit conversions, always check to make sure your answer is reasonable. For example, if you are converting from a larger unit to a smaller unit, such as from kilometers to meters, your answer should be larger than the number you started with.

Solution

1 **Gather Required Information**   There are 1,000 mg in 1 g and 1,000 g in 1 kg. There are 100 cm in 1 m.

2 **Set Up Unit Conversions**   Don't forget to cube the length conversion.

$$367.2 \text{ mg} \times \frac{1 \text{ g}}{1,000 \text{ mg}} \times \frac{1 \text{ kg}}{1,000 \text{ g}}$$

$$823.8 \text{ cm}^3 \times \frac{1 \text{ m}^3}{(100)^3 \text{ cm}^3} = 823.8 \text{ cm}^3 \times \frac{1 \text{ m}^3}{1 \times 10^6 \text{ cm}^3}$$

3 **Cancel Similar Units and Solve**

$$367.2 \text{ mg} \times \frac{1 \text{ g}}{1,000 \text{ mg}} \times \frac{1 \text{ kg}}{1,000 \text{ g}} = 3.672 \times 10^{-4} \text{ kg}$$

$$823.8 \text{ cm}^3 \times \frac{(1^3) \text{ m}^3}{(100)^3 \text{ cm}^3} = 823.8 \text{ cm}^3 \times \frac{1 \text{ m}^3}{1 \times 10^6 \text{ cm}^3} = 8.238 \times 10^{-4} \text{ m}^3$$

$$\frac{3.672 \times 10^{-4} \text{ kg}}{8.238 \times 10^{-4} \text{ m}^3} = 0.44574 \text{ kg/m}^3$$

Problem Set

1. A scientist needs to measure the mass, temperature, and luminous intensity of a lightbulb. What three SI base units will the scientist's measurements include?

2. Perform the following unit conversions: 134 km to cm, 35 g to µg, 0.65 mmol to mol. Show your work.

3. A student measures the length and mass of an object. He records the length as 45.2 cm and the mass as 195.6 mg. Convert the student's measurements to SI base units. Show your work.

4. Scientists often describe energy using units of joules (J). One joule is equal to $1 \text{ kg} \cdot \text{m}^2/\text{s}^2$. Is the joule an SI base unit or a derived unit? Explain your answer.

5. One meter is defined as the distance light travels in 3.335640×10^{-9} s. What is the speed of light in cm/s?

6. Convert 4.5 km/min² to mm/s².

7. **Challenge** The SI unit of pressure is the pascal (Pa). One pascal is equal to $1 \text{ kg/m} \cdot \text{s}^2$. Convert $0.115 \text{ g/cm} \cdot \text{ms}^2$ to kPa.

8. **Challenge** The coulomb (C) is the unit of electric charge. One ampere is equal to 1 coulomb per second. If a battery contains $145 \text{ mA} \cdot \text{hr}$ of electric charge, how many coulombs of electric charge does it contain?

9. **Challenge** Convert $85.6 \text{ mg} \cdot \text{mm}^2/\text{ms}^2$ to joules.

Metric System: Derived Units

SI base units can be combined to form derived units, which can be used to solve a variety of problems.

There are seven SI base units. Scientists combine SI base units to form derived units, which they can then use to describe various quantities that they cannot describe using the base units alone. For example, the cubic meter (m^3) is an SI unit of volume. The newton (N) is the SI unit of force. Its units are $kg \cdot m/s^2$. The joule (J) is the SI unit of heat and energy. Its units are $N \cdot m$, or $m^2 \cdot kg/s^2$. Scientists also sometimes use another energy unit, the calorie, to describe energy measurements. One calorie (cal) is the amount of energy required to raise the temperature of 1 g of water by 1°C. The calorie is one example of a non-SI unit that scientists often use for convenience or to make their work more easily understandable.

OBJECTIVE

• Use derived units to solve problems.

EXAMPLE 1

Solve Problems Using Derived Units

The SI unit of pressure is a derived unit called the *pascal* (Pa). One pascal is equal to 1 N/m^2. A sample of a gas is exerting a total of 38.5 N of force on the sides of its container. The container is a cube with sides of length 93.4 cm. What is the pressure on each face of the container in pascals? Remember, the pascal is based on meters, not centimeters.

Solution

1 Strategize   First, calculate the area of each face of the container, and then divide the total force by the number of sides to determine the force on each side. Then, calculate the pressure on each side by division.

2 Calculate the Area of the Container's Sides   The area of a square is simply the square of its side length. Remember to convert from square centimeters to square meters.

$$(93.4^2)\ cm^2 \times \frac{(1^2)\ m^2}{(100^2)\ cm^2} = 8,720\ cm^2 \times \frac{1\ m^2}{1 \times 10^4\ cm^2} = 0.872\ m^2$$

3 Calculate the Force on Each Side   A cube has six faces, so each face will receive one-sixth of the total force exerted by the gas. Therefore, each face will receive 38.5 N ÷ 6 = 6.41 N of force.

4 Solve   To calculate the pressure, divide the force on each side by the area of each side.

$$\frac{6.41\ N}{0.872\ m^2} = 7.36\ Pa$$

REMEMBER

SI DERIVED UNITS

• A derived unit is a combination of two or more SI base units. The base units that are combined to form a derived unit may be the same or different. For example, square meters (m^2) is a derived unit, and so is meters per second (m/s).

• Some SI derived units, such as the newton (N), the joule (J), the liter (L), and the watt (W), have unique names. Other SI derived units, such as the meter per second and the square meter, do not have unique names. Every SI derived unit with a unique name can also be expressed as a combination of SI base units. For example, one liter is equal to 0.001 m^3, and one watt is equal to 1 $m^2 \cdot kg/s^3$.

EXAMPLE 2

Convert from Joules to Calories

Scientists often use the calorie for heat and energy calculations involving water. The specific heat of water is 4.186 J/g · °C, or 1.00 cal/g · °C, so using calories can make calculations simpler. If a sample of water absorbed 25.3 cal, how many joules of energy did it absorb?

Solution

1 Strategize   First, determine the conversion factor between calories and joules. Use the information about the specific heat of water that is given in the problem to identify the conversion factor.

2 Divide and Simplify   First, set up an equality. Then, rearrange the equality to solve for the desired units. Don't forget to cancel similar units.

$$\frac{1.00\ cal}{(1\ g)(1°C)} = \frac{4.186\ J}{(1\ g)(1°C)}$$

$$(1\ g)(1°C) \times \frac{1.00\ cal}{(1\ g)(1°C)} = (1\ g)(1°C) \times \frac{4.186\ J}{(1\ g)(1°C)}$$

$$1.00\ cal = 4.186\ J$$

conversion factor = 4.186 J/cal

3 Solve   Now, use the conversion factor to convert 25.3 cal to joules.

$$25.3\ cal \times \frac{4.186\ J}{cal} = 106\ J$$

Problem Set

1. Density is a physical property. Explain why the unit for density (g/cm³) is a derived unit.

2. Calculate the volume in cubic centimeters of a sugar crystal that has a length of 1 cm, a width of 0.009 m, and a height of 10 mm.

3. Most substances expand when they are heated. How does heating affect the mass and volume, and therefore the density, of most substances? (Hint: Density is equal to mass divided by volume.)

4. A miner found a mineral fragment with a volume of 1.49 cm³ and a mass of 28.7 g. The density of gold is 19.3 g/cm³. The density of pyrite is 5.0 g/cm³. Which mineral did the miner find?

5. One Calorie (Cal) is equal to 1,000 cal. If a particular food contains 325 Cal, how many joules of energy does it contain (1 cal = 4.186 J)?

6. A particular chemical reaction releases 425.3 J of heat. How many calories of heat does the reaction release?

7. **Challenge**   A chemical reaction produces enough heat to raise the temperature of 5.00 g of water by 3.24°C. How many joules of energy does the reaction release?

8. **Challenge**   The SI unit for power is the watt (W). One watt is equal to 1 J/s. How many watts are used by a device that uses 35.7 cal of energy each minute?

9. **Challenge**   One volt (V) is equal to 1 W/A (A = ampere). Express the unit of the volt in terms of SI base units.

Graphing

Scientists use graphs to summarize and display the data they collect.

Much of chemistry, and science in general, involves collecting data. And much of the information scientists collect is in the form of numeric data (numbers). Scientists then try to figure out the relationships between different sets of data. One way to quickly summarize, display, and begin to interpret different sets of data is to use a graph. A graph is a visual display of data. Graphs can clearly communicate a great deal of information in a small amount of space, and they can make trends in data easier to see.

EXAMPLE 1

Create a Graph from Experimental Data

A student cut a copper wire into pieces with different masses. Then, he measured the volume of each piece. His data are shown in the table below. Create a graph to show the relationship between mass and volume for the student's data.

Mass (g)	Volume (cm³)	Mass (g)	Volume (cm³)
5.2	46.2	29.7	278.1
12.0	103.3	33.9	290.2
16.4	150.5	38.7	343.1
22.6	198.6	40.1	382.3

Solution

1 **Identify Variables** The student measured two quantities, mass and volume. To make the graph, plot one of these variables along the x-axis and the other along the y-axis. Plot the mass along the x-axis and the volume along the y-axis.

2 **Decide on the Scale of Each Axis** Once you have determined which variable will be plotted on which axis, decide on a scale for each axis. Choose a scale that will make the graph as large as possible. Divide each axis to form subdivisions of equal intervals, making sure to include the smallest and largest values of each quantity. Intervals that are multiples of 1, 2, 5, and 10 are easiest to work with. To avoid clutter, do not label each subdivision. The two axes do not need to have the same scale. For these data, the x-axis will run from 0 g to 45 g in intervals of 5 g. The y-axis will run from 40 cm³ to 400 cm³ in intervals of 20 cm³.

3 **Plot the Points** Start with the first pair of values from the data table, and continue to the last. Place a small dot at each data point.

④ Sketch a Line or Curve to Fit the Data   Sketch a line or curve that goes through the vicinity of the majority of the data points. Do not just draw from dot to dot.

⑤ Title the Graph   The title tells others what the graph shows. The title should be informative, but not too long. The picture below shows the completed graph for these data.

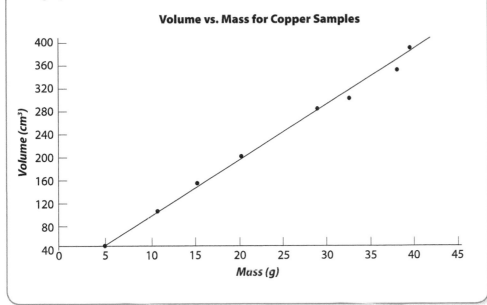

Volume vs. Mass for Copper Samples

(x-axis: Mass (g), y-axis: Volume (cm³))

> **TIP**
>
> For graphs that have *x*- and *y*-axes, write your title in the form "*Y* vs. *X*," not "*X* vs. *Y*."

Problem Set

1. A student's graph will show length along the *x* axis? Her length measurements range from 0.45 cm to 18.42 cm. Approximately what should the range and scale of the *x*-axis of the graph be?

2. A student does an experiment to learn how the concentration of an acid in a solution affects the solution's pH (pH is a measure from 1–14 of the acidity or alkalinity of a solution). What title should the student put on his graph?

3. Create a graph to display the data in the table below.

Heat Added (J)	Temperature (°C)
138	45.3
226	47.2
346	49.6
437	51.7

4. A graph shows the same data as a data table, but with less precision. Why, then, would a scientist want to create a graph to display the data in a data table?

5. **Challenge**   A chemist carries out an experiment to determine how temperature affects the rate of a chemical reaction. Her data show that, as temperature increases, the rate of reaction increases linearly. Draw a sketch of what a graph of the chemist's data may look like. Include titles and axis labels, but do not include units on the axes.

6. **Challenge**   Create a graph of average atomic mass vs. atomic number for the first 18 elements in the periodic table. Describe any trends you notice. (Hint: The atomic number of an element is given at the top of its square in the periodic table. Its average atomic mass is at the bottom. For example, hydrogen's atomic number is 1, and its average atomic mass is 1.0079.)

Scientific Methods in Chemistry

Scientific methods provide organized ways to acquire new knowledge, solve problems, and answer questions.

Scientists use many different methods to gather information and to solve problems. Scientific methods can involve different steps in different orders. Some common steps in scientific methods include asking a question, forming a hypothesis, researching others' work, collecting data, analyzing data, drawing conclusions, and sharing work with others. Although scientific methods are varied, all scientific methods include the collection of data through observation and experiment, and the use of these data to answer questions and test hypotheses.

OBJECTIVE

- Describe how scientists learn about the world.

REMEMBER

SCIENTIFIC METHODS

- Scientific methods are the processes and procedures that scientists use to learn about the world.

- Some scientific investigations are *controlled* experiments. In a controlled experiment, only one condition or variable is allowed to change between tested groups. The other conditions are kept the same between the groups.

- No matter what kind of scientific investigation you carry out, you should always make sure to record your observations or data carefully and accurately.

EXAMPLE 1

Design a Scientific Investigation

A student learns that more sugar will dissolve in hot water than in cold water. He hypothesizes that the sugar will also dissolve more quickly in hot water than in cold water. Describe a scientific investigation the student could do to test his hypothesis.

Solution

1 **Identify Necessary Data**   To test his hypothesis, the student will need to collect data on how quickly sugar dissolves in hot water and in cold water.

2 **Identify Type of Investigation**   Dissolving sugar in water is something that is easily controlled and done in a laboratory, so the student should do an experiment to test his hypothesis. He will need to repeat his measurements several times, to make sure they are accurate.

3 **Solve**   A possible experiment the student could do is summarized below:

- Pour 200 mL of water into each of 10 identical containers.
- Heat the water in five of the containers to 80°C. Cool the water in the other five containers to 10°C. Record the temperature of the water in each container.
- Measure 10 samples of sugar, each with a mass of about 5.0 g. Record the mass of each sample.
- Add one sample of sugar to each container. Record which sample of sugar was added to each container.
- Use mechanical stirrers to stir the water in each container at exactly the same rate. Time how long it takes each sample of sugar to completely dissolve in the water.

TIP

Example 1 is a controlled experiment, because only the temperature of the water varies between groups. All the other conditions (amount of water and sugar, type of container, and rate of stirring) are kept the same.

EXAMPLE 2

Describe Scientific Methods

Explain why the statement "scientists use the scientific method to investigate the natural world" is incorrect. Give examples to support your answer.

TIP

Even among scientists who do the same type of scientific investigation, there is no single scientific method. For example, an organic chemist may use a different experimental method than an inorganic chemist uses.

Solution

1 Recall Relevant Information   The statement implies that there is only one way that scientists investigate the natural world, and that all scientists use this single method. It is true that all scientists make observations and try to answer questions about the natural world, but think about the different ways scientists do their work. Some scientists carry out experiments in laboratories. Others make observations of natural systems, such as the ocean or the atmosphere. Some scientists make computer models of natural systems to help them learn how the world works.

2 Solve   The statement is incorrect because scientists use many different methods to learn about the world. An organic chemist may carry out an experiment in a laboratory to learn about the properties of a specific chemical. A geologist may make observations of a natural system, such as a mountain, to learn how it formed and what it is made of. An atmospheric scientist may make a computer model of the atmosphere to study weather and climate patterns. These scientists all use different steps and procedures to learn about the world. Therefore, they do not all use the same scientific method.

Problem Set

1. Which of the following questions can be answered using scientific methods?
   A. Is it right that people eat meat?
   B. What is the best food to eat for breakfast?
   C. Which tastes better, dark chocolate or milk chocolate?
   D. Which contains more sugar, cola or sweetened iced tea?

2. A student sees a commercial for a paper towel, which claims that the towel can absorb more water than other towels. Describe a scientific investigation the student could do to test the commercial's claims.

3. Explain why a scientist could not use a controlled experiment to answer the question, "How did earth's continents form?"

4. Describe a scientific investigation a student could carry out to test her hypothesis that honeybees are more likely to fly to flowers that are fed with fertilizer than to flowers grown without fertilizer.

5. **Challenge**   A student wants to do an experiment to compare how well different types of laundry soap remove grease stains from cotton cloth. What conditions should the student control in the experiment? What data should she collect?

6. **Challenge**   Explain why scientists often repeat their experiments several times before reporting the results.

Early Theories of the Atom

Modern atomic theory is based on the work of many different scientists.

For thousands of years, scientists have sought to understand matter and the tiny particles that matter is made of. During that time, many different models of the atom have been proposed, tested, and rejected. One of the first people to propose a model of the atom was Democritus, a Greek philosopher. According to Democritus, atoms were indivisible—that is, the atom was the absolute smallest particle of matter possible. In fact, the word *atom* is based on the Greek word *atomos,* which means "indivisible." Since Democritus's time, scientists have learned a great deal about atoms and the structure of matter. John Dalton, Robert Millikan, and J.J. Thomson were three scientists who contributed greatly to our current theory of the atom.

OBJECTIVES

- **Describe the historical development of the concept of the atom.**

- **Describe the contributions of early scientists to the modern theory of the atom.**

EXAMPLE 1

Compare Atomic Models

Describe the similarities and differences between Dalton's model of the atom and Thomson's model of the atom.

Solution

1 **Recall Relevant Information** According to Dalton, atoms were tiny, indivisible spheres, as shown in the left-hand image below. In Thomson's model, which is sometimes called the *plum pudding model*, atoms consist of electrons suspended in a mass of positively charged matter, as shown in the right-hand image below.

Dalton's atomic model   **Thomson's atomic model**

2 **Solve** Both models assume that an atom as a whole has no net electric charge, and that an atom of an element has all the chemical properties of that element. However, Dalton's model assumes that the atom cannot be broken down into smaller pieces. Thomson's model assumes that atoms are themselves made of smaller parts (electrons and positively charged matter).

REMEMBER

EARLY ATOMIC MODELS

- According to Democritus, all matter was made up of atoms, which were indivisible. Democritus's ideas were not based on scientific experiments or observations.

- John Dalton's atomic theory was based on experimentation and observation. As a result, more scientists accepted it than accepted Democritus's ideas.

- J.J. Thomson's experiments with cathode-ray tubes demonstrated that atoms contain smaller, negatively charged particles called *electrons.*

- Robert Millikan's oil drop experiments allowed him and other scientists to calculate the amount of electric charge an electron carries.

EXAMPLE 2

Describe the Effects of J.J. Thomson's Experiments

Which aspect of Dalton's atomic theory did Thomson disprove?

Solution

1 Recall Relevant Information Dalton's atomic theory states the following:

- All elements are made of atoms, which cannot be divided or broken down.
- All atoms of a given element are identical. Atoms of different elements are different.
- Atoms can be mixed together without reacting with one another. Atoms can also be combined chemically to form compounds.
- During a chemical reaction, the atoms in substances are rearranged. Chemical reactions cannot change an atom of one element into an atom of another element.

Thomson's cathode-ray tube experiments showed that atoms contain smaller particles that are negatively charged.

2 Solve Thomson's experiments demonstrated that an atom can be broken down into smaller pieces. Therefore, Thomson disproved Dalton's idea that atoms are indivisible.

TIP

Thomson's model of the atom is sometimes called the *plum pudding model* because of the way the electrons are scattered throughout the positively charged matter in the atom. A plum pudding is an English dessert that contains raisins scattered throughout a bready dough, rather like chocolate chips in a chocolate chip muffin.

TIP

The other three parts of Dalton's atomic theory are still accepted as correct today, although they have been refined somewhat by the work of other scientists.

Problem Set

1. How did Robert Millikan contribute to our understanding of atoms?

2. Describe the similarities and differences between Democritus's ideas about atoms and Dalton's atomic theory.

3. Part of Dalton's atomic theory states that, when atoms combine to form compounds, they always combine in the same whole-number ratio for a given compound. Explain what this statement means.

4. Describe how J.J. Thomson's cathode-ray tube experiments and Robert Millikan's oil drop experiments were related to one another and to the development of modern atomic theory.

5. **Challenge** Explain why Democritus's ideas about atoms cannot be called an atomic theory.

6. **Challenge** Describe how Thomson's cathode-ray tube experiments proved the existence of negatively charged particles in the atom that were later named *electrons*.

The Nuclear Atom

The modern scientific model of the atom consists of a central, positively charged nucleus surrounded by negatively charged electrons.

Thomson's cathode-ray tube experiments showed that atoms contain electrons. Thomson thought that the positively charged material in an atom made up most of the volume of the atom, and that the electrons were embedded in this positively charged material. Ernest Rutherford's gold-foil experiments showed that all the positive charge in an atom is concentrated in a tiny region at its center, called the *nucleus*. We now know that the nucleus is the center of the atom and contains protons and neutrons. Electrons orbit the nucleus at specific energy levels called *orbitals*.

OBJECTIVE

• Describe the composition of the nucleus of the atom.

REMEMBER

THE NUCLEAR ATOM

• After Ernest Rutherford completed his original gold-foil experiments, he hypothesized that the positive charge in the nucleus is carried by individual particles, in the same way that the negative charge is carried by electrons. Later, he proved the existence of these positively charged particles, which he called *protons*.

• Rutherford also hypothesized that there are neutral (uncharged) particles in the nucleus. Later, another scientist, James Chadwick, proved the existence of these particles, which he called *neutrons*.

• Protons and neutrons have about the same mass. They are about 1,800 times more massive than electrons.

• Protons and electrons have the same magnitude of electric charge, but protons carry a positive charge and electrons carry a negative charge.

• Atoms are electrically neutral, so they have the same number of protons and electrons.

EXAMPLE 1

Describe the Rutherford Atom

Draw and label an illustration of the atomic model Rutherford developed after his gold-foil experiments. The illustration should include several electrons and a nucleus.

Solution

❶ Identify Relevant Information   Rutherford's gold-foil experiment proved that the atom has a dense, positively charged center. This center is called the *nucleus*, and it is positively charged. The negatively charged electrons are located outside the nucleus. Rutherford's original model did not include protons and neutrons as individual particles.

❷ Design   The drawing will need to include a small central region to represent the nucleus and other, smaller particles outside the nucleus to represent electrons.

❸ Solve   The illustration below shows the model of the atom that Rutherford developed based on the results of his experiment.

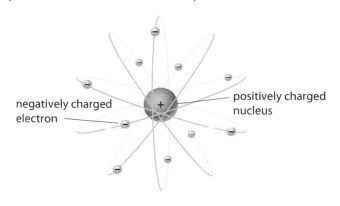

negatively charged electron

positively charged nucleus

EXAMPLE 2

Describe Rutherford's Gold-Foil Experiment

Summarize the setup and results of Rutherford's gold-foil experiment, and explain how those results led Rutherford to formulate a new model of the atom.

Solution

1 Recall Relevant Information   Rutherford's experiment involved a sheet of very thin gold foil, a stream of positively charged particles, and a detector that glowed when it was hit by positively charged particles, as shown below.

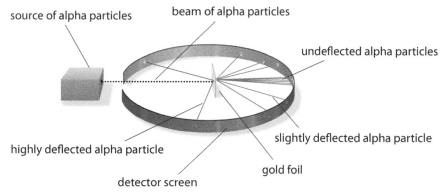

2 Solve   Rutherford fired a stream of positively charged particles at a piece of thin gold foil surrounded by a detector. He observed where on the detector the particles struck. He observed that most of the charged particles traveled straight through the foil, but a few of them were deflected back at large angles. Rutherford concluded that the highly deflected particles had hit relatively massive regions within the gold foil and bounced off. Because only a few of the particles bounced back, Rutherford concluded that most of the mass of an atom is concentrated in a small area, and that most of an atom is empty space.

Problem Set

1. Make a table comparing protons, neutrons, and electrons. Include the relative mass, charge, and location of each particle.

2. Draw a picture to represent the modern model of an atom of helium. Make sure to label your drawing.

3. Explain why the net charge of the nucleus is positive, but an atom has no net charge.

4. Describe the similarities and differences between the model of the atom that Rutherford proposed after his gold-foil experiment and the modern model of the atom.

5. **Challenge**   After his gold-foil experiment, Rutherford recollected, "It was as credible as if you had fired a 15-inch shell [bullet] at a sheet of tissue paper and it came back and hit you." What does this statement tell you about the results he expected to obtain from his experiment?

6. **Challenge**   One of the observations that Rutherford made based on his gold-foil experiment was that the magnitude of the amount of positive charge on an atom's nucleus was about one-half the magnitude of the atomic mass of the element. For example, the magnitude of the positive charge on an atom of gold is 79, and the magnitude of the atomic weight of gold is about 196. Based on what you know about the modern model of the atom, explain Rutherford's observation.

Atomic Number and Mass Number

An atom's atomic number is the number of protons in its nucleus. Its mass number is the number of protons plus the number of neutrons in its nucleus.

An atom is the smallest particle of an element that retains the properties of that element. You may recall that most of an atom is empty space. The rest of an atom consists of a positively charged center (nucleus) containing protons and neutrons, surrounded by a cloud of electrons. Most of the mass of an atom is in its nucleus. Chemists use two different numbers to describe the composition of an atom's nucleus: atomic number and mass number. An atom's *atomic number*, represented by the symbol Z, is the number of protons in the nucleus of the atom. An atom's *mass number*, represented by the symbol A, is the sum of the number of protons and the number of neutrons in the nucleus. The number above each element's chemical symbol in the periodic table is that element's atomic number. The atomic number of an element is what distinguishes it from all other elements. In other words, the number of protons in an atom defines which element it is an atom of. If you know an atom's atomic number and mass number, you can determine the number of protons, neutrons, and electrons in the atom.

OBJECTIVES

- Define *atomic number* and *mass number*.
- Differentiate between an atom's atomic number and its mass number.

REMEMBER

ATOMIC NUMBER AND MASS NUMBER

- An atom's atomic number identifies which element it is an atom of. Each element has a unique atomic number, and all atoms of a given element have the same atomic number.

- An element's atomic number is written above that element's symbol in the periodic table.

- Each atom of an element has a specific mass number. Different atoms of the same element can have different mass numbers because they can have different numbers of neutrons.

- An electrically neutral atom has the same number of electrons as protons.

EXAMPLE 1

Determine the Atomic Number of an Atom

An atom of uranium (U) contains 92 protons and 146 neutrons. An atom of oxygen (O) contains 8 protons and 8 neutrons. An atom of silver (Ag) contains 47 protons and 60 neutrons. Identify the atomic numbers and mass numbers of these atoms.

Solution

1 **Recall Relevant Information**   The atomic number of an atom is the number of protons in the nucleus of the atom. The mass number of an atom is the sum of the number of protons and neutrons in the nucleus of the atom.

2 **Solve**   The atom of uranium contains 92 protons, so its atomic number is 92. It contains 146 neutrons, so its mass number is $92 + 146 = 238$. The atom of oxygen contains 8 protons, so its atomic number is 8. It contains 8 neutrons, so its mass number is $8 + 8 = 16$. The atom of silver contains 47 protons, so its atomic number is 47. It contains 60 neutrons, so its mass number is $47 + 60 = 107$.

EXAMPLE 2

Determine the Number of Protons, Neutrons, and Electrons in an Atom

A particular electrically neutral atom has an atomic number of 11 and a mass number of 23. Identify the atom, and state the number of protons, neutrons, and electrons in the atom.

Solution

1 **Recall Relevant Information** The atomic number of an atom is equal to the number of protons in the atom. It also determines the identity of the atom. The mass number of an atom is equal to the sum of the number of protons and the number of neutrons in the atom. In an electrically neutral atom, the number of protons is equal to the number of electrons.

2 **Solve** The atom's atomic number is 11, so it has 11 protons. It is electrically neutral, so it has 11 electrons. To calculate the number of neutrons in the atom, use the equation $N = A - Z$, where N is the number of neutrons, A is the mass number, and Z is the number of protons. For this atom, $N = 23 - 11 = 12$, so the atom has 12 neutrons. The periodic table shows that the element with atomic number 11 is sodium (Na).

TIP

The mass number of an atom is not the same as the average atomic mass for the element, which is listed below the element's symbol in the periodic table.

Problem Set

1. Can an atom's atomic number ever be smaller than its mass number? Explain your answer.

2. An atom of bromine (Br) contains 35 protons and 45 neutrons. An atom of rhenium (Re) contains 75 protons and 111 neutrons. An atom of plutonium (Pu) contains 94 protons and 150 neutrons. Identify the atomic numbers and mass numbers of these atoms.

3. A prospector finds an element with an atomic number of 79. Is this element gold? Explain your answer.

4. An electrically neutral atom has an atomic number of 76 and a mass number of 188. Identify the atom and state the number of protons, neutrons, and electrons in the atom. (Hint: Refer to the periodic table at the back of the book.)

5. An atom has a mass number of 178. Is this enough information for you to identify the atom? If so, explain why. If not, explain what other information you would need to identify the atom.

6. Identify the number of protons, neutrons, and electrons in an electrically neutral atom of platinum with a mass number of 195. (Hint: Refer to the periodic table at the back of the book.)

7. **Challenge** An electrically neutral atom contains 26 electrons and 30 neutrons. Identify the atom and give its mass number and atomic number.

8. **Challenge** Explain why the periodic table shows the atomic number of each element, but not the mass number. (Hint: Different atoms of the same element can have different numbers of neutrons.)

9. **Challenge** An electrically neutral atom of iodine contains 73 neutrons. Identify the number of protons and electrons in the atom and give its atomic number and its mass number.

Ions

When an atom gains or loses one or more electrons, and as a result becomes electrically charged, the resulting particle is called an *ion.*

Neutral atoms have equal numbers of electrons and protons. An atom becomes an ion when it acquires an electric charge by gaining or losing one or more electrons. The charge on an ion can be determined by calculating the algebraic sum of the protons and electrons, assigning +1 to each proton and –1 to each electron. The resultant charge is written as a superscript to the right of the chemical symbol.

OBJECTIVES

- Define the term *ion.*
- Write symbols for ions.
- Determine the charges on ions from the numbers of subatomic particles in them.

EXAMPLE 1

Determine the Number of Electrons in an Ion

When magnesium chloride ($MgCl_2$) dissolves in water, it separates into Mg^{2+} ions and Cl^- ions. How many electrons are in each Mg^{2+} ion, and how many electrons are in each Cl^- ion?

Solution

1 Collect Determine the number of protons in neutral atoms of Mg and Cl from the atomic numbers listed in the periodic table at the back of the book. In a neutral atom, the number of protons will equal the number of electrons. Magnesium's atomic number is 12, and chlorine's atomic number is 17. Therefore, a neutral atom of Mg has 12 protons and 12 electrons, and a neutral atom of Cl has 17 protons and 17 electrons.

2 Strategize Remember that atoms form ions only by gaining or losing electrons. They cannot gain or lose protons. Therefore, determine how many electrons an Mg atom must gain or lose to acquire a +2 charge, and how many electrons a Cl atom must gain or lose to acquire a –1 charge.

3 Solve An electron has a negative charge, so if an atom gains electrons, it will become a negatively charged ion. Conversely, for an atom to become a positively charged ion, it must lose electrons. The following formula can be used to calculate the number of electrons in an ion:

$$E = P - C$$

In this equation, *C* is the charge on the ion, *P* is the number of protons in the ion, and *E* is the number of electrons in the ion. For Mg^{2+}, $E = 12 - 2 = 10$. For Cl^-, $E = 17 - (-1) = 18$. So, an Mg^{2+} ion has 10 electrons, and a Cl^- ion has 18 electrons.

REMEMBER

IONS

- When indicating the charge in the superscript, write the number first, then the type of charge (for example, Ca^{2+}, not Ca^{+2}).

- For charges of +1 and –1, only the sign is needed as the superscript (for example, Na^+ or F^-).

- Many ions are made up of more than one atom. For example, SO_4^{2-} and OH^- are both ions that contain more than one atom. These ions generally act as single units in chemical reactions.

- Subscripts in chemical formulas indicate the number of atoms of each element in one molecule or formula unit of the substance.

EXAMPLE 2

Writing Symbols for Ions

The atomic structures of two ions are shown to the right.

Write the chemical symbols for these ions.

TIP

Remember that neutrons have no electric charge, so they do not contribute to the overall charge of an ion.

Solution

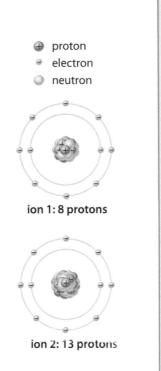

⊕ proton
⊖ electron
○ neutron

ion 1: 8 protons

ion 2: 13 protons

① Collect   Identify the numbers of protons and electrons in each ion. Ion 1 has 8 protons and 10 electrons. Ion 2 has 13 protons and 10 electrons.

② Apply   Remember that the number of protons in an atom determines the atom's atomic number. Therefore, ion 1 is an ion of the element with atomic number 8, and ion 2 is an ion of the element with atomic number 13. Look at the periodic table at the back of the book. It shows that ion 1 must be an oxygen ion, because oxygen has an atomic number of 8. Similarly, ion 2 must be an aluminum ion, because aluminum has an atomic number of 13.

③ Solve   To write the symbol for each ion, write the ion's chemical symbol and its charge. The chemical symbol for oxygen is O, and the chemical symbol for aluminum is Al. To find the net charge on each ion, use the formula $E = P - C$. For ion 1, $E = 8 - 10 = -2$. For ion 2, $E = 13 - 10 = 3$. Therefore, the symbol for ion 1 is O^{2-}, and the symbol for ion 2 is Al^{3+}.

Problem Set

1. Write a definition for *ion* in your own words, and explain how negative and positive ions form from neutral atoms.

2. How many electrons and protons are in an F^- ion? (Hint: Use a periodic table.)

3. How many electrons and protons are in a Ba^{2+} ion?

4. Write the symbol for the ion shown below.

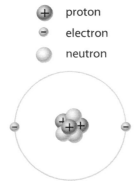

⊕ proton
⊖ electron
○ neutron

5. Of the particles He, He^+, and He^{2+}, which has no electrons? Explain your answer.

6. Write the chemical symbol for an ion with 20 protons, 20 neutrons, and 18 electrons.

7. **Challenge**   How many electrons are in an ammonium ion (NH_4^+)?

8. **Challenge**   An ion formed from a single atom has 18 electrons and a charge of +1. In water, this compound dissociates into ions. Write the chemical symbol for this ion.

9. **Challenge**   The formula for rubidium hydroxide is RbOH. In water, this compound dissociates into ions. The formula for the hydroxide ion is OH^-. What is the charge on the rubidium ion? Explain your answer.

Isotopes and Atomic Mass

Atoms of an element with different numbers of neutrons are isotopes of that element.

If you examine the average atomic masses of most elements in the periodic table, you will see that most of them are not whole numbers or close to whole numbers. This is because the average atomic mass of an element is not the mass of an individual atom of that element. Instead, it is the average mass (in grams) of one mole of a representative sample of the element. The average atomic mass of an element listed in the periodic table is the average of all the isotopes of the element, weighted for relative abundance. Isotopes of an element are atoms of the element with different numbers of neutrons. Isotopes of an element have the same chemical properties but different atomic masses.

EXAMPLE 1

Calculate Average Atomic Mass

Use the information in the table below to calculate the average atomic mass of neon in amu.

Isotope	Abundance	Atomic Mass (amu)
^{20}Ne	90.48%	19.992
^{21}Ne	0.27%	20.994
^{22}Ne	9.25%	21.991

Solution

1 Analyze The average atomic mass of an element is the weighted average of the atomic masses of the isotopes that make it up. So, to calculate the average atomic mass of neon, use the equation below:

$$m_{Ne} = (A_{20})(m_{20}) + (A_{21})(m_{21}) + (A_{22})(m_{22})$$

In this equation, m_{Ne} is the average atomic mass of neon, A_{20} is the abundance of ^{20}Ne, m_{20} is the atomic mass of ^{20}Ne, A_{21} is the abundance of ^{21}Ne, m_{21} is the atomic mass of ^{21}Ne, A_{22} is the abundance of ^{22}Ne, and m_{22} is the atomic mass of ^{22}Ne.

2 Solve

$$m_{Ne} = (A_{20})(m_{20}) + (A_{21})(m_{21}) + (A_{22})(m_{22})$$
$$= (0.9048)(19.992 \text{ amu}) + (0.0027)(20.994 \text{ amu}) + (0.0925)(21.991 \text{ amu})$$
$$= 20 \text{ amu}$$

REMEMBER

ISOTOPES

- Atoms of an element with different numbers of neutrons are isotopes of that element. The number of protons in an atom determines what element it is.

- To write the chemical symbol for an isotope, write the whole number closest to its atomic mass as a superscript to the left of the chemical symbol for the element. For example, carbon-13 has an atomic mass of 13.003 amu, so the chemical symbol for carbon-13 is ^{13}C.

- The average atomic mass of an element that is listed in the periodic table is the weighted average of the atomic masses of all the isotopes of that element.

- By convention, chemists define an atom of carbon-12 (^{12}C) to have a mass of exactly 12 amu. All other atomic masses are defined relative to this mass.

EXAMPLE 2

Identify the Most Abundant Isotope

The average atomic mass of boron is 10.81 amu. The two naturally occuring isotopes boron-10 (^{10}B) and boron-11 (^{11}B) make up close to 100% of the boron that exists. The table to the right gives the atomic masses of single atoms of boron-10 and boron-11. Which isotope is more abundant?

Solution

1 Recall Relevant Information   The average atomic mass of an element is the weighted average of the atomic masses of all of its isotopes. Boron-10 and boron-11 together make up close to 100% of the boron that exists. Therefore, the average atomic mass of boron is equal to the atomic mass of ^{10}B times the fraction of all boron atoms that are ^{10}B plus the atomic mass of ^{11}B times the fraction of all boron atoms that are ^{11}B.

2 Reason and Solve   If boron-10 and boron-11 were equally abundant—that is, if 50% of the boron atoms were ^{10}B and 50% were ^{11}B—then the average atomic mass of boron would be $(0.5)(10.013) + (0.5)(11.009) = 10.51$. Boron's atomic mass is greater than this. Therefore, the heavier isotope, ^{11}B, must be the more abundant one.

TIP

The number in the superscript of a chemical symbol for an isotope (for example, the 20 in ^{20}Ne) indicates the sum of the number of protons and the number of neutrons in an atom of the isotope. Because protons and neutrons have atomic masses near 1 amu, their sum is close to the atomic mass of the isotope.

Isotope	Atomic Mass (amu)
Boron-10	10.013
Boron-11	11.009

Problem Set

1. An atom has 18 protons and 20 neutrons. Write the chemical symbol for the atom. (Hint: Use a periodic table.)

2. Lithium (Li) is made up of 7.59% ^{6}Li and 92.41% ^{7}Li. The atomic mass of ^{6}Li is 6.015 amu. The atomic mass of ^{7}Li is 7.016 amu. Calculate the average atomic mass of lithium.

3. Copper (Cu) has an average atomic mass of 63.55 amu and is made up of the isotopes ^{63}Cu and ^{65}Cu. Assuming these are the only isotopes of copper, which isotope is most abundant?

4. Silicon (Si) is made up of 92.23% ^{28}Si (atomic mass 27.977 amu), 4.68% ^{29}Si (atomic mass 28.976 amu), and 3.09% ^{30}Si (atomic mass 29.974 amu). What is the average atomic mass of silicon in amu?

5. The average atomic mass of rubidium (Rb) is 85.47 amu. Rubidium is made up of isotopes ^{85}Rb and ^{87}Rb. Assuming these are the only isotopes of rubidium, which isotope is more abundant?

6. An atom contains 64 neutrons and has an atomic mass of 112 amu. Write the chemical symbol for one atom of this element.

7. **Challenge**   Bromine (Br) has an average atomic mass of 79.9 amu. Assume that it is made up only of the isotopes ^{79}Br and ^{81}Br. What is the approximate ratio of ^{79}Br to ^{81}Br?

8. **Challenge**   Carbon (C) has two isotopes, ^{12}C (atomic mass 12.000 amu) and ^{13}C (atomic mass 13.003 amu). The average atomic mass of carbon is 12.011 amu. Calculate the abundance of each isotope of carbon.

9. **Challenge**   Chlorine (Cl) is made up of 75.78% ^{35}Cl (atomic mass 34.969 amu) and 24.22% ^{37}Cl. Chlorine's average atomic mass is 35.45 amu. Calculate the atomic mass of ^{37}Cl.

The Bohr Atom

The Bohr model of the atom explains many properties of atoms by portraying electrons as traveling around the nucleus in fixed, circular orbits with fixed energies.

According to the Bohr model of the atom, electrons move around the nucleus in circular orbits at fixed distances from the nucleus. Each orbit also has a fixed (or *quantized*) level of energy. Each of these orbits, or shells, can hold a specific number of electrons. The Bohr model explains absorption and emission spectra and many of the trends in the periodic table. However, it has since been replaced by other atomic models, because it cannot explain all of the observed properties of atoms.

EXAMPLE 1

Use the Bohr Model of an Atom to Explain Elemental Properties

The picture below shows a Bohr model of an atom of lithium. Use the model to explain why lithium tends to form Li^+ ions.

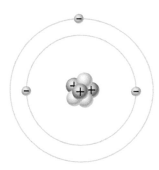

Solution

1 Collect In the Bohr model, electrons travel in orbits with specific energy levels and cannot exist between these levels. In addition, each orbit has a fixed capacity for holding electrons. When one orbit (shell) of an atom is full, any remaining electrons will occupy the orbit of next highest energy. The lithium atom shown above has three electrons—two in its innermost shell and one in its valence (outermost) shell.

2 Solve The innermost energy level has two electrons, and thus is full. Lithium's single valence electron is farther away from the positively charged nucleus than are its two inner electrons. Therefore, its valence electron is much less strongly held than the other two electrons. The valence electrons of an atom are the electrons that participate in chemical reactions. As a result, it is relatively easy for lithium to lose its valence electron, forming a Li^+ ion.

REMEMBER

THE BOHR ATOM

- The Bohr model is not the complete, current model of the atom.
- Although the Bohr model does not explain all properties of atoms, it is accurate enough to serve as an introduction to atomic structure.
- In the Bohr model of the atom, the first electron shell can hold up to two electrons, the second electron shell can hold up to eight electrons, and the third electron shell can hold up to eighteen electrons.

Identify Characteristics of the Bohr Model

Describe the similarities and differences between the Bohr model of the atom and the Rutherford model of the atom.

Solution

1 **Recall Relevant Information** In the Rutherford model, an atom consists of a tiny, dense, positively charged nucleus surrounded by electrons. The electrons orbit the nucleus along specific paths, and those paths can exist anywhere around the nucleus. In the Bohr model, the electrons orbit the positively charged nucleus in specific paths, or shells.

2 **Solve** Both the Bohr atom and the Rutherford atom consist of electrons orbiting a positively charged nucleus. However, in the Bohr model, electrons can exist only in certain energy levels around the nucleus. They cannot just orbit along any path. This is different from the Rutherford model, in which electrons could exist anywhere outside the nucleus.

The Rutherford model of the atom is sometimes called the *planetary model*, because in the Rutherford model, electrons orbit the nucleus in the way that planets orbit the sun.

Problem Set

1. Which of these statements correctly describes the electrons in the Bohr model of the atom?
   A. They are embedded in positively charged matter.
   B. They can be found anywhere outside the nucleus.
   C. They orbit the nucleus in fixed paths.
   D. They are all the same distance from the nucleus.

2. Carbon (C) atoms have six electrons. According to the Bohr model of the atom, how many valence electrons do they have? Explain your answer.

3. According to the Bohr model of the atom, how many valence electrons does an atom of boron (B) have? (Boron's atomic number is 5.) Explain your answer.

4. The Bohr model of an atom of aluminum (Al) shown in the next column is complete except for the placement of the electrons in the three electron shells. Complete the Bohr model of aluminum by drawing a small circle with a minus sign inside to represent each of the electrons in the appropriate shells (represented by gray circles). (Hint: Use a periodic table to determine the number of electrons in an aluminum atom.)

Bohr model of an aluminum atom

5. **Challenge** Draw a picture to represent the Bohr model of an atom of oxygen (O). According to your drawing, how many electrons in an oxygen atom can participate in chemical reactions?

6. **Challenge** Use a Bohr model of a magnesium (Mg) atom to explain why magnesium tends to form Mg^{2+} ions.

Electron Orbitals

In the modern model of the atom, electrons exist in specific orbitals within subshells, which are in turn grouped into electron shells.

In the Bohr model of the atom, electrons can exist only in specific electron shells. The modern atomic model expands on this idea. In the modern model, electrons exist within specific regions of space known as *electron clouds*. They do not orbit the nucleus along single, circular paths. The electron cloud of an atom can be divided into different shells. The electron shells are represented by numbers. The number 1 represents the innermost shell, the number 2 represents the next shell, and so on. Each shell is, in turn, made up of between one and four subshells, which are represented by the letters *s*, *p*, *d*, and *f*. Each subshell consists of one or more orbitals. One orbital can hold up to two electrons. An *s* subshell has one orbital, a *p* subshell has three orbitals, a *d* subshell has five orbitals, and an *f* subshell has seven orbitals. Electrons fill the orbitals in a specific pattern.

OBJECTIVES

- Interpret diagrams of electron configurations using standard notation.
- Create energy level diagrams for various atoms.

REMEMBER

ORBITALS

- Two electrons cannot occupy the same place at the same time.
- The periodic table reflects how shells and subshells fill as atomic number increases.
- Subshells represent energy levels.
- Each orbital can hold a maximum of two electrons. Each type of subshell consists of a different number of orbitals, so each type of subshell can hold a different number of electrons.

EXAMPLE 1

Write the Electron Configuration for an Atom

Draw an orbital diagram to show the electron configuration of manganese (Mn).

Solution

1 Collect and Strategize Manganese's atomic number is 25, so it has 25 electrons. The diagram to the right gives the order in which the electron subshells fill. First, draw an empty orbital diagram, using arrows to represent electrons. Then, fill in the electrons starting with the lowest energy level, continuing to fill until 25 electrons have been drawn according to orbital filling rules.

2 Solve The diagram below shows the completed electron diagram for manganese. Notice that the five electrons in the 3*d* orbitals each half-fill an orbital, rather than pairing up. This follows an orbital filling rule stating that an orbital fills up first with electrons of the same spin. Also notice that each pair of electrons consists of one "spin-up" electron (up arrow) and one "spin-down" electron (down arrow).

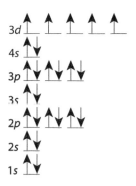

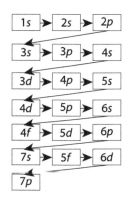

This flowchart shows the order in which electron shells are filled. Notice that the 4*s* shell is filled before the 3*d* shell.

EXAMPLE 2

Write an Electron Configuration for an Element

Write the standard electron configuration for the element bromine (Br).

Solution

1 Collect and Strategize Bromine's atomic number is 35, so it has 35 electrons. Write the symbols for the different subshells in the order in which they fill with electrons. Stop when 35 electrons have been accounted for.

2 Solve and Check The electron configuration for bromine is $1s^2\ 2s^2\ 2p^6\ 3s^2\ 3p^6\ 4s^2\ 3d^{10}\ 4p^5$. To check this configuration, add the superscripts together to ensure that they sum to 35, as shown below:

$$2 + 2 + 6 + 2 + 6 + 2 + 10 + 5 = 35$$

A standard electron configuration uses symbols to represent the different subshells. For example, the p subshell of the second electron shell is represented by the symbol $2p$. The number of electrons in the subshell is represented by a superscript on the subshell's letter. For example, a full $3s$ subshell is written as $3s^2$.

Problem Set

1. Identify the maximum number of electrons that can occupy an s subshell, a p subshell, a d subshell, and an f subshell. Explain your answer.

2. Write the standard electron configuration for an electrically neutral atom of sodium (Na).

3. Draw an orbital diagram to show the electron configuration of an atom of carbon (C).

4. Draw an orbital diagram to show the electron configuration of an aluminum ion with a +3 charge (Al^{3+}). (Hint: Atoms lose their valence electrons first when they form positive ions.)

5. An electrically neutral atom has the electron configuration $1s^2\ 2s^2\ 2p^6\ 3s^2\ 3p^4$. What element is it an atom of?

6. Write the electron configurations for the first four elements in group 1A (the first vertical column) of the periodic table at the back of the book. Use the configurations to explain why these elements tend to form ions with a +1 charge.

7. **Challenge** Write the standard electron configuration of a chloride ion (Cl^-).

8. **Challenge** The energy level diagram below represents an ion with a charge of −2.

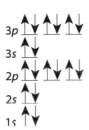

What is the ion?

9. **Challenge** In the periodic table at the back of the book, the transition metals fall in the B groups. (A group in the periodic table is a vertical column.) In terms of electron configuration, how are these elements similar? Why do you think there are ten transition metals in each period (horizontal row) of the periodic table?

The Quantum Atom and Atomic Spectra

Quantum theory explains the structure of the atom and relates the electronic structure of atoms to the values of the discrete energies observed for emission spectra.

The modern model of the atom is called the *quantum mechanical model*. According to the quantum mechanical model, an atom's electrons exist in a region of space known as an *electron cloud*. There is no way to know exactly where an electron is within this cloud at any given time, but the quantum mechanical model allows us to determine the areas where it is most likely to be. Like the Bohr model, the quantum mechanical model assumes that electrons can exist only in certain areas that correspond to specific levels of energy. When subjected to electromagnetic radiation, atoms absorb, and then emit, radiation in discrete, narrow frequency bands. An atom emits energy when one of its electrons drops from a higher energy level to a lower energy level. The resulting emission spectra correspond to the energies of the orbitals in the atom's electron cloud.

OBJECTIVES

- Describe energy ranges of the electromagnetic spectrum.
- Relate emission spectra to electronic configuration of atoms.

REMEMBER

THE QUANTUM ATOM AND ATOMIC SPECTRA

- Atomic absorption and emission spectra reveal the electronic structure and electronic energy levels of atoms.
- Quantum theory explains electron configuration, energy levels, and emission spectra.
- Simple relationships exist between wavelength, frequency, energy, and speed of electromagnetic radiation.

EXAMPLE 1

Relate Atomic Absorption Spectra to Atomic Models

Different elements absorb electromagnetic radiation of different wavelengths. For example, sodium atoms will not absorb the same wavelengths of light as chlorine atoms will. Explain this observation using the quantum mechanical model of the atom.

Solution

1 Recall   Different wavelengths of electromagnetic radiation have different amounts of energy. The wavelength of an electromagnetic wave is inversely proportional to its energy—that is, the larger the wavelength, the lower the energy of the wave. According to the quantum mechanical model, the electrons in an atom can exist only in certain areas, which have specific energies. An electron can move to a higher energy level only if the atom absorbs a specific amount of energy.

2 Solve   The energy levels in which electrons exist are different in different atoms. An atom will absorb energy only if that energy allows an electron to move to a higher energy level. Therefore, atoms of different elements must absorb different amounts of energy to allow their electrons to move to higher energy levels. Different wavelengths of electromagnetic radiation have different amounts of energy, so different elements will absorb the wavelengths of radiation that correspond to the energies needed to move their electrons to higher energy levels.

TIP

The wavelength and frequency of electromagnetic radiation are also inversely related: the higher the wavelength, the lower the frequency. Therefore, frequency and energy are directly related: the higher the frequency, the greater the energy.

EXAMPLE 2

Relate Emission Spectra to Observable Effects

When it is excited by absorbing energy, an atom of beryllium (Be) emits visible blue light. In contrast, an atom of boron (B) emits yellow and orange light. Use the electromagnetic spectrum shown below to identify which of these emissions corresponds to energy levels that are farther apart energetically from each other.

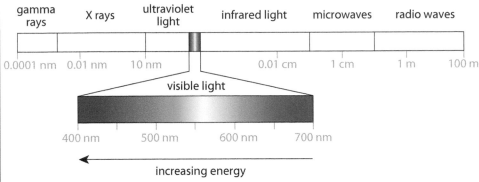

Solution

1 **Collect and Strategize** An atom emits energy when one of its electrons drops from a higher energy level to a lower energy level. The greater the difference in energy levels of an atom, the higher the energy of the light it emits. The amount of energy in electromagnetic radiation is inversely related to its wavelength. Yellow and orange light have longer wavelengths than blue light does, so blue light has more energy than yellow and orange light do.

2 **Solve** Beryllium emits light with greater energy (smaller wavelength) than boron does. The energy released in beryllium to produce the blue light indicates that the electron that released the energy dropped through a greater energy transition than the one that dropped in boron to produce the yellow and orange light. Therefore, beryllium's emission corresponds to electrons moving from energy levels that are farther apart in energy than those in boron.

Problem Set

1. Astronomers can use the electromagnetic emission spectra of distant stars to determine their elemental compositions. Explain how this is possible.

2. Atom A emits mainly X rays when it is excited. Atom B emits mainly gamma rays. Which emission corresponds to a transition between energy levels that are closer in energy? Explain your answer. (Hint: Refer to the electromagnetic spectrum in Example 2 above.)

3. One of the energy-level drops that an electron in a certain atom can undergo releases light with a wavelength of about 323 nm. What type of radiation does this atom give off during this energy-level drop? (Hint: Refer to the electromagnetic spectrum in Example 2 above. 1 nm $= 1 \times 10^{-9}$ m.)

4. Atom A absorbs mainly violet light. When it loses an electron to form an A^+ ion, the ion absorbs mainly green light. Which absorption corresponds to a transition between energy levels that are closer in energy? Explain your answer.

5. **Challenge** Hydrogen has only one electron, yet its absorption and emission spectra contain many lines. Explain how this is possible.

6. **Challenge** Explain why more energy is generally required to cause an inner electron to jump to a higher energy level than to cause a valence electron to jump to a higher energy level.

Atomic Number and the Periodic Law

Dimitri Mendeleev devised the first widely accepted periodic table by arranging the elements in a pattern based on increasing atomic mass and repeating properties.

In 1869, Dimitri Mendeleev published his first version of the periodic table. He knew the relative atomic masses of the elements that had been discovered at that time. When he listed the elements in order of increasing atomic mass, he observed that certain properties repeated at regular intervals. He called this the *periodic law*, and he arranged his table to illustrate this law by putting elements with similar properties in the same column.

OBJECTIVES

- Describe the structure of the first widely accepted periodic table.
- Explain the periodic law.

EXAMPLE 1

Describe Mendeleev's Periodic Table

The diagram below shows the first four periods (rows) of Mendeleev's periodic table. Describe the similarities and differences between the diagram and the first four periods of the modern periodic table.

H						
Li	Be	B	C	N	O	F
Na	Mg	Al	Si	P	S	Cl
K	Ca		Ti	V	Cr	Mn	Fe, Cu, Ni

REMEMBER

MENDELEEV'S PERIODIC TABLE

- Mendeleev had never seen the Bohr model of the atom and had no knowledge of subatomic particles.
- Mendeleev had only partially accurate atomic masses and chemical properties to work with.

Solution

① Observe Turn to the back of the book and examine the first four rows of the modern periodic table shown there. Compare the locations of the elements in both periodic tables and the layout of both tables.

② Solve The first three rows of both tables are very similar. Mendeleev's periodic table does not show the noble gases helium (He), neon (Ne), or argon (Ar), but otherwise the order of the elements in the first three rows of both tables is the same: H, Li, Be, B, C, N, O, F, Na, Mg, Al, Si, P, S, Cl. The fourth row of Mendeleev's table differs from the modern table more significantly. In particular, Mendeleev placed some of the elements we now call *transition metals*, such as titanium (Ti) and vanadium (V), in the same columns as nontransition metals.

EXAMPLE 2

Use Atomic Models to Explain the Periodic Law

How does the modern model of the atom explain the repeating chemical properties of the elements?

Solution

1 **Recall Relevant Information** The chemical properties of an element depend largely on the element's electron arrangement—specifically, its number and distribution of valence electrons. Elements with the same number and arrangement of valence electrons therefore have similar properties. In the modern model of the atom, electrons occupy energy levels in an atom, and they fill those energy levels in a specific order. The atomic number of an element determines how many electrons are in an atom of that element, because in a neutral atom the number of electrons equals the number of protons.

2 **Solve** The nature of orbital filling proposed by the modern atomic model leads to repetition in the number of valence electrons in different elements, even though each element has a unique number of electrons. For example, although lithium and sodium have different numbers of total electrons, they each have only a single valence electron (in the $2s$ subshell for lithium and the $3s$ subshell for sodium). Because valence electron arrangements repeat at regular intervals as atomic number increases, chemical properties that depend on electron arrangement repeat at the same intervals.

TIP

The repeating properties of the elements in the periodic table lead to trends in properties through the rows and columns of the table.

Problem Set

1. Which of these is a characteristic of the modern periodic table, but **not** of Mendeleev's periodic table?
   A. elements arranged by increasing atomic mass
   B. elements placed in columns according to chemical properties
   C. distribution of elements determined by electron configuration
   D. heavier elements in lower rows

2. Write your own definition for *periodic law*.

3. Mendeleev did not include the noble gases (He, Ne, Ar, and so on) in his periodic table. Consider their reactivity. State a possible reason for this omission.

4. Describe how Mendeleev developed his periodic table.

5. **Challenge** Mendeleev left several blank spaces in his periodic table. Why do you think he left those spaces blank, instead of simply placing the next heaviest element in them?

6. **Challenge** Based on where Mendeleev positioned the elements iron (Fe), copper (Cu), and nickel (Ni), what can you conclude about their properties? Explain your answer.

Problem Set 20

The Periodic Table

You can learn about an element's physical and chemical properties from its location in the periodic table.

The periodic table is a chart that lists all the elements. Elements that share similar qualities are located near each other on the periodic table. The location of an element in the periodic table can help you predict that element's properties. The horizontal rows on the periodic table are called *periods*. In each of the table's seven periods, elements are listed from left to right in order of increasing atomic number—that is, the number of protons in an atom's nucleus. All elements in a period have the same number of electron shells. The number of the row in which an element is located tells you how many electron shells the element has. The vertical columns on the periodic table are called *groups*. Elements in the same group have the same number of valence electrons. Therefore, elements in the same group tend to have similar chemical and physical properties.

OBJECTIVE

- Describe the characteristics of the periodic table.

REMEMBER

PERIODS AND GROUPS

- Elements in a period (row) have the same number of electron shells. That number is equal to the number of the period. So, for example, elements in period 3 have electrons in the first, second, and third electron shells.

- Elements in the same group (column) have the same number of valence electrons and typically have similar physical and chemical properties. For elements in the A groups (1A, 2A, 3A, and so on), the number of valence electrons is equal to the number of the group. So, for example, elements in group 6A all have six valence electrons.

- Some groups of elements have specific names. The elements in group 1A are called the *alkali metals*. The elements in group 2A are called the *alkaline earth metals*. The elements in the B groups are called the *transition metals*. The elements in group 7A are called the *halogens*, and the elements in group 8A are called the *noble gases*.

EXAMPLE 1

Identify an Element's Period and Group

Common table salt, or sodium chloride, forms from the elements sodium (Na) and chlorine (Cl). Identify an element that has the same number of electron shells as sodium and another element that has the same number of valence electrons as chlorine.

Solution

1 Recall Relevant Information Elements in the same row, or period, have the same number of electron shells. Elements in the same column, or group, have the same number of valence electrons. Therefore, look for an element that is in the same period as sodium and another element that is in the same group as chlorine.

2 Study the Periodic Table Examine the periodic table at the back of the book. Sodium is in the third period, and chlorine is in group 7A. Therefore, sodium has three electron shells, and chlorine has seven valence electrons.

3 Solve Magnesium, aluminum, silicon, phosphorus, sulfur, chlorine, and argon are all in the third row, so these elements are in the same period as sodium, and they all have three electron shells. Fluorine, bromine, iodine, and astatine are all in group 7A, the same group as chlorine, so they all have seven valence electrons.

EXAMPLE 2

Predict an Element's Properties

Neon (Ne) is a gas that glows red in vacuum-discharge tubes in the presence of electricity. These tubes are often twisted into words and shapes to make neon signs. Neon is also very nonreactive—that is, it does not form compounds easily. Identify two elements that probably have properties similar to neon.

Solution

1 **Recall Relevant Information** Elements in the same group on the periodic table tend to have similar properties because they have the same number of valence electrons. Look at the periodic table at the back of the book. Notice that neon is in group 8A. Therefore, other elements in group 8A probably have properties similar to neon.

2 **Solve** Helium, argon, krypton, xenon, and radon are all in group 8A. Therefore, they all probably have properties similar to neon.

TIP

Elements in group 8A are also known as noble gases. Their full outer electron shells make them very nonreactive and stable.

Problem Set

1. Silicon dioxide (SiO_2) is one of the most common compounds on earth. It is found in most rocks on and below earth's surface. It is the major component of most kinds of sand. Identify an element with the same number of valence electrons as silicon, and another element with the same number of electron shells as oxygen. Explain your answer.

2. Which of the following elements probably has the most properties in common with gold (Au)?
   A. lead (Pb)
   B. copper (Cu)
   C. aluminum (Al)
   D. rubidium (Rb)

3. Identify the element that has the same number of valence electrons as germanium and the same number of electron shells as iodine.

4. Lithium (Li) tends to form ions with a charge of +1. Identify two other elements that probably form ions with +1 charges. Explain your answer.

5. **Challenge** Calcium carbonate ($CaCO_3$) makes up many marine animals' shells. Small amounts of strontium (Sr) can take the place of some of the calcium (Ca) in these animals' shells. Explain why strontium can substitute for calcium in calcium carbonate. (Hint: These marine animals use chemical reactions to form their shells.)

6. **Challenge** Scientists in Russia created a few atoms of ununoctium, element number 118, in 2006. Ununoctium is in group 8A. With which elements does ununoctium most likely share chemical and physical properties? Explain your answer.

Electron Arrangement Patterns

You can use the periodic table to figure out how many electrons an element has available to bond with other elements.

The periodic table is full of useful information about each element's physical and chemical characteristics. One piece of information you can derive from the table is how many electrons an element has available for bonding, which can tell you something about its chemical reactivity. Remember that electrons fill orbitals in a specific order. That filling order is reflected in the elements' positions in the table. Elements in groups 1A and 2A, along with helium in group 8A, are known as the *s*-block elements, because their valence electrons are located only in an *s* subshell. Likewise, elements in groups 3A–7A are known as the *p*-block elements, because they have some valence electrons in a *p* subshell. Transition metals are also called *d*-block elements, and those at the bottom of the table (the lanthanides and actinides) are known as the *f*-block. The period number for the *s* and *p* blocks indicates which subshell the electrons fill. For example, in the first period, the 1*s* subshell is being filled. In the second period, the 2*s* and 2*p* subshells are being filled. Therefore, an element's position in the periodic table tells you how many valence electrons it has. For example, for the group A elements, the number of valence electrons is equal to the group number.

OBJECTIVE

- Describe how the arrangement of elements in the periodic table corresponds to the order of electron shell filling.

REMEMBER

ELECTRON FILLING PATTERNS

- The order in which electrons fill subshells is reflected in blocks on the periodic table: Groups 1A and 2A are the *s*-block, groups 3A–8A are the *p*-block, the B group elements are the *d*-block, and the lanthanides and actinides are the *f*-block.

- The subshell number is the same as the period number for the *s*- and *p*-blocks. It starts at 3 in the fourth period for the *d*-block.

- To figure out how many electrons are available for bonding, count from left to right from the beginning of a block.

EXAMPLE 1

Identify the Number of Valence Electrons an Element Has

Arsenic (As) is a metalloid. It has some industrial uses, but most of its compounds are toxic to people and other living things. How many valence electrons does an atom of arsenic have?

Solution

1 **Examine the Periodic Table**   First, locate arsenic on the periodic table at the back of the book. Notice that it is in group 5A. Therefore, it is a member of the *p*-block elements.

2 **Solve and Check**   For the group A elements, the group number indicates the number of valence electrons in the elements in the group. Since arsenic is in group 5A, it has five valence electrons. To check this, write the electron configuration for arsenic. Arsenic has 33 electrons, so its electron configuration is $1s^2\, 2s^2\, 2p^6\, 3s^2\, 3p^6\, 4s^2\, 3d^{10}\, 4p^3$. The valence electrons are in the 4*s* and 4*p* subshells, and there are $2 + 3 = 5$ valence electrons.

EXAMPLE 2

Predict Electron Configuration Based on Location

Without counting electrons, predict the electron configuration of aluminum (Al). How many valence electrons does it have? In which subshells are they located?

Solution

1 **Recall Relevant Information** The period number of an element indicates which electron shell its valence electrons are located in. The group number of a group A element indicates how many valence electrons it has. Examine the periodic table at the back of the book. Notice that aluminum is in group 3A, period 3.

2 **Solve and Check** Aluminum is in group 3A, so it must have three valence electrons. It is in period 3, so its valence electrons must be located in the third electron shell. The first and second electron shells must be full. Therefore, aluminum must have two electrons in the 1s subshell, two electrons in the 2s subshell, and six electrons in the 2p subshell. Two of its three valence electrons are in the 3s subshell, and the last one is in the 3p subshell. Therefore, its electron configuration must be $1s^2\,2s^2\,2p^6\,3s^2\,3p^1$. To check, find the total number of electrons, which is $2 + 2 + 6 + 2 + 1 = 13$. Aluminum has 13 electrons, so the predicted electron configuration is correct.

TIP

Remember that the 3d subshell fills after the 4s subshell, but before the 4p subshell. That pattern occurs for other d and f subshells as well. Therefore, be extra careful predicting electron configurations and numbers of valence electrons for transition metals, lanthanides, and actinides.

Problem Set

1. Carbon (C) is one of the most important elements in biological molecules. How many valence electrons does carbon have? Identify one other element with this same number of valence electrons.

2. Calcium (Ca) is an important component of human bones and teeth. Without counting electrons, predict the electron configuration of calcium.

3. Francium (Fr) has one valence electron, and the electron is in the 7s subshell. Without looking at the periodic table, state the group and period in which francium is located.

4. An element has two valence electrons. They are both located in an s subshell. Give two possibilities for the identity of the element.

5. **Challenge** Scientists think that earth's core (its innermost layer) is made primarily of iron (Fe) and nickel (Ni). Without counting electrons, predict the electron configurations of iron and nickel.

6. **Challenge** Describe the general pattern of the valence electron configuration of all the elements in group 8A.

Trends Within the Periodic Table

You can predict the chemical and physical properties of an element from its position in the periodic table.

The periodic law states that many physical and chemical properties recur when the elements are arranged in order of increasing atomic number. The periodic table arranges elements into horizontal rows called *periods* and vertical columns called *groups* or *families*. As you move from left to right across a period, electrons are added one at a time to a particular energy level. As you move from top to bottom in a group, electrons are added to increasingly higher energy levels. The patterns in electron filling produce trends in electronegativity, ionization energy, and relative sizes of ions and atoms.

OBJECTIVES

- Analyze periodic trends.
- Use periodic trends to predict properties of elements in the periodic table.

EXAMPLE 1

Predict Trends in Atomic Radius

Predict how the atomic radius of the elements in a group changes as you move from top to bottom in the group.

Solution

1. **Recall Relevant Information**   As you move from top to bottom in a group, the elements have progressively greater numbers of electrons, and those electrons are found in progressively more distant electron shells.

2. **Solve**   As you move down a group, the number of electron shells in the elements increases. Therefore, atomic radius probably increases as you move down a group.

REMEMBER

TRENDS WITHIN THE PERIODIC TABLE

- In general, atomic radius increases from top to bottom in a group and decreases from left to right across a period.

- In general, first ionization energy decreases from top to bottom in a group and increases from left to right across a period.

- In general, electronegativity decreases from top to bottom in a group and increases from left to right across a period, except for the noble gases.

EXAMPLE 2

Explain Trends in Ionization Energy

The first ionization energy of an atom is the amount of energy required to remove a single valence electron from the neutral atom in the gas phase. For example, the first ionization energy of sodium is the energy of the following reaction:

$$Na_{(g)} \rightarrow Na^+_{(g)} + e^-$$

First ionization energies tend to decrease as you move from top to bottom in a group, and they tend to increase as you move from left to right across a period. Explain these observations.

Solution

⊖ valence electron
⊖ inner ("shielding") electron

1 Recall Relevant Information   All the elements in a group have the same number of valence electrons, but as you move down a group, the number of protons and of electron shells increases. As you move from left to right across a period, the number of protons and electrons increases, but the valence electrons are being added to the same electron shell or subshell. The first ionization energy must be enough to overcome the attraction between a valence electron and the nucleus.

2 Solve   As you move down a group, first ionization energy decreases because the valence electrons are farther away from the nucleus. Although the positive charge of the nucleus increases as the number of protons increases, the valence electrons are shielded from much of the additional attraction by the inner electrons, as shown to the right. Elements that are farther down in the group have more inner, shielding electrons, so the attraction between the valence electrons and the nucleus is weaker. The weaker attraction makes the valence electrons easier to remove from the atom.

As you move across a period, the number of protons in the nucleus also increases, but there is no increase in shielding from the inner electrons—for example, carbon (C) has the same number of inner electrons as lithium (Li). Therefore, the attraction between the nucleus and the valence electrons becomes stronger as you move across a period, and the first ionization energy increases as a result.

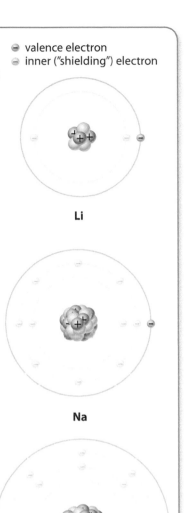

Li

Na

K

TIP

The shielding effect from inner electrons increases more rapidly than the positive charge on the nucleus as you move down a column. Therefore, the increased shielding mainly controls the trends in elemental properties as you move down a group.

TIP

Although electrons do not actually travel in circular orbits around atomic nuclei, scientists often draw models of atoms with electrons in circular orbits, as shown here, for simplicity. Also for simplicity, scientists often show atomic nuclei as solid spheres of positive charge, even though nuclei actually contain protons and neutrons.

EXAMPLE 3

Predict Relative Electronegativities

Identify the element with the lowest electronegativity and the element with the highest electronegativity n the periodic table.

Solution

1 Recall Relevant Information   Electronegativity is a measure of how readily an atom attracts electrons when it is part of a compound. In general, elements with high first ionization energies tend to have high electronegativities, and vice versa.

An important exception to this trend is the noble gases, which all have very low electronegativities because they tend not to form compounds. First ionization energy is generally highest in the upper-right corner of the periodic table. It is generally lowest in the lower-left corner.

2 **Solve** Cesium (Cs) is the least electronegative element in the periodic table. (Although francium is located lower in group 1A than cesium is, francium is unstable, so its electronegativity is difficult to define.) Fluorine (F) is the element in the upper-right corner of the periodic table (if you exclude the noble gases), so it is the most electronegative element in the periodic table.

EXAMPLE 4

Predict Differences in Ionic Radius

For each of the following pairs of species, identify which species has the largest radius: Na and Na^+, Mg^{2+} and Ca^{2+}, and F and F^-.

Solution

1 **Recall Relevant Information** The size of a neutral atom depends mainly on two things: the magnitude of the positive charge on the nucleus and the number of inner electrons shielding the valence electrons from the nucleus. It is therefore reasonable to assume that the size of an ion would depend on similar factors. Therefore, for each pair of species, compare the magnitude of the positive charge on the nucleus to the number of shielding electrons. For an atom to form a positive ion (cation), it must lose one or more electrons. For an atom to form a negative ion (anion), it must gain one or more electrons. As you move from left to right across a period, the number of valence electrons increases, but the number of electron shells stays the same. As you move from top to bottom in a group, the number of valence electrons stays the same, but the number of electron shells increases.

2 **Reason** When an atom becomes an ion, only the number of electrons changes. The number of protons in the nucleus, and therefore the magnitude of the positive charge on the nucleus, does not change. In general, only the valence electrons are affected when an ion forms, so the number of shielding, inner electrons also does not change. Therefore, when Na becomes Na^+ by losing an electron, the same magnitude of positive charge affects one less electron. When F becomes F^-, the same magnitude of positive charge affects one more electron. As you move down a group, the positive charge on the nucleus increases, but so does the number of inner, shielding electrons. Therefore, although Ca^{2+} and Mg^{2+} both have the same amount of "extra" positive charge, there is more shielding between the Ca^{2+} nucleus and the valence electrons than there is between the Mg^{2+} nucleus and its valence electrons.

3 **Solve** A sodium ion (Na^+) and a sodium atom (Na) both have the same amount of positive charge and shielding. However, in the ion, the positive charge is attracting fewer electrons, so the electrons are more closely held. Therefore, Na^+ is smaller than Na. In contrast, a fluoride ion (F^-) is larger than a fluorine atom (F). In the F^- ion, the positive nuclear charge is acting on more electrons than it is in the neutral atom. Therefore, the electrons in the F^- are more closely held. Because there is more shielding between the Ca^{2+} nucleus and its valence electrons than between the Mg^{2+} nucleus and its valence electrons, the Ca^{2+} ion will be larger than the Mg^{2+} ion.

TIP

Every cation is smaller than its corresponding neutral atom. Every anion is larger than its corresponding neutral atom.

EXAMPLE 5

Describe Periodic Trends

Draw a sketch of the periodic table, and use arrows to indicate the trends in atomic radius, first ionization energy, and electronegativity on the sketch.

TIP

The strength of the attraction between the atom's nucleus and its valence electrons is the main factor that determines atomic radius, first ionization energy, and electronegativity. As the strength of attraction increases, the atomic radius decreases, and the first ionization energy and electronegativity increase.

Solution

1 Recall Relevant Information   Atomic radius generally increases from top to bottom in a group and decreases from left to right across a period. First ionization energy generally decreases from top to bottom in a group and increases from left to right across a period. Electronegativity generally decreases from top to bottom in a group and increases from left to right across a period.

2 Solve   The sketch below shows the trends in atomic radius (red arrow), first ionization energy (blue arrow), and electronegativity (green arrow) in the periodic table. In each case, the arrow points in the direction of increasing values.

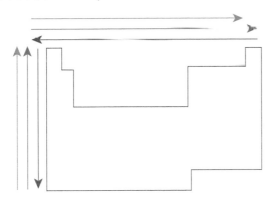

Problem Set

1. Calcium ions (Ca²⁺) are necessary for the regulation of body fluids, transmission of nerve impulses, and heart activity. Which has the larger radius, a calcium atom or a calcium ion?

2. Which probably has the greater first ionization energy, lithium (Li) or neon (Ne)? Explain your answer.

3. List the following elements in order of increasing electronegativity: tellurium (Te), chlorine (Cl), and barium (Ba).

4. Draw a sketch of what a graph of atomic radius vs. atomic number would look like for the period 3 elements.

5. **Challenge**   Some elements can form ions with different charges. For example, nitrogen (N) can form N³⁻, N³⁺, and N⁵⁺ ions. List the following species from largest radius to smallest radius: N³⁺, N³⁻, N, and N⁵⁺. Explain your answer.

6. **Challenge**   The second ionization energy of an element is the energy required to remove a single valence electron from a cation of the element with a charge of +1 (for example, to remove an electron from Ca⁺ to form Ca²⁺). Explain why the second ionization energy for an element is generally greater than the element's first ionization energy.

Metals

Metals make up the vast majority of elements in the periodic table, and they have distinct physical and chemical properties that make them useful in a variety of applications.

About 75 percent of all the elements are classified as metals. Except for hydrogen (H), all of the elements in groups 1A and 2A are metals, and all of the elements in the B groups are also metals. Some elements in groups 3A–6A are also considered metals. In addition to their position on the periodic table, metals have other qualities that distinguish them from nonmetals and metalloids. In general, metals are shiny, have high densities, and are solid at room temperature. They are also malleable, which means they can be hammered into different shapes without breaking, and ductile, which means they can be pulled into thin sheets or wires. Metals are also good conductors of heat and electricity. Chemically, most metals combine easily with nonmetals. Metals typically form positive ions when they react with other elements.

OBJECTIVES

- Locate metals in the periodic table.
- Discuss some of the properties of metals.

EXAMPLE 1

Use the Periodic Table to Identify Metals

Bismuth (Bi), a pinkish solid, is used in many cosmetics and medicines. Is bismuth a metal?

Solution

① Examine the Periodic Table

Examine the periodic table at the back of the book. Notice that bismuth is in group 5A. Some of the elements in this group are considered metals, but others are not. The diagram to the right shows the elements in groups 3A–6A that are considered metals. In this diagram, the metals are highlighted in orange.

					8A
3A	4A	5A	6A	7A	He
B	C	N	O	F	Ne
Al	Si	P	S	Cl	Ar
Ga	Ge	As	Se	Br	Kr
In	Sn	Sb	Te	I	Xe
Tl	Pb	Bi	Po	At	Rn

② Solve According to the diagram to the right, bismuth is classified as a metal.

REMEMBER

METALS

- All metals except mercury are solids at room temperature. Mercury is liquid at room temperature.
- Although all metals have similar properties, their properties vary. For example, copper and silver conduct electricity better than many other metals, and beryllium is much less malleable and ductile than many other metals.

TIP

You can use an element's location on the periodic table to determine whether it is a metal.

EXAMPLE 2

Describe Physical Properties of Metals

Chromium (Cr) is added to some kinds of steel. It makes the steel harder and less prone to corrosion, or rusting. Predict some properties of chromium.

Solution

1 **Recall Relevant Information** Examine the periodic table at the back of the book. Notice that chromium is in group 6B. All of the group B elements are metals, so chromium is a metal. Some of the distinguishing characteristics of metals include malleability, ductility, high density, high electrical and thermal conductivity, and low specific heat. Most metals are shiny, grayish solids at room temperature.

2 **Solve** Because chromium is a metal, it probably has most or all of the characteristics of metals. It is probably a shiny, grayish solid at room temperature, it probably conducts heat and electricity well, it is probably both malleable and ductile, and it probably has a high density and a low specific heat.

TIP

Remember that not all metals have identical properties. Just knowing that an element is a metal can give you insights into some of its likely properties, but you cannot definitely predict all of the properties of a metal just by knowing it's a metal.

Problem Set

1. Use the periodic table at the back of the book to identify which of the following elements is a metal:
   A. C
   B. F
   C. Ne
   D. Sr

2. Metal wires form the core of most power cords. Which physical qualities of metals make them good materials to put inside power cords?

3. Most types of jewelry incorporate metals. Which physical qualities of metals make them good materials for making jewelry?

4. Use the periodic table at the back of the book to identify the metal in the following list: krypton, sulfur, phosphorus, tellurium, gallium, selenium. Explain your answer.

5. **Challenge** The properties of a metal depend largely on the way the metal atoms interact with one another. Which of the following elements probably has atomic interactions that are most similar to those of gold: potassium, helium, or nitrogen? Explain your answer.

6. **Challenge** Metals generally form positively charged ions when they react with other elements. Do most metals more easily gain or lose electrons? Explain your answer.

Nonmetals

Nonmetals take up the upper right-hand corner of the periodic table, and they have distinct physical and chemical properties that distinguish them from metals and metalloids.

Only about 16 percent of the elements in the periodic table are classified as nonmetals. With the exception of hydrogen (H) in group 1A, all nonmetals are found in the top right-hand corner of the periodic table, in groups 4A–8A. Nonmetals have different properties from metals. Also, the properties of nonmetals are generally less uniform than those of metals. Most nonmetals aren't solid at room temperature, and those that are solid generally have a dull appearance. They aren't malleable or ductile, and they generally have low densities. Nonmetals are also poor conductors of heat and electricity. Chemically, nonmetals react easily with metals. Nonmetals generally form negative ions when they react with other elements.

OBJECTIVES

- Locate nonmetals in the periodic table.
- Discuss some of the properties of nonmetals.

EXAMPLE 1

Use the Periodic Table to Identify Nonmetals

Phosphorus (P), a solid that comes in colors ranging from white to reddish black, is found in a variety of different products, such as explosives, pesticides, toothpastes, and detergents. Is phosphorus a nonmetal?

Solution

1 Locate and Remember
Examine the periodic table at the back of the book. Notice that phosphorus is in group 5A. Some of the elements in this group are considered nonmetals, but others are not. The diagram to the right shows the elements in groups 3A–8A that are considered nonmetals. In this diagram, the nonmetals are highlighted in pink, green, and blue.

2 Solve The diagram to the right shows that phosphorus is classified as a nonmetal.

3A	4A	5A	6A	7A	8A
					He
B	C	N	O	F	Ne
Al	Si	P	S	Cl	Ar
Ga	Ge	As	Se	Br	Kr
In	Sn	Sb	Te	I	Xe
Tl	Pb	Bi	Po	At	Rn

REMEMBER

NONMETALS

- With the exception of hydrogen (H) in group 1A, all nonmetals are in the top right-hand corner of the periodic table, in groups 4A to 8A.
- Nitrogen, oxygen, fluorine, chlorine, and the noble elements (group 8A) are all gases at room temperature. Bromine is a liquid at room temperature. All of the other nonmetals are solids at room temperature.
- Nonmetal atoms tend to form negatively charged ions (anions).

EXAMPLE 2

Describe Physical Properties of Nonmetals

Sulfur (S) is an element that is widely used in fertilizers, matches, gunpowder, and insecticides. It forms dull and brittle yellow crystals at room temperature. Is sulfur a metal or a nonmetal? Answer without looking at a periodic table.

Solution

1 **Recall Relevant Information**   Unlike metals, most nonmetals are brittle— that is, they break instead of bending or stretching when they are put under stress. In their solid forms, most nonmetals are not shiny like metals.

2 **Solve**   Sulfur has physical characteristics shared by nonmetals, including being dull and brittle as a solid. Therefore, sulfur is a nonmetal.

TIP

Nonmetals tend to have a wider variety of colors than metals have. Even a single nonmetal can have a range of colors. For example, carbon can exist as a black solid (charcoal) or as a colorless solid (diamond).

Problem Set

1. Use the periodic table at the back of the book to identify which of the following elements is classified as a nonmetal:
   A. Ar
   B. Cd
   C. Na
   D. Sn

2. Xenon (Xe), an element found in some kinds of light bulbs, is an odorless, colorless gas at room temperature. It is inert, so it doesn't react easily with other elements. Is xenon a metal or a nonmetal? Answer **without** looking at a periodic table. Explain your answer.

3. Fluorine (F) and chlorine (Cl) are both gases at room temperature. When they react with other elements, they tend to form negatively charged ions very easily. Are fluorine and chlorine metals or nonmetals? Answer **without** looking at a periodic table. Explain your answer.

4. Use the periodic table at the back of the book to identify the three nonmetals in the following list: yttrium, iodine, manganese, uranium, helium, hydrogen, ruthenium, strontium.

5. **Challenge**   A scientist is studying a sample of an unknown element. The element is a dull, black solid at room temperature. It does not conduct heat well, and it is very brittle. Identify four groups in the periodic table in which this element might be located. Explain your answer.

6. **Challenge**   Selenium (Se) is a dull, brittle solid at room temperature. When it reacts with other elements, it tends to form Se^{2-} ions. Is selenium a metal or a nonmetal? Answer **without** looking at a periodic table. Explain your answer.

Metalloids

Metalloids, elements that sit in a jagged line on the right side of the periodic table, have properties that are similar to those of both metals and nonmetals.

Metalloids are elements situated between metals and nonmetals, both on the periodic table and in their physical and chemical properties. Remember that metals take up the left and middle of the periodic table, and nonmetals spread out from the table's top right-hand corner. Dividing those two classes of elements are metalloids, which form a jagged or staircase line between metals and nonmetals that stretches diagonally between groups 3A and 6A. Only seven elements on the periodic table are metalloids: boron (B), silicon (Si), germanium (Ge), arsenic (As), antimony (Sb), tellurium (Te), and astatine (At). Metalloids have some properties that are similar to those of metals, but other properties that are more similar to those of nonmetals. For example, metalloids are solids, like most metals. However, some of them are dull, like nonmetals. Metalloids are malleable and ductile like metals. They conduct electricity and heat better than nonmetals, but not as well as metals do.

OBJECTIVES

- Locate metalloids in the periodic table.
- Discuss some of the properties of metalloids.

EXAMPLE 1

Use the Periodic Table to Identify Nonmetals

Which metalloids are in the fifth period of the periodic table?

Solution

1 **Examine the Periodic Table**
Remember that a period on the periodic table is a horizontal row. The metalloids are located in groups 3A–7A, as shown in the diagram to the right. In this diagram, the metalloids are highlighted in purple.

2 **Solve** The fifth period includes the metalloids antimony (Sb) and tellurium (Te).

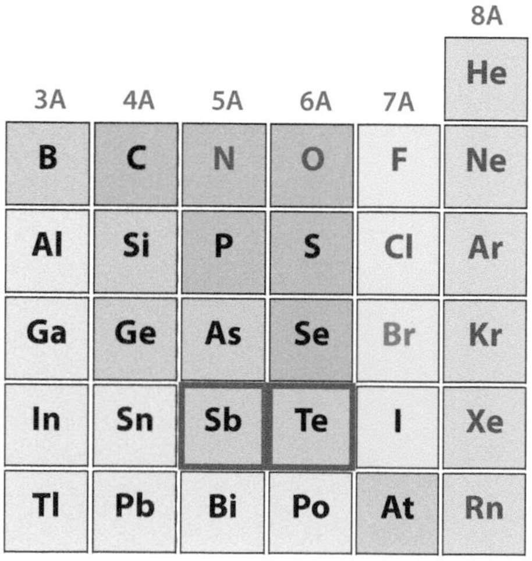

					8A
3A	4A	5A	6A	7A	He
B	C	N	O	F	Ne
Al	Si	P	S	Cl	Ar
Ga	Ge	As	Se	Br	Kr
In	Sn	Sb	Te	I	Xe
Tl	Pb	Bi	Po	At	Rn

REMEMBER

METALLOIDS

- Only seven elements on the periodic table are metalloids: boron (B), silicon (Si), germanium (Ge), arsenic (As), antimony (Sb), tellurium (Te), and astatine (At).
- All metalloids are solid at room temperature.

EXAMPLE 2

Describe Properties of Metalloids

Gold (Au) is a metal, sulfur (S) is a nonmetal, and boron (B) is a metalloid. Rank these three elements from highest to lowest in terms of their electrical conductivity.

TIP

Metalloids have physical and chemical properties that fall between those of metals and nonmetals.

Solution

1 **Recall Relevant Information**   Metalloids have properties that fall between those of metals and nonmetals. They conduct electricity and heat better than nonmetals do, but not as well as metals do.

2 **Solve**   Of these three elements, gold is the best electrical conductor, boron is an intermediate electrical conductor, and sulfur is the poorest electrical conductor.

Problem Set

1. Use the periodic table at the back of the book to identify which of the following elements is classified as a metalloid:
   A. Ac
   B. Ag
   C. Ar
   D. As

2. Use the periodic table at the back of the book to put the following elements in order from the best conductor of electricity to the poorest conductor of electricity: selenium (Se), tin (Sn), antimony (Sb).

3. Which element is probably a better conductor of heat, silicon (Si) or phosphorous (P)? Explain your answer. (Hint: Examine a periodic table.)

4. Use the periodic table at the back of the book to put the following elements in order from least malleable to most malleable: nickel (Ni), germanium (Ge), iodine (I). Explain your answer.

5. **Challenge**   A scientist is studying a sample of an unknown substance. The scientist determines that the substance is a metalloid with four valence electrons. Which two elements could the unknown substance be? Explain your answer. (Hint: Use a periodic table. Remember that the group number of an element indicates the number of valence electrons it has.)

6. **Challenge**   Identify two metalloids that have the same number of electron shells as krypton (Kr). Explain your answer. (Hint: Use a periodic table. Remember that the period an element is in indicates how many electron shells the element has.)

Inner Transition Metals

The lanthanide and actinide series of elements, which are generally shown at the bottom of the periodic table, have physical and chemical properties that differ from those of the other transition metals.

Look at the periodic table at the back of the book. Notice that two rows of elements are separated from the main body of the table. The top row is called the lanthanide series, named after the element lanthanum (La), and includes elements with atomic numbers 57–70. The bottom row is called the actinide series, named after actinium (Ac), and includes elements with atomic numbers 89–102. Long ago, the lanthanides and actinides were grouped together with the other transition metals. However, chemists eventually discovered that these *inner transition metals* have chemical and physical properties that differ from the other transition metals. Many of these elements are so similar to one another that they are difficult to distinguish. All of the inner transition metals are silvery in color. They are all very shiny, but they tarnish easily in air. All are good conductors of electricity. They all react easily and explosively with nonmetals. However, one major difference separates elements with atomic numbers greater than 92 from the rest of the inner transition metals. These elements, which have atomic numbers greater than that of uranium (U), are known as the *transuranium elements*. They do not occur in nature. Transuranium elements are all radioactive, with half-lives significantly shorter than the age of the earth. Therefore, if they were ever present on our planet, they decayed long ago. Scientists can synthesize these elements using machines such as nuclear reactors and particle accelerators.

OBJECTIVES

- Locate the inner transition metals on the periodic table.
- Identify the transuranium elements and describe how they form.

REMEMBER

LANTHANIDES AND ACTINIDES

- The lanthanide series includes elements with atomic numbers from 57–70.
- The actinide series includes elements with atomic numbers from 89–102.
- As a whole, lanthanides and actinides are called inner transition metals. These elements have very similar properties, which differ from those of the other transition metals.

EXAMPLE 1

Use the Periodic Table to Identify Inner Transition Metals

Neodymium (Nd) occurs naturally as part of several minerals, including xenotime, monazite, and bastnasite. Magnets made from neodymium are quite powerful. Is neodymium an inner transition metal?

Solution

1 Recall Relevant Information   The inner transition metals include elements with atomic numbers between 57 and 70 and between 89 and 102. The portion of the periodic table shown below shows the inner transition metals.

57 La Lanthanum 138.91	58 Ce Cerium 140.12	59 Pr Praseodymium 140.91	60 Nd Neodymium 144.24	61 Pm Promethium (145)	62 Sm Samarium 150.4	63 Eu Europium 151.96	64 Gd Gadolinium 157.25	65 Tb Terbium 158.93	66 Dy Dysprosium 162.50	67 Ho Holmium 164.93	68 Er Erbium 167.26	69 Tm Thulium 168.93	70 Yb Ytterbium 173.04
89 Ac Actinium (227)	90 Th Thorium 232.04	91 Pa Protactinium 231.04	92 U Uranium 238.03	93 Np Neptunium (237)	94 Pu Plutonium (244)	95 Am Americium (243)	96 Cm Curium (247)	97 Bk Berkelium (247)	98 Cf Californium (251)	99 Es Einsteinium (252)	100 Fm Fermium (257)	101 Md Mendelevium (258)	102 No Nobelium (259)

2 Solve   Look at the diagram above. Neodymium's atomic number is 60. Therefore, neodymium is an inner transition metal.

EXAMPLE 2

Describe the Formation of Transuranium Elements

Which of the following elements is a synthesized element that does not occur naturally on earth?

    A. Ar

    B. Bk

    C. Cd

    D. Dy

Solution

1   **Examine the Periodic Table**   Look at the periodic table at the back of the book. Argon (Ar) is element number 18. Berkelium (Bk) is element number 97. Cadmium (Cd) is element number 48. Dysprosium (Dy) is element number 66.

2   **Recall Relevant Information**   The transuranium elements do not occur naturally on earth. Scientists can study them only by creating them in a laboratory using a nuclear reactor or particle accelerator. The transuranium elements are elements with atomic numbers greater than 92.

3   **Solve**   Argon, cadmium, and dysprosium are not transuranium elements, but berkelium is. (The element was named after the University of California at Berkeley.) Therefore, the correct answer is B.

TIP

The transuranium elements are not the only synthesized elements on the periodic table. Technetium (Tc) is also synthesized.

Problem Set

1. Use the periodic table at the back of the book to identify which of the following elements is an inner transition metal.
   A. W
   B. Xe
   C. Yb
   D. Zn

2. Einsteinium (Es), named after Albert Einstein, does not exist naturally on earth. Explain how scientists can study einsteinium even though it does not naturally occur.

3. How are the transuranium elements different from most other elements on the periodic table?

4. Use the periodic table at the back of the book to classify each of the following elements as a transition metal, an inner transition metal, or a transuranium element: molybdenum, lutetium, cerium, holmium, thorium, americium, fermium, rhenium. (Hint: Some of the elements can be classified in more than one way.)

5. **Challenge**   Geologists use radioactive elements to determine the ages of geologic materials. Three commonly used radioactive decay series are Lu-Hf, Sm-Nd, and U-Pb. Which of these series consists of two inner transition metals?

6. **Challenge**   In terms of electron arrangements, how are the inner transition metals different from the naturally occurring transition metals?

Monatomic Ions

Atoms tend to lose or gain electrons in such a way as to end up with full valence electron shells.

OBJECTIVE

- **Use the octet rule to predict the charges on monatomic ions.**

Atoms can bond, or join together, by losing, gaining, or sharing electrons. When a single, electrically neutral atom loses or gains electrons, it forms a monatomic ion. An atom that loses electrons becomes a cation, or positively charged ion. An atom that gains electrons becomes an anion, or negatively charged ion. However, atoms cannot gain or lose just any number of electrons. Atoms tend to gain or lose specific numbers of electrons. The number of electrons an atom loses or gains when it forms an ion is related to the neutral atom's valence electron configuration. Remember that a full valence electron shell is a very stable configuration for an atom. Therefore, atoms tend to gain or lose a number of electrons that leaves them with a full outer electron shell. In most common elements, a full outer electron shell contains eight electrons. Therefore, the rule that an atom gains or loses electrons to form a full valence electron shell is often called the *octet rule*. (The prefix *oct-* means "eight.")

EXAMPLE 1

Predict the Charge on a Monatomic Ion

Oxygen and potassium are among the 10 most abundant elements in earth's crust. Predict the charges on a monatomic oxygen ion and a monatomic potassium ion.

Solution

1 **Examine the Periodic Table** Locate oxygen (O) and potassium (K) on the periodic table at the back of the book. Oxygen is in group 6A. Potassium is in group 1A.

2 **Recall Relevant Information** Elements in group 6A have six valence electrons (two in an *s* subshell and four in a *p* subshell). Elements in group 1A have one valence electron (in an *s* subshell). Atoms tend to gain or lose electrons in such a way as to leave them with a full valence electron shell.

3 **Solve** To fill its 2*p* subshell, an oxygen atom must gain two electrons. Therefore, oxygen most commonly forms O^{2-} ions. To fill its fourth electron shell, a potassium atom would have to gain seven valence electrons. However, if a potassium atom lost the single valence electron in its 4*s* subshell, its valence electron configuration would be $3s^2\ 3p^6$. Therefore, losing a single electron would give a potassium atom a full valence electron shell. Losing one electron is much easier than gaining seven. Therefore, potassium most commonly forms K^+ ions.

REMEMBER

MONATOMIC IONS

- Most metal atoms lose one, two, or three valence electrons to achieve an octet.

- Most nonmetals gain one, two, or three valence electrons to achieve an octet.

- Loss of an electron from a neutral atom results in an ion with a positive charge. Because metals tend to lose electrons, they become cations when they react and form compounds.

- Nonmetals tend to gain electrons, so they become anions when they react and form compounds.

EXAMPLE 2

Identify the Ion Formed by an Atom

Which of the following ions would an atom of calcium (Ca) most likely form?

    A. Ca^+

    B. Ca^{2+}

    C. Ca^{2-}

    D. Ca^{6-}

Solution

1 **Recall Relevant Information**   Locate calcium on the periodic table at the back of the book. Calcium is in period 4, group 2A. Therefore, an atom of calcium has two valence electrons in a $4s$ subshell. Atoms tend to gain or lose a number of electrons that leaves them with a full valence electron shell.

2 **Solve**   Examine each answer choice to determine whether the ion shown has a full valence electron shell. A Ca atom must lose one electron to form a Ca^+ ion, so Ca^+ has one valence electron in a $4s$ subshell. A Ca atom must lose two electrons to form a Ca^{2+} ion, so Ca^{2+} has eight valence electrons (two in a $3s$ subshell and six in a $3p$ subshell) because it has lost both of its $4s$ electrons. A Ca atom must gain two electrons to form a Ca^{2-} ion, so Ca^{2-} has four valence electrons (two in a $4s$ subshell and two in a $4p$ subshell). A Ca atom must gain six electrons to form a Ca^{6-} ion, so Ca^{6-} has eight valence electrons (two in a $4s$ subshell and six in a $4p$ subshell). Neither Ca^+ nor Ca^{2-} has a full valence electron shell, so choices A and C are incorrect. Although Ca^{6-} has a full fourth electron shell, an atom is much more likely to lose two electrons than it is to gain six electrons. Therefore, choice B is correct.

TIP

In general, the more electrons an atom must lose or gain to attain a full valence electron shell, the less likely it is that the atom will lose or gain those electrons. Most atoms do not gain or lose more than three electrons to form ions.

Problem Set

1. Explain why the noble gases generally do not form bonds with other elements.

2. What charge would you expect an ion of sodium (Na) to have? Explain your answer.

3. Carbon (C) atoms do not generally form monatomic ions. What do you think is the reason for this?

4. An atom of sulfur (S) forms a monatomic ion. Which of the following ions does it most likely form? (Hint: Use a periodic table.)
     A. S^{2+} **B.** S^{6+}
     C. S^{2-} **D.** S^{6-}

5. **Challenge** A half-full electron subshell is not as stable as a full subshell, but it is more stable than a subshell that is more than half full or less than half full. Explain why nitrogen (N) is less likely to form monatomic ions than oxygen (O) is, even when the difference in the number of electrons each atom must gain is taken into account.

6. **Challenge** The formula unit for magnesium chloride is electrically neutral. Write the chemical formula for magnesium chloride. (Hint: It consists only of magnesium ions and chloride ions.)

Polyatomic Ions

You can determine how two atoms will bond based on their electronegativities and first ionization energies.

A polyatomic ion is a group of two or more atoms that are bound together and that have an overall electric charge. The atoms in a polyatomic ion are bonded together through the sharing of electrons. Polyatomic ions tend to be made up of atoms that do not gain or lose electrons easily. Instead, the atoms in a polyatomic ion share their valence electrons so that all the atoms in the ion have a full valence electron shell. You can predict whether two atoms will share or transfer electrons when they bond by comparing their electronegativities. Remember that the electronegativity of an atom is a measure of how strongly it attracts electrons in a bond. Two atoms with similar electronegativities will tend to share electrons when they form a bond. Atoms with very different electronegativities will tend to transfer electrons when they form a bond. The farther apart two elements are on the periodic table, the larger the difference in their electronegativities.

OBJECTIVES

- Identify polyatomic ions.
- Explain how electronegativity differences can be used to predict the nature of chemical bonding.

EXAMPLE 1

Identify Polyatomic Ions

Which of the following lists includes only polyatomic ions?

 A. Sr^{2+}, NH_4^+, H^+

 B. $ClO_3^-, CrO_4^{2-}, C_2O_4^{2-}$

 C. O^{2-}, O^-, O_2^{2-}

 D. CCl_4, CO_3^{2-}, CN^-

Solution

1 **Collect and Strategize** A polyatomic ion is a group of two or more atoms that are bonded together and have a net electric charge. To answer this question, examine each answer choice and determine whether all the species listed contain more than one atom and have a net electric charge.

2 **Solve** Sr^{2+}, H^+, O^{2-}, and O^- are each made of only a single atom, so they are not polyatomic ions. CCl_4 does not have a net electric charge, so it is not an ion. Therefore, choices A, C, and D do not list only polyatomic ions, and choice B is the correct answer.

REMEMBER

POLYATOMIC IONS

- A polyatomic ion consists of two or more atoms with a net electric charge.

- The atoms in a polyatomic ion can be atoms of the same element or of different elements.

- Most polyatomic ions consist of atoms with similar electronegativities.

EXAMPLE 2

Rank Bonds in Terms of Electron Sharing

Rank the following bonds in order from the greatest sharing of electrons to the least sharing of electrons: K–Cl, Br–Br, Be–O, S–O.

Solution

1 Recall Relevant Information Elements with similar electronegativities tend to share electrons when they form bonds. Elements with very different electronegativities tend to transfer electrons when they form bonds—that is, one atom gains electrons, and the other atom loses them. In general, the farther apart two elements are on the periodic table, the more different their electronegativities are.

2 Examine the Periodic Table Locate the elements in each pair on the periodic table at the back of the book. Potassium (K) is in group 1A. Chlorine (Cl) and bromine (Br) are in group 7A. Sulfur (S) and oxygen (O) are in group 6A. Beryllium (Be) is in group 2A.

3 Solve Potassium and chlorine are on opposite sides of the periodic table. Therefore, they have very different electronegativities and will tend to transfer electrons rather than share them. The two bromine atoms have identical electronegativities, so they will share electrons rather than transferring them. Beryllium and oxygen are far apart, but not as far apart as potassium and chlorine. Sulfur and oxygen are in the same group, so they will have similar, but not identical, electronegativities. Therefore, the correct order is Br–Br > S–O > Be–O > K–Cl. To confirm, examine the electronegativity of each atom in the table at the back of the book. Potassium and chlorine have the most dissimilar electronegativity values.

Common Polyatomic Ions	
Name	**Formula**
Acetate	CH_3COO^-
Ammonium	NH_4^+
Carbonate	CO_3^{2-}
Hydroxide	OH^-
Nitrate	NO_3^-
Phosphate	PO_4^{3-}
Sulfate	SO_4^{2-}

Problem Set

1. Name the polyatomic ion in each of the following compounds: Na_3PO_4, NH_4Cl, KOH. (Hint: Examine the table on this page.)

2. Put the following bonds in order from the smallest degree of electron sharing to the largest: O–Se, Li–Br, C–S, N–N. (Hint: Use a periodic table.)

3. Identify which of these pairs of elements is most likely to be part of a polyatomic ion: S and O, Cl and Mg, K and F. Explain your answer.

4. Is bromine (Br) more likely to share electrons when bonding with magnesium (Mg) or with selenium (Se)? Explain your answer.

5. **Challenge** The electronegativity value for nitrogen (N) is 3.0. The electronegativity value for oxygen (O) is 3.5. The electronegativity value for lithium (Li) is 1.0. Use this information to explain why NO_3^- is a common polyatomic ion, but LiO^- is not.

6. **Challenge** Aluminum phosphate is a compound used to help baked goods rise. The phosphate polyatomic ion (PO_4^{3-}) has three extra electrons. The extra electrons are distributed around the atoms in the ion. Aluminum is a metal with three valence electrons. Explain how aluminum phosphate ($AlPO_4$) is an example of a compound with bonds formed by both the sharing of electrons and the transfer of electrons.

The Ionic Bond and Salts

Cations and anions attract one another and form ionic bonds. Compounds held together by ionic bonds are called *salts*.

Positively charged ions are called *cations* and negatively charged ions are called *anions*. These oppositely charged ions have an electrical attraction for one another and can form ionic bonds. Substances that contain ionic bonds are called *salts*. In the solid state, salts form crystals. If you could see the ions making up a crystal, you would see that the cations and anions in the salt are arranged in a regular, repeating pattern, which is reflected in the shape of the crystal. The net amounts of positive and negative charge in a salt are always exactly equal, so the salt has no overall electrical charge. Therefore, you can predict the chemical formula for an ionic compound if you know the charges on the ions in the compound.

OBJECTIVES

- Define an ionic bond.
- Describe the arrangement of ions in a solid salt.

EXAMPLE 1

Write the Chemical Formula of an Ionic Compound

Barium chloride is a salt that gives some fireworks a bright green color. Write the chemical formula for barium chloride, which forms from Ba^{2+} and Cl^- ions.

Solution

1 **Recall Relevant Concepts** To form a Ba^{2+} ion, a Ba atom must lose two electrons. To form a Cl^- ion, a Cl atom must gain one electron. To maintain electric neutrality, any electrons lost by Ba atoms must be gained by Cl atoms.

2 **Solve** Each Cl atom can gain only one electron, but a Ba atom loses two electrons to form a Ba^{2+} ion. The two electrons that the Ba atom loses must be taken up by two Cl atoms (one electron per atom). Therefore, each Ba^{2+} ion must be bonded to two Cl^- ions, and the chemical formula for barium chloride must be $BaCl_2$. To check that this formula is correct, add the charges on the ions in the formula. The net charge on a $BaCl_2$ formula unit is $+2 + 2(-1) = +2 + (-2) = 0$, so $BaCl_2$ is the correct formula.

REMEMBER

IONIC BONDS

- An ionic bond is the result of electrostatic attraction between positively charged ions (cations) and negatively charged ions (anions).

- The net electric charge on an ionic compound is always zero.

- An ionic compound can be made up of monatomic ions, polyatomic ions, or both.

- Metals, oxygen, and the halogens (group 7A) most commonly form ionic compounds. Oxygen and the halogens tend to form anions. Metals tend to form cations.

EXAMPLE 2

Predict the Formation of an Ionic Bond

Which of the following pairs of atoms is most likely to form an ionic bond?

    A. C and N

    B. Si and O

    C. Br and Br

    D. Li and Cl

Solution

1 **Recall Relevant Information** For a pair of atoms to form an ionic bond, one of the atoms must lose electrons to become a cation, and the other atom must gain those electrons to become an anion. Remember that elements with similar electronegativities tend to share electrons, rather than transferring them. The closer two elements are on the periodic table, the more similar their electronegativities are. Therefore, the elements that are farthest apart on the periodic table are most likely to transfer electrons and form an ionic bond.

2 **Solve** Locate each element on the periodic table at the back of the book. Lithium (Li) is in group 1A. Carbon (C) and silicon (Si) are both in group 4A. Nitrogen (N) is in group 5A. Oxygen (O) is in group 6A. Chlorine (Cl) and bromine (Br) are both in group 7A. Of the pairs given, lithium and chlorine are farthest apart on the periodic table. Therefore, they are most likely to form an ionic bond, and the correct answer is D.

TIP

When describing the bonding in a compound or writing the chemical formula for a compound, always locate the elements in the compound on the periodic table first. The position of an element on the periodic table can give you a lot of information about its chemical properties, including the types of bonds it tends to form.

Problem Set

1. Which of the following pairs of elements is most likely to form an ionic bond?
   A. S and O
   B. K and F
   C. C and O
   D. F and F

2. Explain why salts are electrically neutral.

3. Define the term *crystal* in your own words.

4. Potassium nitrate, also called *saltpeter*, is a chemical compound that contains monatomic potassium ions (K^+) and polyatomic nitrate ions (NO_3^-). Write the chemical formula for potassium nitrate. (Hint: The compound is electrically neutral.)

5. **Challenge** When solid iron (Fe) is exposed to air and water, it rusts. Rust is an ionic compound, iron oxide. It consists of Fe^{3+} ions and O^{2-} ions. What is the chemical formula for iron oxide?

6. **Challenge** Potassium chloride is an ionic compound that is often used as a substitute for table salt (sodium chloride). Potassium chloride tastes salty like sodium chloride, but it affects the body differently. Therefore, people who are on low-sodium diets often use potassium chloride as a substitute for table salt. Write the chemical formulas for table salt (sodium chloride) and potassium chloride. (Hint: Use a periodic table to determine the charge on each ion.)

Properties of Ionic Compounds

Most ionic compounds are solids at room temperature, have high melting points, and conduct electricity well when they dissolve in water or are melted.

Many important minerals and gems, including garnet, ruby, emerald, hematite (an iron ore), and fluorite, are ionic compounds. The ions in ionic compounds form a regular, repeating pattern in the solid state. This pattern results in the formation of crystals, which are solids with regular atomic structures. The arrangement of the ions in a crystal determines the shape of the crystal, which is why gems and minerals form crystals with specific shapes. Remember that the ions in an ionic compound are held together by electrostatic attraction—that is, the cations and anions are attracted to each other because they have opposite electric charges. The ionic bonds in ionic compounds are very strong. These strong bonds affect many of the properties of ionic compounds.

OBJECTIVES

- Describe some common properties of ionic compounds.
- Explain why salt solutions tend to be excellent conductors of electricity.

EXAMPLE 1

Describe Properties of Ionic Compounds

A scientist is studying the properties of an ionic compound. Which of these properties does the compound most likely have?

    A. It has a net positive charge.

    B. It does not dissolve in water.

    C. It is a gas at room temperature.

    D. It has a very high melting point.

Solution

1 **Recall Relevant Information** Ionic compounds are held together by ionic bonds, which are very strong. Ionic compounds dissolve most easily in polar solvents. Water is a polar solvent.

2 **Solve** Examine each of the answer choices to determine if it describes a common property of ionic compounds. Ionic compounds have no net charge, so choice A is incorrect. Most ionic compounds dissolve easily in water, so choice B is incorrect. Most ionic compounds are solids at room temperature, so choice C is incorrect. Most ionic compounds have high melting points, because the ionic bonds between their ions are so strong. Therefore, the correct answer is D.

REMEMBER

PROPERTIES OF IONIC COMPOUNDS

- Most ionic compounds (salts) are solids at room temperature. In the solid state, the ions in the compound are arranged in a regular, repeating pattern. This pattern produces a specific crystal shape in the solid compound.

- Ionic bonds are very strong.

- Most ionic compounds have very high melting points.

- Most ionic compounds dissolve easily in water.

EXAMPLE 2

Explain the Electrical Conductivity of Salt Solutions

Most salts dissolve easily in water. Explain why salt solutions tend to be much better conductors of electricity than pure water is.

Solution

1. **Recall Relevant Information**   For an electric current to flow, charged particles must move from one place to another. In a metal wire, the charged particles that carry the current are electrons. In a liquid, ions carry electric current. Pure water contains very few ions. When a salt dissolves in water, the ions in the salt dissociate, or separate.

2. **Solve**   In pure water, there are very few ions to carry electric current. However, when a salt dissolves in water, the ions in the salt dissociate. These ions, which are electrically charged, can move easily through the solution. They can rapidly carry an electric current through the solution, so salt solutions conduct electricity better than pure water does.

Problem Set

1. Name three properties of most ionic compounds.

2. Sucrose, or common table sugar, is not an ionic compound. Sodium chloride, or common table salt, is an ionic compound. Which would probably conduct electricity better, water mixed with sugar or water mixed with salt? Explain your answer.

3. Plastics are polymers. They are made up of chains of atoms that are bonded together by sharing electrons rather than by transferring electrons from one atom to another. Which would you expect to have a higher melting point when dissolved in water, the salt calcium chloride ($CaCl_2$) or the plastic polyethylene? Explain your answer.

4. Car batteries contain a concentrated solution of sulfuric acid in water. Sulfuric acid is an ionic compound. Explain how the sulfuric acid solution might help the car battery produce electricity.

5. **Challenge**   Most salts conduct electricity better when they are melted, or molten, than when they are in the solid state. Suggest a reason why most molten salts conduct electricity well.

6. **Challenge**   Crystals have very regular shapes. When NaCl crystals are allowed to form slowly, they grow in the shape of cubes. Why do crystals of ionic compounds have regular, geometric shapes?

Naming Ionic Compounds

The names of ionic compounds follow specific rules.

An ionic compound forms when one or more positively charged ions, or *cations,* bond with one or more negatively charged ions, or *anions*. When naming compounds, chemists rely on a list of rules to make sure that everyone uses the same words to describe the same compound. Here are some rules for naming simple ionic compounds:

- The first word in the compound's name is the name of the first ion in the chemical formula.
- The second word in the compound's name is the name of the second ion in the chemical formula.
- The name of a monatomic cation is just the name of the element. For example, sodium forms only Na^+ ions, which are simply called sodium ions. If an element can form more than one kind of cation, roman numerals are used to indicate the charge on the cation. For example, iron can form Fe^{2+} or Fe^{3+} ions, which are known as iron(II) ions and iron(III) ions, respectively.
- The name of a monatomic anion is the first syllable of the element's name plus the suffix *–ide*. For example, O^{2-} is an oxide ion.

OBJECTIVE

- **Name ionic compounds.**

EXAMPLE 1

Name an Ionic Compound

The compound with the formula $CaBr_2$ is an ionic compound. What is the name of this compound?

    A. calcium bromine

    B. calcium bromide

    C. bromide calcium

    D. bromine calcide

Solution

1 **Collect** Identify the elements that make up the compound. Look at the periodic table at the back of the book. Notice that the symbol Ca stands for calcium and the symbol Br stands for bromine.

2 **Apply Naming Rules** Calcium is the first element in the formula, so the first word in the name will be *calcium*. Bromine is the second element in the formula. To obtain the second word in the name, replace the end of *bromine* with *–ide* to yield *bromide*.

3 **Solve** Combining the words from Step 2 yields the name of the compound: calcium bromide. Therefore, B is the correct answer.

REMEMBER

NAMING IONIC COMPOUNDS

- The name of an ionic compound is the name of the cation followed by the name of the anion.
- Monatomic ions are ions that form from single atoms.
- Polyatomic ions are ions that are made up of two or more atoms.
- Cations are positively charged ions.
- Anions are negatively charged ions.
- Many transition metals (group B elements) can form more than one kind of cation. For example, iron can form Fe^{2+} and Fe^{3+} ions, and copper can form Cu^+ and Cu^{2+} ions.

EXAMPLE 2

Write the Formula for an Ionic Compound

Iron(II) ions can combine with hydroxide ions to form iron(II) hydroxide. Write the chemical formula for iron(II) hydroxide.

Solution

1 **Recall Relevant Information**   The first word in the name of an ionic compound is the name of the first ion in the formula. The second word is the name of the second ion in the formula.

2 **Apply**   The first word in iron(II) hydroxide is *iron(II)*. The roman numerals indicate that the charge on the iron(II) ion is +2. Iron(II) ion is a monatomic cation. Therefore, the first symbol in the chemical formula will be the symbol for iron, Fe. The second word in the name is *hydroxide*, which is the name of a polyatomic anion, OH^-. (The table to the right shows the names and formulas of some common polyatomic ions.) Therefore, the second symbol in the formula will be OH.

3 **Solve**   The overall charge on iron(II) hydroxide must be 0, so the positive and negative charges must cancel out. Two −1 charges are required to balance one +2 charge. Therefore, each formula unit of iron(II) hydroxide will have one iron(II) ion and two hydroxide ions. The formula for iron(II) hydroxide is therefore $Fe(OH)_2$.

Common Polyatomic Ions	
Name	**Formula**
Acetate	CH_3COO^-
Ammonium	NH_4^+
Carbonate	CO_3^{2-}
Hydroxide	OH^-
Nitrate	NO_3^-
Phosphate	PO_4^{3-}
Sulfate	SO_4^{2-}

Problem Set

1. Write the name of the ionic compound that has the chemical formula LiCl. (Hint: Refer to the periodic table at the back of the book.)

2. Write the chemical formula for the compound sodium hydroxide. (Hint: Refer to the table of common polyatomic ions.)

3. Write the chemical formula for copper(II) bromide, the compound that forms when copper(II) ions bond with bromide ions. (Hint: The compound, like all compounds, is electrically neutral.)

4. Sulfuric acid is a very strong acid. Its proper chemical name is hydrogen sulfate. Write the chemical formula for sulfuric acid. (Hint: Refer to the table of common polyatomic ions. Hydrogen has a +1 charge in sulfuric acid.)

5. **Challenge**   The ionic compound FeS has a strong odor, like rotten eggs. The compound contains an S^{2-} ion. What is the name of the compound?

6. **Challenge**   Write the name and chemical formula of the compound that forms when ammonium ions combine with SO_4^{2-} ions. (Hint: Refer to the table of common polyatomic ions.)

Bonding in Metals

The mobility of valence electrons in metals explains many of the characteristic properties of metals, such as electrical and thermal conductivity, malleability, ductility, and strength.

Atoms can form chemical bonds by transferring or sharing electrons. The type of bonding between the atoms in a substance influences the substance's properties. In metals, valence electrons are delocalized, meaning that all the atoms share all the valence electrons. These free-moving electrons are sometimes referred to as a *sea of electrons*. The valence electrons are not centered around a specific atom. Instead, they are free to move throughout the metal. Delocalization of electrons explains many of the physical properties of metals.

OBJECTIVES

- **Describe how a metallic bond forms.**
- **Explain the properties of metals in terms of metallic bonding.**

EXAMPLE 1

Illustrate Metallic Bonding

Draw a picture to show the arrangement of atoms and valence electrons in a metal.

Solution

1 **Recall Relevant Information**   In a metal, valence electrons are free to move throughout the metal. They are not bound to a specific metal atom. The metal cations (metal atoms without their valence electrons) are arranged in a regular pattern, forming a crystal. The electrostatic attraction between the electrons and the cations forms the metallic bonds that hold the metal together. Therefore, the drawing should include large, positively charged ions arranged in a regular pattern, with tiny, negatively charged electrons randomly but evenly distributed between the cations.

2 **Solve**   A sample sketch is shown below.

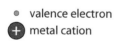 valence electron
metal cation

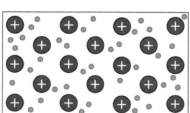

REMEMBER

METALLIC BONDS

- In a sample of a metal, neutral metal atoms do not exist. Instead, the metal is made up of metal cations and of electrons that are free to move throughout the metal.

- The cations in a solid metal are arranged in an orderly, repeating pattern.

- Although all metals have metallic bonds, they do not all have identical properties. Some metals are more malleable or ductile than others, and some metals conduct electricity better than others.

EXAMPLE 2

Explain the Electrical Conductivity of Metals

Copper metal is an excellent conductor of electricity, which is why it is used in most electrical wiring. Explain in terms of bonding why copper is such a good conductor of electricity.

Solution

1 **Recall Relevant Information** Copper is a transition metal. Transition metals, like all metals, have metallic bonds. Electrons are delocalized in metallic bonds. They are free to move throughout the metal. For an electric current to flow through a material, charged particles, such as electrons, must be able to move through the material.

2 **Solve** Copper conducts electricity because the electrons are free to move and are not bound to specific atoms. If an electric potential causes an electron to enter one end of an electrical wire, repulsion between electrons will expel an electron from the other end of the wire.

TIP

Only the valence electrons of metal atoms are delocalized. Inner electrons are not delocalized.

Problem Set

1. In a sample of which of the following elements would you expect to find a delocalized sea of electrons? Use the periodic table to justify your answer.
   A. Ar
   B. C
   C. Na
   D. S

2. What holds together the atoms in a metal?

3. Explain in terms of the forces between atoms why metals tend to be strong and have high melting points.

4. Explain why a solid metal can be considered a crystal.

5. **Challenge** Explain why solid sodium (Na) can conduct electricity well, but solid sodium chloride (NaCl) cannot.

6. **Challenge** Explain how metallic bonding makes most metals malleable and ductile.

The Covalent Bond and Molecules

The atoms in molecules are joined by covalent bonds, which form when atoms share electrons.

Molecules are particles containing two or more atoms joined by covalent bonds. Covalent bonds form between atoms when the atoms share electrons. Covalent bonds most commonly form between atoms of nonmetals. Most covalent bonds form when atoms share a single pair of electrons. However, some covalent bonds form when atoms share two pairs of electrons, and some form when atoms share three pairs of electrons. A covalent bond that consists of a single pair of shared electrons is called a *single bond*, one that consists of two pairs of shared electrons is a *double bond*, and one that consists of three pairs of shared electrons is a *triple bond*. Like ionic bonds, covalent bonds tend to form in a way that gives each atom in the bond a full valence (outer) electron shell. Many compounds are made up of molecules that consist of two nonmetal atoms bonded together. Some rules for naming these compounds are given below:

- The first word in the compound's name is the name of the first element in the chemical formula.
- The second word in the compound's name is the name of the second element in the chemical formula. Keep the first syllable of the second element's name, and replace the rest of its name with *–ide*.
- Prefixes are used to indicate the number of atoms of each element in the molecule.

EXAMPLE 1

Name a Covalent Compound

The compound with the formula CO_2 is covalently bonded. Which of these is the correct name for the compound?

    A. oxygen carbide

    B. dioxygen carbide

    C. carbon oxide

    D. carbon dioxide

Solution

1   **Collect**   First, identify the elements that make up the compound. Look at the periodic table at the back of the book. Notice that the symbol C stands for carbon, and the symbol O stands for oxygen.

REMEMBER

COVALENT COMPOUNDS

- Covalent bonds form when atoms share electrons.
- Every covalent bond consists of one or more pairs of shared electrons — that is, atoms do not share only a single electron.
- As with ionic bonds, covalent bonds generally form in ways that give all the atoms involved full valence electron shells.
- Most molecules are made of atoms of more than two elements. The rules for naming these compounds are more complex than those presented here.

2 **Apply**   The carbon atom is the first atom in the formula, so the first word in the name will be *carbon*. Oxygen is the second atom in the formula. To obtain the second word in the name, replace the end of *oxygen* with the suffix *–ide*, which yields *oxide*. There are two oxygen atoms in the molecule, so the prefix *di–* will precede the *oxide*.

3 **Solve**   Combining the words from Step 2 yields the name of the compound: carbon dioxide. Therefore, choice D is the correct answer.

EXAMPLE 2

Write the Formula for a Covalent Compound

Write the chemical formula for sulfur tetrachloride.

Solution

1 **Recall Relevant Information**   The first word in the name of a covalent compound is the name of the first element in the formula. The second word is based on the name of the second element in the formula. Each name may be modified with a prefix to indicate the number of atoms of the element in the molecule.

2 **Apply**   The first word in sulfur tetrachloride is *sulfur*, so the first chemical symbol in the formula must be the chemical symbol for sulfur. The periodic table shows that the chemical symbol for sulfur is S. The second word, *tetrachloride*, has the prefix *tetra–*. Therefore, there must be four of the second element in each molecule of the compound. *Chloride* begins with *chlor–*, which is the beginning of *chlorine*. Therefore, the second element in the compound must be chlorine. The periodic table shows that the chemical symbol for chlorine is Cl.

3 **Solve**   S (sulfur) must be the first symbol in the formula, and Cl (chlorine), must be the second. There are four chlorine atoms in each molecule of sulfur tetrachloride. Therefore, the chemical formula for sulfur tetrachloride is SCl_4.

TIP

In chemical names, the prefix *mono–* means "one," the prefix *di–* means "two," the prefix *tri–* means "three," the prefix *tetra–* means "four," and the prefix *penta–* means "five." The prefix *mono–* is generally not used for the first word in a compound. For example, CO_2 is carbon dioxide, not monocarbon dioxide.

EXAMPLE 3

Describe How Covalent Bonds Form

Carbon tetrachloride (CCl_4) is a covalently bonded compound. Describe how the bonds between the carbon atom and the chlorine atoms form.

Solution

1 **Gather**   First, identify the number of valence electrons in each type of atom. Examine the periodic table at the back of the book. Notice that carbon is in group 4A, and chlorine is in group 7A. Therefore, each carbon atom has four valence electrons, and each chlorine atom has seven valence electrons.

2 **Apply**   Atoms tend to form bonds in a way that gives each atom a full valence electron shell. Chlorine and carbon atoms each require eight valence electrons to have a full valence electron shell. Therefore, a carbon atom must share four electrons with other atoms to have a full valence electron shell. A chlorine atom must share one electron with another atom to have a full valence electron shell.

3 **Solve**   The carbon atom shares one pair of electrons with each chlorine atom. Because the atoms share the electrons, both electrons in each pair can be considered to belong to both atoms. The diagram below shows how the atoms share electrons. Each dot represents a valence electron.

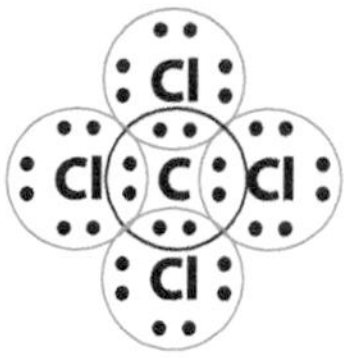

When the carbon and chlorine atoms share electrons in this way, each atom has eight valence electrons. The green circles show the chlorine atoms' valence electrons. The black circle shows the carbon atom's valence electrons.

EXAMPLE 4

Identify Single, Double, and Triple Bonds

The diagrams below show how electrons are shared in three covalent compounds. Identify the bonds in each compound as single bonds, double bonds, or triple bonds. Each dot represents a valence electron.

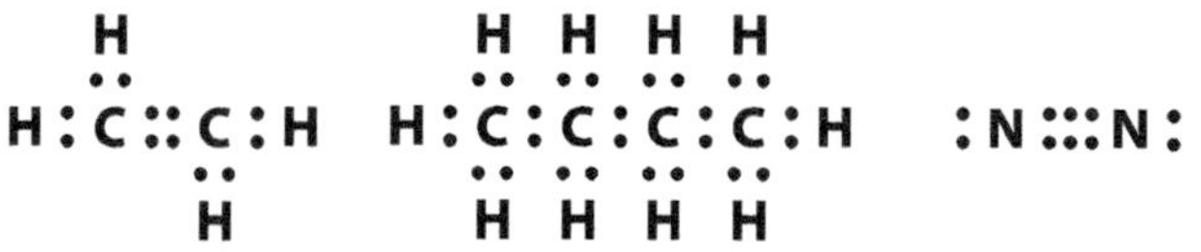

$$
\begin{array}{ccc}
\text{H} & \text{H H H H} & \\
\overset{\bullet\bullet}{\text{H}:\text{C}::\text{C}:\text{H}} & \text{H}:\text{C}:\text{C}:\text{C}:\text{C}:\text{H} & :\text{N}:::\text{N}: \\
\text{H} & \text{H H H H} & \\
\text{ethene (C}_2\text{H}_4\text{)} & \text{butane (C}_4\text{H}_{10}\text{)} & \text{nitrogen (N}_2\text{)}
\end{array}
$$

Solution

1 **Recall Relevant Information**   A single covalent bond consists of one pair of shared electrons. A double covalent bond consists of two pairs of shared electrons. A triple covalent bond consists of three pairs of shared electrons. In diagrams like the ones above, electrons that are located between two atoms are shared electrons.

TIP

A covalent bond always consists of one, two, or three pairs of electrons. Therefore, all covalent bonds contain an even number of electrons. There is no such thing as a quadruple covalent bond.

2 **Examine the Diagram** There is a single pair of electrons between each carbon atom and each hydrogen atom in ethene. There are two pairs of electrons between the two carbon atoms in ethene. There is a single pair of electrons between all of the atoms in butane. There are three pairs of electrons between the atoms in nitrogen.

3 **Solve** The C–H bonds in ethene and butane and the C–C bonds in butane are single bonds. The C–C bond in ethene is a double bond. The N–N bond in nitrogen is a triple bond.

Problem Set

1. Write the name of the covalent compound with the formula SO_2.

2. Write a definition of *molecule* in your own words.

3. Which of these chemical formulas is the correct formula for the covalent compound phosphorus trichloride?
   A. PCl
   B. P_3Cl
   C. PCl_3
   D. P_3Cl_3

4. Write the formal chemical names for water (H_2O) and ammonia (NH_3).

5. The diagram below shows the bonding in carbon dioxide (CO_2). Identify the bonds in the compound as single, double, or triple bonds.

$$\overset{\cdot\cdot}{\underset{\cdot\cdot}{O}} :: C :: \overset{\cdot\cdot}{\underset{\cdot\cdot}{O}}$$

6. Write the chemical formula for dinitrogen monoxide. (Hint: Refer to the periodic table at the back of the book.)

7. **Challenge** What is the chemical formula for the covalent compound dinitrogen tetraoxide?

8. **Challenge** The diagram below shows the bonding in methanoic acid (HCOOH). Explain how each covalent bond in the molecule provides a full valence electron shell to each atom.

9. **Challenge** Write the name of the covalent compound shown below:

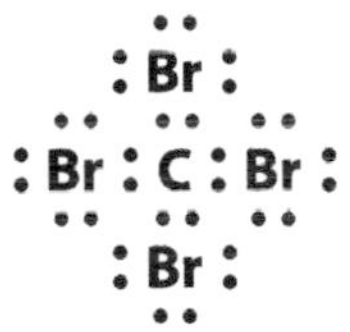

$$\begin{array}{c} \overset{\cdot\cdot}{:Br:} \\ \overset{\cdot\cdot}{:Br:}\,C\,\overset{\cdot\cdot}{:Br:} \\ \overset{\cdot\cdot}{:Br:} \end{array}$$

(Hint: Write the chemical formula first. The central atom is the first chemical symbol in the chemical formula.)

Lewis Dot Structures

You can use symbols for elements and dot representations of electrons to model how electrons are arranged in an atom and how bonding occurs.

OBJECTIVE

- Draw or interpret a Lewis dot structure for a molecule.

Electrostatic interactions between the nucleus of an atom and electrons of another atom serve as the basis for bonding. In most cases, the electrons involved in bonding are valence electrons. Because it can be hard to visualize how electrons interact, chemists use Lewis dot structures to represent how the valence electrons behave during bonding.

EXAMPLE 1

Draw Lewis Dot Structures for Covalent Compounds

Draw the Lewis dot structure for ammonia (NH_3).

Solution

① Collect   Draw a Lewis dot structure for each atom in the molecule. A Lewis dot structure uses one dot to represent each valence electron. Hydrogen (group IA) has one valence electron, and nitrogen (group 5A) has five. The Lewis dot structures for the atoms are as shown below.

$$H \cdot \quad \overset{\cdot\cdot}{\underset{\cdot}{\cdot N \cdot}} H \cdot$$
$$H \cdot$$

② Solve   The number of valence electrons in the molecule is equal to the sum of the number of valence electrons on the atoms in the molecule. Therefore, ammonia will have $1 + 1 + 1 + 5 = 8$ valence electrons. Nitrogen will be the central atom. Each hydrogen atom will share one electron with the nitrogen atom to form a covalent bond, represented by a straight line. This will result in each hydrogen atom having two valence electrons and the nitrogen atom having eight valence electrons.

$$H - \overset{\cdot\cdot}{\underset{|}{N}} - H$$
$$H$$

③ Check   To double-check that the structure is correct, count the number of electrons in the Lewis dot structure. It should equal the total number of valence electrons in the atoms in the molecule. The Lewis dot structure for ammonia shown above contains eight electrons, as it should. In addition, each atom has a full outer electron shell, as it should in a stable molecule.

REMEMBER

RULES FOR LEWIS DOT STRUCTURES

- All atoms should have eight electrons surrounding them (except H, He, and Be, which should have two electrons each).

- Only valence electrons are shown in Lewis dot structures.

- In a covalent bond, each atom must share one of its electrons with the other atom—that is, a covalent bond always involves a pair of electrons.

- The total number of valence electrons in a molecule is equal to the sum of the number of valence electrons in each atom in the molecule.

EXAMPLE 2

Draw Lewis Dot Structures for Molecules with Multiple Bonds

Draw the Lewis dot structure for molecular oxygen (O_2).

Solution

1 Collect Each oxygen atom has six valence electrons, so the oxygen molecule should have 12. Start by drawing the two oxygen atoms.

2 Predict and Check As a first attempt, draw a structure in which the oxygen atoms share two electrons (one electron pair). However, when the molecule is drawn that way, each oxygen atom has only seven valence electrons, as shown below:

3 Solve and Check To draw the molecule correctly, change the single bond between the oxygen atoms to a double bond. This arrangement yields a molecule with 12 valence electrons, and also gives each oxygen atom a full octet.

TIP

Lewis dot structures are also called *electron dot structures* or simply *Lewis structures*. Pairs of shared electrons (covalent bonds) can be shown in different ways. For example, the oxygen molecule in this example may be shown in the following ways:

Problem Set

Draw Lewis dot structures for each of the following molecules.

1. H_2S

2. CH_4

3. H_2O

4. C_2H_6

5. CO_2

6. N_2

7. **Challenge** To write the Lewis dot structure for a negatively charged ion, add extra electrons as needed to produce the correct charge. Draw the Lewis dot structure for the hydroxide ion (OH^-).

8. **Challenge** Draw the Lewis dot structure for the ammonium ion (NH_4^+).

9. **Challenge** Atoms in period 3 or greater of the periodic table can accept more than eight valence electrons. Draw the Lewis dot structure for SF_4.

Molecular Shapes

The repulsion between electrons in bonds and lone pairs determines the shapes and polarities of molecules.

It is common to write the formulas for compounds in their condensed forms, such as H_2O or CO_2. However, these forms do not give any information about the shape or polarity of a molecule. The shape and polarity of a molecule have important effects on the compound's chemical properties. Therefore, it is important to be able to predict the shape and polarity of a molecule. Chemists use the valence shell electron pair repulsion (VSEPR) theory to predict molecular shapes and polarities. According to the VSEPR theory, electrons in bonds or in lone pairs repel one another. As a result, the bonds and lone pairs in a molecule tend to be as far apart as possible in three dimensions.

OBJECTIVE

- Use Lewis dot structures to predict the shapes and polarities of common molecules.

EXAMPLE 1

Explain the Shape of a Molecule with No Lone Pairs

The picture below shows the three-dimensional structure of a molecule of methane (CH_4).

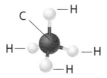

Use a Lewis dot structure for methane to explain the three-dimensional shape of the methane molecule.

Solution

1 **Strategize** Lewis dot structures show all the valence electrons in a molecule. According to the VSEPR theory, the valence electrons determine the shape of a molecule. Therefore, to explain the shape of the methane molecule, first draw a Lewis dot structure for it. Then, examine the bonds and any lone pairs to figure out how they affect the shape of the molecule.

2 **Apply** The Lewis dot structure for methane is shown below. Notice that the carbon atom shares one pair of electrons with each hydrogen atom.

$$\text{H}-\overset{\displaystyle \text{H}}{\underset{\displaystyle \text{H}}{\text{C}}}-\text{H}$$

REMEMBER

MOLECULAR SHAPES

- Bonds and lone pairs tend to be oriented in space in a way that minimizes the repulsion between the valence electrons in the molecule.

- Lone pairs of electrons have a stronger repulsive force than bonded pairs of electrons do.

- When electron distribution in a molecule or in a bond is not uniform, the molecule or bond is said to be *polar*.

3 **Solve** The electrons in the four bonds are all negatively charged. Therefore, they repel one another. This repulsion causes the bonds to be oriented in a way that maximizes their distance from one another. The four bonds can be thought of as bars or sticks that all radiate from a central point (the carbon atom). To maximize the distance between them, the ends of the four bonds (the hydrogen atoms) must form the points of a shape called a *tetrahedron*, as shown below:

Therefore, because this tetrahedral shape maximizes the distances between the bonds, it is the most stable shape for the CH_4 molecule.

EXAMPLE 2

Explain the Shape of a Molecule with Lone Pairs

The picture below shows the three-dimensional structure of a molecule of ammonia (NH_3).

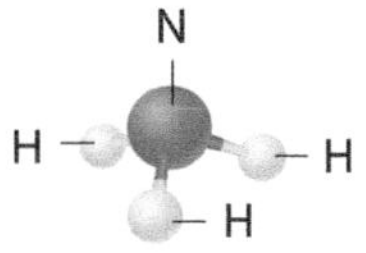

Use a Lewis dot structure for NH_3 to explain the shape of the ammonia molecule.

Solution

1 **Strategize** As you did for methane in Example 1, draw a Lewis dot structure for ammonia. Then, examine the bonds and any lone pairs to determine how they affect the shape of the ammonia molecule.

2 **Apply** The Lewis dot structure for ammonia is shown below. Notice that the nitrogen atom shares one pair of electrons with each hydrogen atom. The nitrogen atom also has one lone pair of electrons that is not shared with any other atom.

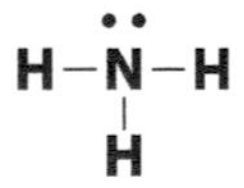

$$H-\overset{\cdot\cdot}{\underset{|}{N}}-H$$
$$H$$

TIP

Lewis dot structures show molecules in two dimensions, but real molecules exist in three dimensions. Therefore, it is important to think in three dimensions when predicting molecular shapes. Making physical models can be helpful in visualizing shapes in three dimensions.

3 **Solve** The electrons in the three bonds and the electrons in the lone pair are all negatively charged. Therefore, they repel one another. In the methane molecule, those repulsions caused the four bonds to form a tetrahedral shape. In the ammonia molecule, there are only three bonds. The lone pair of electrons exerts a greater repulsive force on the bonds than the bonds exert on one another. Therefore, the lone pair of electrons on the ammonia molecule forces the bonds away from a perfect tetrahedral orientation. That is why the angles between the bonds in the ammonia molecule are smaller than those in the methane molecule.

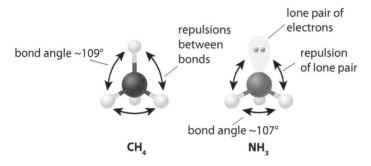

A lone pair of electrons repels other electrons more than a pair of bonded electrons does.

EXAMPLE 3

Predict the Polarity of a Molecule

Use Lewis dot structures to explain why a water molecule (H_2O) is polar, but a carbon dioxide molecule (CO_2) is not.

Solution

1 **Recall Relevant Information** A polar molecule is one in which the electron density is not the same everywhere in the molecule. As a result, one part of the molecule has a slight net positive charge, and another part has a slight net negative charge. Any bond between two atoms of different elements is polar, because the two atoms have different electronegativities. The electrons in a bond between atoms of two different elements will tend to exist around the more electronegative element more often than around the less electronegative element. As a result, the more electronegative element will have a negative partial charge, and the less electronegative element will have a positive partial charge. A molecule as a whole is polar if the polarities of its individual bonds do not cancel each other out.

2 **Draw Lewis Dot Structures** The diagrams below show the Lewis dot structures for water and carbon dioxide:

$$H \underset{\text{water}}{\overset{\cdot\cdot}{\underset{}{O}}} H \qquad \underset{\text{carbon dioxide}}{O = C = O}$$

TIP

Atoms of the same element have the same electronegativity. Therefore, bonds between atoms of the same element are always completely nonpolar.

3 **Solve**   Notice that the water molecule is bent, because of the repulsion of the two lone pairs on the oxygen atom. In contrast, the carbon dioxide molecule is linear, because there are no lone pairs on the carbon atom. Oxygen is much more electronegative than carbon or hydrogen. Therefore, the electrons in the bonds in each molecule will tend to exist around the oxygen atoms more often than around the hydrogen or carbon atoms. The oxygen atoms will have negative partial charges, and the hydrogen and carbon atoms will have positive partial charges. These charges can be represented as arrows pointing from positive to negative, as shown below:

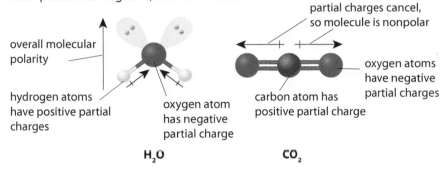

overall molecular polarity

hydrogen atoms have positive partial charges

oxygen atom has negative partial charge

H_2O

partial charges cancel, so molecule is nonpolar

carbon atom has positive partial charge

oxygen atoms have negative partial charges

CO_2

The carbon dioxide molecule is symmetrical. The negative partial charges on the two oxygen atoms balance each other out. Therefore, the molecule as a whole is not polar. In contrast, the partial charges on the water molecule do not cancel each other out. The water molecule as a whole is therefore polar.

TIP

To determine whether a molecule is polar, imagine that the arrows representing the partial charges are ropes attached to a ball. (The ball represents the central atom.) Imagine pulling on the ropes at the same time with the same amount of force. If the ball would move as a result of pulling on the ropes, the partial charges do not cancel each other out, and the molecule is polar. If the ball would not move, the partial charges cancel each other out, and the molecule is nonpolar.

Problem Set

1. Explain why covalent bonds and nonbonded electron pairs repel each other.

2. Carbon tetrachloride (CCl_4) was once commonly used in dry cleaning. However, most dry cleaners today use other chemicals, because CCl_4 is highly toxic. Draw or describe the shape of a molecule of carbon tetrachloride. (Hint: Draw the Lewis dot structure first.)

3. Is a molecule of NH_3 polar or nonpolar? Explain your answer. (Hint: Think about the symmetry of the molecule.)

4. Draw or describe the shape of a molecule of phosphorus trichloride (PCl_3). (Hint: Draw the Lewis dot structure first.)

5. More than 70 percent of the air on earth is made of molecular nitrogen (N_2). Draw or describe the shape of a molecule of N_2. (Hint: Draw the Lewis dot structure first.)

6. Hydrogen sulfide (H_2S) is a compound that occurs naturally in volcanoes and hot springs. It has a strong odor. Is a molecule of hydrogen sulfide polar or nonpolar? (Hint: Compare the molecule to a water molecule.)

7. **Challenge**   Is a molecule of carbon tetrafluoride (CF_4) polar or nonpolar? Explain your answer. (Hint: Draw the Lewis dot structure first. Think about the symmetry of the molecule.)

8. **Challenge**   Why is a molecule of H_2O polar, whereas molecules of H_2 and O_2 are nonpolar? (Hint: A molecule with no polar bonds cannot be a polar molecule.)

9. **Challenge**   Draw or describe the shape of a molecule of chloramine (NH_2Cl). (Hint: Nitrogen is the central atom.)

Van der Waals Forces

Weak forces based on electric charges can bring atoms and molecules together.

Weak attractions and repulsions known as van der Waals forces can cause atoms or molecules to attract or repel one another. There are three main types of van der Waals forces: dipole interactions, dispersion forces, and hydrogen bonds. Dipole interactions occur between polar molecules. The positive partial charge on one polar molecule attracts the negative partial charge on another polar molecule, pulling the molecules together. Dispersion forces occur because electrons are constantly moving. At any moment, a neutral atom or molecule may have a negative side and a positive side. These slight charges are transient—that is, they last only a very short time. However, even that small amount of time can be enough for the atoms or molecules to attract or repel one another slightly. The bigger the atom or molecule is, the more electrons are in motion, and the larger the dispersion forces between them. The third type of van der Waals force, the hydrogen bond, occurs between molecules that contain hydrogen atoms covalently bonded to highly electronegative atoms, such as O, N, or F. A relatively strong electrostatic attraction forms between a hydrogen atom bound to an O, N, or F atom and an O, N, or F atom on another molecule. This attraction is known as a hydrogen bond. Van der Waals forces can affect the boiling and melting points of substances. In general, the stronger the van der Waals attractions between atoms or molecules in a substance are, the higher the substance's melting and boiling points are.

OBJECTIVES

- Identify van der Waals forces, including dipole interactions and dispersion forces.
- Relate van der Waals forces to the boiling and melting points of substances.
- Describe hydrogen bonds.

REMEMBER

VAN DER WAALS FORCES

- Van der Waals forces are electrostatic attractions and repulsions — that is, they arise because similar electric charges repel, and opposite electric charges attract.

- Only polar molecules can produce dipole interactions.

- Dispersion forces occur when the cloud of electrons that surrounds an atom momentarily migrates to one side of an atom, giving that side a temporary negative charge and the other side a temporary positive charge.

- Hydrogen bonds occur between hydrogen atoms and atoms of highly electronegative elements (generally O, N, or F). Hydrogen bonds are *not* bonds between two hydrogen atoms.

EXAMPLE 1

Describe the van der Waals Forces in a Substance

Sulfur dichloride (SCl_2), a cherry-red liquid, is made up of polar molecules. What primary van der Waals force pulls groups of these molecules together?

Solution

1 Recall Relevant Information   There are three main types of van der Waals forces: dipole interactions, dispersion forces, and hydrogen bonds. Dipole interactions occur only between polar molecules. Dispersion forces occur in all molecules. Hydrogen bonds occur only in molecules that contain hydrogen atoms.

2 Solve   Sulfur dichloride is a polar molecule, so dipole interactions will pull SCl_2 molecules together. Dispersion forces may also affect SCl_2 molecules. Hydrogen bonds will not exist between SCl_2 molecules, because these molecules do not contain hydrogen atoms.

EXAMPLE 2

Predict the Effects of van der Waals Forces on Boiling Point

Helium (He) and neon (Ne) are both noble gases that can be condensed into liquids. Use what you know about van der Waals forces to predict which of these substances probably has the higher boiling point.

TIP

Atoms with more electrons typically have higher boiling points because more electrons can participate in dispersion forces.

Solution

1 **Recall Relevant Information**   The electrons in an atom are constantly moving. Sometimes, through random chance, they are unevenly distributed in the atom. When this occurs, one side of the atom becomes slightly positively charged, and the other side becomes slightly negatively charged. At any given moment, many of the atoms in a sample of a substance have such partial electric charges. The partial charges produce electrostatic attractions and repulsions between the atoms (dispersion forces). The more electrons an atom has, the stronger these dispersion forces are. In general, the stronger the dispersion forces in a substance are, the higher the substance's melting and boiling points are.

2 **Solve**   Helium and neon are nonpolar and do not contain hydrogen atoms. Therefore, the only van der Waals forces affecting them are dispersion forces. The number of electrons in their atoms will determine the strength of the dispersion forces in the two substances. The periodic table shows that neon has 10 electrons, and helium has 2. Because neon has more electrons than helium does, neon likely has a higher boiling point.

Problem Set

1. In which of these substances would dipole interactions be strongest?
   A. H_2
   B. CH_4
   C. H_2O
   D. O_2

2. Which of the alkaline earth metals (group 2A) would you expect to have the highest boiling point? Explain your answer.

3. Phosphorus trichloride (PCl_3) and ammonia (NH_3) are both polar molecules. Identify a type of van der Waals force that exists in ammonia but not in phosphorus trichloride. Explain your answer.

4. Which liquid element has the higher boiling point, bromine (Br) or mercury (Hg)? Explain your answer.

5. **Challenge**   Fluorine (F_2) and chlorine (Cl_2) both exist as gases at room temperature and pressure. Bromine (Br_2) is a liquid at room temperature and pressure, and iodine (I_2) and astatine (At) are solids at room temperature and pressure. Explain these observations in terms of van der Waals forces.

6. **Challenge**   Explain why hydrogen bonds occur in water (H_2O), but not in hydrogen gas (H_2).

The Conservation of Mass

Chemical reactions cannot create or destroy matter.

In chemical reactions, starting materials interact to form one or more new kinds of matter. The starting materials in chemical reactions are called *reactants*, and the resulting materials are called *products*. Chemists use chemical equations to represent chemical reactions. In a chemical equation, the reactants are written on the left-hand side of an arrow, and the products are written on the right-hand side of the arrow, as shown below:

$$\underbrace{A + B}_{\text{reactants}} \longrightarrow \underbrace{C + D}_{\text{products}}$$

The law of conservation of mass states that matter cannot be created or destroyed during a chemical reaction. This means that the number of atoms of a given element on one side of a chemical equation must equal the number of atoms of that element on the other side of the equation. In other words, the equation must be balanced. There are no exceptions to this rule.

EXAMPLE 1

Identify Products and Reactants

One formula unit of lye, or sodium hydroxide (NaOH), can combine with one formula unit of hydrochloric acid (HCl) to form one formula unit of table salt (NaCl) and one molecule of water (H_2O). Identify the reactants and products of this reaction, and write a chemical equation for the reaction.

Solution

1 Recall Definitions The substance or substances that are consumed during a chemical reaction are the reactants. The substance or substances that are produced during a chemical reaction are the products. When writing a chemical equation, write the reactants on the left-hand side of the arrow, and write the products on the right-hand side of the arrow.

2 Solve Sodium hydroxide and hydrochloric acid are the reactants, and table salt and water are the products. To write the chemical equation, write the reactants first, joined by a plus sign, as shown below:

NaOH + HCl

Then, draw an arrow and write the products, as shown below:

NaOH + HCl → NaCl + H_2O

OBJECTIVES

- Define *reactants* and *products* in a chemical reaction.
- Identify the reactants and products in a chemical equation.
- Describe the importance of the law of conservation of mass as it relates to chemical equations.

REMEMBER

CHEMICAL EQUATIONS

- The arrow in a chemical equation always points from reactants to products.

- The arrow in a chemical equation is like the equals sign in a mathematical equation. A chemical equation is balanced only when the number of atoms of each element is the same on both sides of the arrow.

- The law of conservation of mass states that matter cannot be created or destroyed during chemical reactions. This means that the total mass of the reactants in a chemical reaction must be equal to the total mass of the products of the chemical reaction.

EXAMPLE 2

Identify a Balanced Equation

Potassium iodide (KI) can react with chlorine gas (Cl_2) to form potassium chloride (KCl) and iodine molecules (I_2). A scientist writes the chemical equation below to represent this reaction:

$$KI + Cl_2 \rightarrow KCl + I_2$$

Does this chemical equation correctly represent the reaction that actually occurs?

Solution

1 **Recall Relevant Information** The law of conservation of mass specifies that matter cannot be created or destroyed. That means that the number of atoms of each element should be the same on both sides of the arrow in a chemical equation.

2 **Examine the Equation** Count the number of atoms of each element in the equation. The table below shows those counts for this equation:

Element	Number of Atoms in Reactants	Number of Atoms in Products
K	1	1
I	1	2
Cl	2	1

3 **Solve** There are more iodine (I) atoms in the products than in the reactants, and there are more chlorine (Cl) atoms in the reactants than in the products. Therefore, the equation as written is not consistent with the law of conservation of energy. It is not balanced, so it does not correctly represent the reaction that actually occurs.

TIP

The subscripts in the chemical formula for a substance indicate the number of atoms of a given element that are in each molecule or formula unit of the substance.

Problem Set

1. Identify the products and reactants of the following reaction:

   $$2Mg + O_2 \rightarrow 2MgO$$

2. A student writes the following chemical equation for the reaction between sodium (Na) and oxygen (O_2):

   $$4Na + O_2 \rightarrow 2Na_2O$$

   Is the student's equation consistent with the law of conservation of mass?

3. One atom of carbon (C) can combine with one molecule of oxygen gas (O_2) to produce one molecule of carbon dioxide (CO_2). Write the chemical equation for this reaction.

4. Does the equation below follow the law of conservation of mass?

   $$C_6H_{12}O_6 \rightarrow C_2O_5OH + CO_2$$

5. **Challenge** Two formula units of rust (Fe_2O_3) form when three molecules of oxygen gas (O_2) combine with four atoms of iron (Fe). Write the chemical equation for this reaction.

6. **Challenge** When a piece of paper burns, only ashes are left behind. The ashes have less mass than the paper. Explain this observation in terms of the law of conservation of mass.

Balancing Chemical Equations

A balanced chemical equation shows the ratios of reactants and products in a chemical reaction.

The law of conservation of mass states that the total mass of the reactants in a reaction must be exactly the same as the total mass of the products of the reaction. A chemical equation represents what happens during a chemical reaction. Because mass must be conserved during a chemical reaction, the chemical equation for the reaction must be balanced. That is, the number of atoms of each element must be the same on both sides of the equation. Chemists use coefficients to balance chemical equations.

EXAMPLE 1

Write and Balance a Chemical Equation

Calcium (Ca), a group 2A element, can react with water (H_2O) to form calcium hydroxide ($Ca(OH)_2$), a white solid that is barely soluble in water, and hydrogen gas (H_2). Write a balanced chemical equation for the reaction between calcium and water.

Solution

1 Identify Reactants and Products Calcium and water are consumed during the reaction, so they are the reactants. Calcium hydroxide and hydrogen are produced during the reaction, so they are the products.

2 Write a Preliminary Chemical Equation The equation below shows the reactants and products of the reaction:

$$Ca + H_2O \rightarrow Ca(OH)_2 + H_2$$

3 Determine Whether the Preliminary Equation Is Balanced Count the number of calcium, hydrogen, and oxygen atoms on each side of the chemical equation above. The table below shows the numbers of each type of atom on each side of the equation:

Element	Number of Atoms in Reactants	Number of Atoms in Products
Ca	1	1
O	1	2
H	2	4

There are more oxygen and hydrogen atoms in the products than there are in the reactants. Therefore, the equation is not balanced.

REMEMBER

BALANCING CHEMICAL EQUATIONS

- *Coefficients* are the numbers found before the chemical symbols or formulas (the chemical *species*) in a chemical equation.
- The coefficient 1 is never used in chemical equations.
- Only coefficients can be changed when balancing a chemical equation. Subscripts cannot be changed.
- Every element in a reaction must appear in equal quantity on the reactant side and the product side of the equation.

4 **Use Coefficients to Balance the Equation** The calcium atoms are balanced in the equation as written. Start balancing the equation by balancing the oxygen atoms. There must be two oxygen atoms in the reactants to balance the equation. The only reactant that contains oxygen is H_2O. Each molecule of H_2O contains one oxygen atom, so add the coefficient 2 to the H_2O to balance the oxygen atoms. This addition yields the following equation:

$$Ca + 2H_2O \rightarrow Ca(OH)_2 + H_2$$

Now, recount the number of atoms of each element in the reactants and products. The table below shows the new numbers of each type of atom on each side of the equation:

Element	Number of Atoms in Reactants	Number of Atoms in Products
Ca	1	1
O	2	2
H	4	4

All of the atoms are now balanced. Therefore, the balanced chemical equation for the reaction between calcium and water is the one shown below:

$$Ca + 2H_2O \rightarrow Ca(OH)_2 + H_2$$

TIP

Make sure that the formula for a compound is correct when writing an equation that you intend to balance. If the compound's formula is written incorrectly, it will be impossible to correctly balance the equation. If you are having a difficult time balancing an equation, check that the formulas for all compounds are written properly.

Problem Set

1. Balance the following chemical equation:

   $$NaOH + Cl_2 \rightarrow NaOCl + NaCl + H_2O$$

2. Explain why changing subscripts is not an acceptable way to balance a chemical equation.

3. Methane (CH_4) and oxygen (O_2) can react to produce carbon dioxide (CO_2) and water (H_2O). Write a balanced chemical equation for this reaction.

4. Balance the following chemical equation:

   $$H_2 + O_2 \rightarrow H_2O$$

5. Balance the following chemical equation:

   $$N_2 + H_2 \rightarrow NH_3$$

6. Vanadium pentoxide (V_2O_5) can react with hydrogen (H_2) to form vanadium trioxide (V_2O_3) and water (H_2O). What is the coefficient on H_2 when the equation for this reaction is balanced?

7. **Challenge** An aqueous solution of ammonium chloride (NH_4Cl) and barium hydroxide ($Ba(OH)_2$) is heated, and the compounds react to give off ammonia gas (NH_3). Barium chloride ($BaCl_2$) and water (H_2O) are also products. Write a balanced chemical equation for this reaction.

8. **Challenge** Lead metal (Pb) can be produced by heating solid lead(II) sulfide (PbS) with solid lead(II) sulfate ($PbSO_4$), resulting in liquid lead (Pb) and sulfur dioxide gas (SO_2). Write a balanced equation for this reaction.

9. **Challenge** Balance the following chemical equation:

   $$PCl_5 + H_2O \rightarrow H_3PO_4 + HCl$$

Problem Set 39

Combustion Reactions

Combustion reactions occur when substances react with oxygen.

Combustion is a process in which substances combine with oxygen gas (O_2). Combustion is accompanied by the production of heat or the production of both heat and light. Combustion reactions often occur between hydrocarbons and oxygen. A hydrocarbon is a compound made entirely of hydrogen and carbon. Hydrocarbons are some of earth's most important energy resources because they produce a huge amount of energy when they combust. The products of a hydrocarbon combustion reaction are carbon dioxide and water. Hydrocarbon combustion occurs in automobiles, homes, and factories.

OBJECTIVES

- Identify a combustion reaction.
- Complete and balance equations for combustion reactions.

REMEMBER

COMBUSTION REACTIONS

- Combustion occurs when a substance reacts with molecular oxygen (O_2).
- Although most combustion reactions you will see involve hydrocarbons or other organic molecules, a combustion reaction does not have to involve those substances. However, a combustion reaction must have molecular oxygen as a reactant.

EXAMPLE 1

Identify a Combustion Reaction

Which of the following chemical equations describes a combustion reaction?

A. $H_2 + I_2 \rightarrow 2HI$

B. $2H_2 + O_2 \rightarrow 2H_2O$

C. $PbS + PbSO_4 \rightarrow 2Pb + 2SO_2$

D. $AgNO_3 + NaBr \rightarrow AgBr + NaNO_3$

Solution

1 Recall Relevant Information In a combustion reaction, an element or compound reacts with molecular oxygen (O_2).

2 Assess the Answer Choices A combustion reaction must have oxygen as a reactant. In choice A, the reactants are H_2 and I_2. In choice B, the reactants are H_2 and O_2. In choice C, the reactants are PbS and $PbSO_4$. In choice D, the reactants are $AgNO_3$ and NaBr.

3 Solve Choice B is the only equation that contains molecular oxygen as a reactant. Therefore, B is the correct answer.

EXAMPLE 2

Write the Balanced Chemical Equation for a Combustion Reaction

Heptane (C_7H_{16}) is an important component in gasoline. Write the balanced chemical equation for the combustion of heptane.

Solution

1 Recall Relevant Information Heptane is a hydrocarbon (it is made up of hydrogen and carbon). The simple word equation for the combustion of a hydrocarbon in oxygen is shown below:

hydrocarbon + oxygen → water + carbon dioxide

2 Write a Preliminary Chemical Equation Heptane and oxygen are the reactants, and carbon dioxide and water are the products. Therefore, the preliminary chemical equation is shown below:

$$C_7H_{16} + O_2 \rightarrow CO_2 + H_2O$$

3 Solve Use coefficients to balance the equation. Balance the hydrogen atoms first, as shown below:

$$C_7H_{16} + O_2 \rightarrow CO_2 + 8H_2O$$

Next, balance the carbon atoms, as shown below:

$$C_7H_{16} + O_2 \rightarrow 7CO_2 + 8H_2O$$

Finally, balance the oxygen atoms, as shown below:

$$C_7H_{16} + 11O_2 \rightarrow 7CO_2 + 8H_2O$$

TIP Always balance the oxygen atoms last in a combustion equation. Oxygen always appears as a pure element in a combustion equation, so it is easy to change the number of atoms of oxygen in the reactants without affecting the other elements in the reaction.

Problem Set

1. Which of the following chemical equations describes a combustion reaction?
   A. $H_2 + Br_2 \rightarrow 2HBr$
   B. $Cl_2 + 2NaBr \rightarrow Br_2 + 2NaCl$
   C. $CH_3OH + O_2 \rightarrow CO_2 + 2H_2O$
   D. $2Na + 2H_2O \rightarrow 2NaOH + H_2$

2. Natural gas is a mixture of hydrocarbon gases. It is primarily composed of methane (CH_4). Write a balanced chemical equation for the combustion of methane.

3. Cellular respiration involves the combustion of glucose to produce energy. Write the equation for the combustion of glucose ($C_6H_{12}O_6$). (Hint: The products of the reaction are carbon dioxide and water.)

4. Explain why smothering a campfire—that is, preventing air from reaching the burning wood—causes the fire to go out. (Hint: Wood burning is a combustion reaction.)

5. **Challenge** Gasohol is a blend of gasoline and alcohol. The alcohols that can be added to gasoline include ethanol (C_2H_5OH) and butanol (C_4H_9OH). Write chemical equations for the combustion of ethanol and butanol. (Hint: The products of each reaction are carbon dioxide and water.)

6. **Challenge** Not all combustion reactions release carbon dioxide and water. Write the chemical equations for the combustion of magnesium metal (Mg) and sodium (Na). (Hint: Both reactions will form ionic compounds of the metal and oxygen.)

Synthesis Reactions

Synthesis reactions occur when two or more substances react to form a single substance.

Synthesis reactions are also called *combination reactions*. In a synthesis reaction, two or more substances react to form a single substance. The reactants of most synthesis reactions are either two elements or two compounds. The product of a synthesis reaction is a compound. Synthesis reactions are important in many fields of chemistry. Many experimental chemists work to develop new methods of synthesizing various chemicals.

OBJECTIVES

- Identify a synthesis reaction.
- Complete and balance equations for synthesis reactions.

EXAMPLE 1

Identify a Synthesis Reaction

Which of the following chemical equations describes a synthesis reaction?

A. $H_2O_{(g)} \rightarrow H_2O_{(l)}$

B. $2HgO_{(s)} \rightarrow 2Hg_{(l)} + O_{2\,(g)}$

C. $2Na_{(s)} + Cl_{2\,(g)} \rightarrow 2NaCl_{(s)}$

D. $4NH_{3\,(g)} + 7O_{2\,(g)} \rightarrow 4NO_{2\,(g)} + 6H_2O_{(l)}$

Solution

1 Recall Relevant Information In a synthesis reaction, two or more pure substances react to form one new compound.

2 Assess the Answer Choices A synthesis reaction must have two or more reactants and a single product. In choice A, the reactant is gaseous H_2O, and the product is liquid H_2O. In choice B, the reactant is HgO, and the products are Hg and O_2. In choice C, the reactants are Na and Cl_2, and the product is NaCl. In choice D, the reactants are NH_3 and O_2, and the products are NO_2 and H_2O.

3 Solve Choice C is the only equation with two or more reactants and a single product. Therefore, C is the correct answer.

REMEMBER

SYNTHESIS REACTIONS

- Synthesis reactions occur when at least two substances react to form a single substance.
- Most chemical reactions involve at least two reactants. However, a chemical reaction is a synthesis reaction only if it has multiple reactants and a single product.

EXAMPLE 2

Write Balanced Chemical Equations for Synthesis Reactions

When solid magnesium (Mg) burns in air, it combines with oxygen (O_2) to produce magnesium oxide (MgO), which is a white powder. Because air also contains nitrogen (N_2), some magnesium nitride (Mg_3N_2), a greenish-yellow powder, also forms. Write balanced chemical equations for the synthesis of both magnesium oxide and magnesium nitride.

TIP

The general form for a synthesis equation is A + B → AB. In this equation, A and B are elements or compounds, and AB is a compound.

Solution

1 Recall Relevant Information In a synthesis reaction, two or more substances react to form one new compound.

2 Write Preliminary Chemical Equations Magnesium and oxygen are the reactants in the first reaction, and magnesium and nitrogen are the reactants in the second reaction. Magnesium oxide is the product in the first reaction, and magnesium nitride is the product in the second reaction. Therefore, the preliminary chemical equations for the two reactions are the ones shown below:

$$Mg + O_2 \rightarrow MgO$$
$$Mg + N_2 \rightarrow Mg_3N_2$$

3 Solve The preliminary equations are unbalanced. Use coefficients to balance the equations, as shown below:

$$2Mg + O_2 \rightarrow 2MgO$$
$$3Mg + N_2 \rightarrow Mg_3N_2$$

Problem Set

1. When hydrogen gas (H_2) burns in oxygen (O_2), water (H_2O) forms. Write the balanced chemical equation for the synthesis of water from hydrogen gas and oxygen gas.

2. Which of the following chemical equations describes a synthesis reaction?
   A. $H_2 + I_2 \rightarrow 2HI$
   B. $Cl_2 + KI \rightarrow KCl + I_2$
   C. $FeO + C \rightarrow Fe + CO$
   D. $2Mg + H_2SO_4 \rightarrow Mg_2SO_4 + H_2$

3. Graphite and diamond are both forms of pure carbon (C). The conversion from graphite to diamond can be represented by the equation below:

   $$C_{(graphite)} \rightarrow C_{(diamond)}$$

   Explain why this is not a synthesis reaction, even though it has only one product.

4. Aluminum oxide (Al_2O_3) is a compound that is used to give wood flooring a protective coating. It forms when aluminum (Al) and oxygen (O_2) react. Write the balanced chemical equation for the synthesis of aluminum oxide.

5. **Challenge** Solid phosphorus exists in several different crystalline forms called *allotropes*. One of these allotropes is white phosphorus, which has the chemical formula P_4. Phosphorus trichloride (PCl_3) forms when white phosphorus (P_4) reacts with chlorine gas (Cl_2). Write the balanced chemical equation for the synthesis of PCl_3.

6. **Challenge** Explain why elements can be reactants in, but never products of, synthesis reactions.

Decomposition Reactions

A decomposition reaction is a reaction in which one substance breaks down into two or more substances.

In a decomposition reaction, a single compound breaks down into two or more products. These products may be either elements or compounds. Most decomposition reactions occur when a compound absorbs energy, generally in the form of heat or electricity. The new conditions caused by the input of energy cause the compound to become unstable and break down. Decomposition reactions can have important consequences in many situations. For example, common aspirin (acetylsalicylic acid) can decompose over time to form salicylic acid and acetic acid. (Acetic acid is the main acid in vinegar, which is why old aspirin may smell like vinegar.) Many other medications also decompose over time. Although many of the decomposition products of medications are harmless, some can be toxic, which is why most medications have expiration dates.

OBJECTIVES

- Identify a decomposition reaction.
- Complete and balance equations for decomposition reactions.

EXAMPLE 1

Identify a Decomposition Reaction

Which of the following equations describes a decomposition reaction?

A. $H_2O_{(s)} \rightarrow H_2O_{(l)}$

B. $2Cl_2O_{5\ (g)} \rightarrow 2Cl_{2\ (g)} + 5O_{2\ (g)}$

C. $ZnS_{(s)} + 2HCl_{(aq)} \rightarrow ZnCl_{2\ (aq)} + H_2S_{(g)}$

D. $4NH_{3\ (g)} + 7O_{2\ (g)} \rightarrow 4NO_{2\ (g)} + 6H_2O_{(g)}$

Solution

1 **Recall Relevant Information** In a decomposition reaction, a single compound breaks down into two or more products.

2 **Assess the Answer Choices** A decomposition reaction must have one reactant and two or more products. The reactant must be a compound. In choice A, the reactant is solid H_2O, and the product is liquid H_2O. In choice B, the reactant is Cl_2O_5, and the products are Cl_2 and O_2. In choice C, the reactants are ZnS and HCl, and the products are $ZnCl_2$ and H_2S. In choice D, the reactants are NH_3 and O_2, and the products are NO_2 and H_2O.

3 **Solve** Choice B is the only equation with one compound as a reactant and two or more substances as products. Therefore, B is the correct answer.

REMEMBER

DECOMPOSITION REACTIONS

- Decomposition reactions occur when a single compound breaks down to form two or more new substances.

- Most chemical reactions involve at least two products. However, a chemical reaction is a decomposition reaction only if it has a single compound as a reactant and two or more substances as products.

EXAMPLE 2

Write the Balanced Chemical Equation for a Decomposition Reaction

A few compounds decompose into their constituent elements upon heating. For example, when red mercury(II) oxide (HgO) is heated, it decomposes to form liquid metallic mercury (Hg) and oxygen gas. Write the balanced chemical equation for the decomposition of mercury(II) oxide.

TIP

The general form for a decomposition reaction is AB → A + B. In this equation, A and B are elements or compounds, and AB is a compound.

Solution

1 **Recall Relevant Information**   Mercury(II) oxide is a binary compound. A binary compound is a compound that is made up of two different elements. During a decomposition reaction, one compound breaks down into two or more products.

2 **Write the Preliminary Chemical Equation**   Mercury(II) oxide is the reactant, and Hg and O_2 are the products. Therefore, the preliminary chemical equation for the reaction is the one shown below:

$$HgO \rightarrow Hg + O_2$$

3 **Solve**   The preliminary equation is unbalanced. Use coefficients to balance the equation, as shown below:

$$2HgO \rightarrow 2Hg + O_2$$

Problem Set

1. When an electric current passes through liquid water, the water breaks down to form hydrogen gas (H_2) and oxygen gas (O_2). Write the balanced chemical equation for the electrolysis of water.

2. Which of the following equations describes a decomposition reaction?
   A. $H_{2\,(g)} + Br_{2\,(g)} \rightarrow 2HBr_{(g)}$
   B. $2Na_{(s)} + Cl_{2\,(g)} \rightarrow 2NaCl_{(s)}$
   C. $2N_2O_{5\,(g)} \rightarrow O_{2\,(g)} + 4NO_{2\,(g)}$
   D. $Cl_{2\,(g)} + KI_{(s)} \rightarrow KCl_{(s)} + I_{2\,(g)}$

3. Calcium carbonate ($CaCO_3$) is the primary compound in the rock limestone. It is also the main compound in the shells of most ocean invertebrates, such as mussels, clams, and snails. When calcium carbonate is heated, it decomposes to form calcium oxide (CaO) and carbon dioxide (CO_2). Write the balanced chemical equation for the decomposition of calcium carbonate.

4. Decomposition reactions are sometimes described as being the opposite of synthesis reactions. Explain why this description is accurate.

5. **Challenge**   Explain why an element can be the product of a decomposition reaction, but cannot be the reactant in a decomposition reaction.

6. **Challenge**   Metal chlorates are compounds consisting of a metal ion and one or more chlorate ions (ClO_3^-). Metal chlorates decompose to form the corresponding metal chloride and oxygen gas. Write the balanced chemical equations for the decomposition of potassium chlorate ($KClO_3$) and barium chlorate ($Ba(ClO_3)_2$).

Single-Displacement Reactions

A single-displacement reaction is a reaction in which atoms of one element replace atoms of another element in a compound.

In a single-displacement reaction, one element replaces another in a compound. The reactants in a single-displacement reaction are an element and a compound, and the products of a single-displacement reaction are also an element and a compound. During the reaction, the elemental reactant replaces one of the elements in the compound. The element that is replaced becomes a pure element. Therefore, all single-displacement reactions are also redox reactions. Single-displacement reactions are commonly used to produce pure elements from compounds.

OBJECTIVES

- Identify a single-displacement reaction.
- Complete and balance equations for single-displacement reactions.

EXAMPLE 1

Identify a Single-Displacement Reaction

Which of the following chemical equations describes a single-displacement reaction?

A. $H_{2\ (g)} + I_{2\ (g)} \rightarrow 2HI_{(g)}$

B. $2HgO_{(s)} \rightarrow 2Hg_{(l)} + O_{2\ (g)}$

C. $2Cl_2O_{5\ (g)} \rightarrow 2Cl_{2\ (g)} + 5O_{2\ (g)}$

D. $Cl_{2\ (g)} + 2NaBr_{(aq)} \rightarrow Br_{2\ (l)} + 2NaCl_{(aq)}$

Solution

1 Recall Relevant Information In a single-displacement reaction, one element replaces another element in a compound.

2 Assess the Answer Choices A single-displacement reaction must have an element and a compound as reactants and an element and a compound as products. In choice A, the reactants are H_2 and I_2, and the product is HI. In choice B, the reactant is HgO, and the products are Hg and O_2. In choice C, the reactant is Cl_2O_5, and the products are Cl_2 and O_2. In choice D, the reactants are Cl_2 and NaBr, and the products are Br_2 and NaCl.

3 Solve Choice D is the only equation with an element (Cl_2) and a compound (NaBr) as reactants and an element (Br_2) and a compound (NaCl) as products. Therefore, D is the correct answer.

REMEMBER

SINGLE-DISPLACEMENT REACTIONS

- Single-displacement reactions occur when one element replaces another in a compound.
- The reactants in a single-displacement reaction must be an element and a compound. The products must also be an element and a compound.

EXAMPLE 2

Write the Balanced Chemical Equation for a Single-Displacement Reaction

The thermite reaction between aluminum (Al) and iron(III) oxide (Fe_2O_3) gives off large amounts of heat. The products of the reaction are iron (Fe) and aluminum oxide (Al_2O_3). The reaction is often used on railway systems to weld railroad tracks. Write the balanced chemical equation for the thermite reaction.

Solution

1 **Recall Relevant Information** During a single-displacement reaction, one element replaces another in a compound.

2 **Write the Preliminary Chemical Equation** Aluminum and iron(III) oxide are the reactants, and iron and aluminum oxide are the products. Therefore, the preliminary chemical equation for the reaction is the one shown below:

$$Al + Fe_2O_3 \rightarrow Fe + Al_2O_3$$

3 **Solve** The preliminary equation is unbalanced. Use coefficients to balance the equation, as shown below:

$$2Al + Fe_2O_3 \rightarrow 2Fe + Al_2O_3$$

TIP

The general form of a single-displacement reaction can be written in two ways:
$AB + C \rightarrow AC + B$ and
$AB + C \rightarrow A + CB$. In these equations, A, B, and C are elements, and AB, AC, and CB are compounds.

Problem Set

1. Magnesium metal (Mg) reacts with sulfuric acid (H_2SO_4) to form magnesium sulfate ($MgSO_4$) and hydrogen gas (H_2). Write the balanced equation for this single-displacement reaction.

2. Which of the following chemical equations describes a single-displacement reaction?
   A. $H_{2\ (g)} + Cl_{2\ (g)} \rightarrow 2HCl_{(g)}$
   B. $FeO_{(s)} + C_{(s)} \rightarrow Fe_{(s)} + CO_{(g)}$
   C. $MgCO_{3\ (s)} \rightarrow MgO_{(s)} + CO_{2\ (g)}$
   D. $CuCl_{2\ (aq)} + AgNO_{3\ (aq)} \rightarrow CuNO_{3\ (aq)} + AgCl_{(s)}$

3. When zinc (Zn) reacts with hydrochloric acid (HCl), zinc chloride ($ZnCl_2$) and hydrogen gas (H_2) are formed. Write the balanced equation for this single-displacement reaction.

4. When a piece of zinc metal (Zn) is placed in a solution of copper(II) nitrate ($Cu(NO_3)_2$), a precipitate of metallic copper (Cu) is formed. Write the balanced chemical equation for this single-displacement reaction.

5. **Challenge** When solid copper is placed in a solution of aluminum sulfate ($Al_2(SO_4)_3$), aluminum precipitates, leaving behind a solution of copper(II) sulfate ($CuSO_4$). Write the balanced chemical equation for this reaction.

6. **Challenge** The alkali metals (group 1A) react with water in single-displacement reactions to form metal hydroxides and hydrogen gas. Write the balanced chemical equations for the reaction of water with potassium and with lithium.

Double-Displacement Reactions

A double-displacement reaction is a reaction in which two compounds react by exchanging ions or elements to form two new compounds.

In a double-displacement reaction, two compounds exchange ions or elements to form new compounds. In many double-displacement reactions, one or both of the new compounds that form are in a different phase than the reactants. For example, many double-displacement reactions occur when aqueous solutions of two compounds mix and a solid precipitate or a gas forms. Another common group of double-displacement reactions is neutralization reactions, in which an acid and a base react to form a salt and water.

OBJECTIVES

- Identify a double-displacement reaction.
- Complete and balance equations for double-displacement reactions.

EXAMPLE 1

Identify a Double-Displacement Reaction

Which of the following chemical equations describes a double-displacement reaction?

A. $4Al_{(s)} + 3O_{2\ (g)} \rightarrow 2Al_2O_{3\ (s)}$

B. $Na_2CO_{3\ (s)} \rightarrow Na_2O_{(s)} + CO_{2\ (g)}$

C. $Zn_{(s)} + 2HCl_{(aq)} \rightarrow ZnCl_{2\ (aq)} + H_{2\ (g)}$

D. $ZnS_{(s)} + 2HCl_{(aq)} \rightarrow ZnCl_{2\ (aq)} + H_2S_{(g)}$

Solution

1 **Recall Relevant Information**   In a double-displacement reaction, two compounds exchange atoms or ions to form two new compounds.

2 **Assess the Answer Choices**   A double-displacement reaction must have two compounds as reactants and two compounds as products. In choice A, the reactants are Al and O_2, and the product is Al_2O_3. In choice B, the reactant is Na_2CO_3, and the products are Na_2O and CO_2. In choice C, the reactants are Zn and HCl, and the products are $ZnCl_2$ and H_2. In choice D, the reactants are ZnS and HCl, and the products are $ZnCl_2$ and H_2S.

3 **Solve**   Choice D is the only equation with two compounds as reactants and two compounds as products. Therefore, D is the correct answer.

REMEMBER

DOUBLE-DISPLACEMENT REACTIONS

- In a double-displacement reaction, two compounds exchange ions or atoms to form two new compounds.

- Many double-displacement reactions result in the formation of a compound in a different phase from the reactants, such as a gas or a solid precipitate.

- Most acid-base neutralization reactions are double-displacement reactions.

EXAMPLE 2

Write the Balanced Chemical Equation for a Double-Displacement Reaction

To determine the concentration of a sulfuric acid (H_2SO_4) solution, a student titrated it with a known concentration of a sodium hydroxide (NaOH) solution. Write the balanced chemical equation for the reaction of sulfuric acid and sodium hydroxide.

TIP

The general form for a double-displacement reaction is $AB + CD \rightarrow AD + CB$. In this equation, A, B, C, and D are atoms or elements, and AB, CD, AD, and CB are compounds.

Solution

1 **Recall Relevant Information**   A neutralization reaction is a type of double-displacement reaction. Neutralization reactions occur because of the formation of the very stable covalent water molecule from hydrogen ions and hydroxide ions.

2 **Write the Preliminary Chemical Equation**   Sulfuric acid and sodium hydroxide are the reactants. The compounds will exchange ions to form the products. Therefore, sodium sulfate (Na_2SO_4) and water must be the products. The preliminary chemical equation is the one shown below:

$$H_2SO_4 + NaOH \rightarrow Na_2SO_4 + H_2O$$

3 **Solve**   The preliminary equation is unbalanced. Use coefficients to balance the equation, as shown below:

$$H_2SO_4 + 2NaOH \rightarrow Na_2SO_4 + 2H_2O$$

Problem Set

1. When an aqueous solution of sodium chloride (NaCl) is mixed with an aqueous solution of silver nitrate ($AgNO_3$), the result is a solution of sodium nitrate ($NaNO_3$) and a precipitate of solid silver chloride (AgCl). Write the balanced chemical equation for this double-displacement reaction.

2. Which of the following chemical equations describes a double-displacement reaction?
   A. $2N_2O_{5\ (g)} \rightarrow O_{2\ (g)} + 4NO_{2\ (g)}$
   B. $Cl_{2\ (g)} + KI_{(s)} \rightarrow KCl_{(s)} + I_{2\ (g)}$
   C. $2Na_{(s)} + 2H_2O_{(l)} \rightarrow 2NaOH_{(aq)} + H_{2\ (g)}$
   D. $AgNO_{3\ (aq)} + NaBr_{(aq)} \rightarrow AgBr_{(s)} + NaNO_{3\ (aq)}$

3. Many statues are made from limestone. The primary mineral in limestone is calcium carbonate ($CaCO_3$). Limestone structures are corroded by the sulfuric acid (H_2SO_4) in acid rain. Write the balanced equation for this double-displacement reaction. (Hint: Identify the products first.)

4. Silver bromide (AgBr) is insoluble in water. Calcium bromide ($CaBr_2$) and silver nitrate ($AgNO_3$) are soluble in water. Write the equation for the double-displacement reaction between an aqueous solution of calcium bromide and an aqueous solution of silver nitrate.

5. **Challenge**   Barium chloride ($BaCl_2$) and potassium carbonate (K_2CO_3) can react in a double-displacement reaction. Write the balanced chemical equation for this reaction.

6. **Challenge**   A particular double-displacement reaction produces hydrogen sulfide (H_2S) and iron(II) chloride ($FeCl_2$). Write the balanced chemical equation for this reaction.

Oxidation-Reduction Reactions

Oxidation-reduction reactions, or redox reactions, occur when elements or compounds exchange electrons.

When a chemical species (an atom, ion, or molecule) is oxidized, it loses electrons. When a chemical species is reduced, it gains electrons. A chemical reaction in which one or more species donate electrons to one or more other species is called an oxidation-reduction, or *redox*, reaction. In essence, redox reactions are like two separate reactions taking place at once. Oxidation and reduction always occur together—one reaction can't happen without the other one. Consequently, you need a special technique to balance redox reactions that reflects this electron exchange. You can do this by splitting the reaction into two half-reactions. One half-reaction shows the oxidation reaction. The other half-reaction shows the reduction reaction. For reactions that happen in acidic solutions, use the following steps to balance the reaction:

- Balance all elements except H and O in each half-reaction.
- Balance the O by adding H_2O.
- Balance the H by adding H^+.
- Multiply each half-reaction by an integer so that the number of electrons in each is the same.
- Combine the half-reactions and cancel out anything that's the same on both sides of the equation.

OBJECTIVES

- Describe oxidation and reduction.
- Identify oxidation numbers.
- Explain what happens in oxidation-reduction (redox) reactions.
- Balance simple oxidation-reduction equations.

EXAMPLE 1

Identify Oxidation and Reduction of Elements

The formation of sodium chloride from sodium metal and chlorine gas is a redox reaction. The balanced equation for this reaction is shown below:

$$2Na + Cl_2 \rightarrow 2NaCl$$

Which element is oxidized in this reaction? Which is reduced?

Solution

1 **Determine the Charge on Each Atom and Ion**   Sodium (Na) and chlorine (Cl_2) are both elements. They consist of neutral atoms, which have no electric charge. Sodium chloride (NaCl) is an ionic compound. It consists of sodium ions (Na^+) and chloride ions (Cl^-).

2 **Solve**   For a sodium atom to become a sodium ion, it must lose an electron. For a chlorine atom to become a chloride ion, it must gain an electron. Therefore, sodium is oxidized, and chlorine is reduced.

REMEMBER

REDOX REACTIONS

- Oxidation occurs when an atom loses electrons. Oxidation causes an atom's oxidation number or charge to become more positive.
- Reduction occurs when an atom gains electrons. Reduction causes an atom's oxidation number or charge to become more negative.
- Any electrons lost by one atom must be gained by another atom. In other words, oxidation and reduction always happen together.

EXAMPLE 2

Identify Oxidation Numbers in Compounds

Permanganic acid ($HMnO_4$) can react with potassium chlorite ($KClO_2$) to produce manganese dioxide (MnO_2), potassium perchlorate ($KClO_4$), and water. Identify the oxidation number of each atom in each of these compounds.

TIP

The total charge on a molecule or ion is equal to the sum of the oxidation numbers of the atoms in that molecule or ion.

Solution

1 **Identify Ionic Charges**   Permanganic acid consists of hydrogen ion (H^+) and permanganate ion (MnO_4^-). Potassium chlorite consists of potassium ion (K^+) and chlorite ion (ClO_2^-). Potassium perchlorate consists of potassium ion and perchlorate ion (ClO_4^-). Manganese dioxide and water are not ionic compounds.

2 **Solve**   The oxidation number of a monatomic ion is equal to its ionic charge. Therefore, potassium has an oxidation number of $+1$ in both of the potassium-containing compounds, and the hydrogen ion has an oxidation number of $+1$ in permanganic acid. The oxidation number of oxygen is -2 in all compounds except peroxides and fluorides. None of the compounds that contain oxygen are peroxides or fluorides, so the oxidation number of oxygen in all five compounds is -2. The oxidation number of hydrogen is $+1$ in all molecules except metal hydrides. Water is not a metal hydride, so the oxidation number of the hydrogen atoms in water is $+1$. Use the ionic charges and the oxidation number of oxygen to calculate the oxidation numbers of Mn and Cl. The net charge on the permanganate ion is -1. Therefore, use the following equation to calculate the oxidation number of Mn in this ion (x is the oxidation number of Mn):

$$x + (4)(-2) = -1$$
$$x - 8 = -1$$
$$x = +7$$

The oxidation number of Mn in $KMnO_4$ is $+7$. The net charge on the chlorite ion is -1. Therefore, calculate the oxidation number of Cl in the chlorite ion as shown below:

$$x + (2)(-2) = -1$$
$$x - 4 = -1$$
$$x = +3$$

The oxidation number of Cl in $KClO_2$ is $+3$. Similarly, for Mn in MnO_2, the calculation is as follows:

$$x + (2)(-2) = 0$$
$$x - 4 = 0$$
$$x = +4$$

The oxidation number of Mn in MnO_2 is $+4$. Finally, the calculation for Cl in $KClO_4$ is shown below:

$$x + (4)(-2) = -1$$
$$x - 8 = -1$$
$$x = +7$$

The oxidation number of Cl in $KClO_4$ is $+7$.

EXAMPLE 3

Identify Oxidation and Reduction of Compounds

The unbalanced equation below represents the redox reaction described in Example 2:

$$HMnO_4 + KClO_2 \rightarrow MnO_2 + KClO_4 + H_2O$$

Which species is oxidized in this reaction? Which species is reduced?

Solution

1 Identify Oxidation Number Changes   The oxidation numbers of each species in the reaction were determined in Example 2. Hydrogen has an oxidation number of $+1$ on both sides of the equation. Oxygen has an oxidation number of -2 on both sides of the equation. Manganese has an oxidation number of $+7$ in $HMnO_4$ and an oxidation number of $+4$ in MnO_2. Chlorine has an oxidation number of $+3$ in $KClO_2$ and an oxidation number of $+7$ in $KClO_4$.

2 Solve   The oxidation numbers of hydrogen and oxygen do not change, so hydrogen and oxygen are neither oxidized nor reduced. Manganese gains electrons, so it is reduced. Chlorine loses electrons, so it is oxidized.

EXAMPLE 4

Balance the Equation for a Redox Reaction

Balance the equation given in Example 3.

Solution

1 Write Half-Reactions   Each chlorine atom must lose four electrons to change oxidation number from $+3$ to $+7$. Therefore, the oxidation half-reaction is shown below:

$$ClO_2^- \rightarrow ClO_4^- + 4e^-$$

Each manganese atom must gain three electrons to change oxidation number from $+7$ to $+4$. Therefore, the reduction half-reaction is shown below:

$$MnO_4^- + 3e^- \rightarrow MnO_2$$

2 Balance Each Half-Reaction   The chlorine and manganese atoms are already balanced in each half-reaction. Add water (H_2O) to balance the oxygen atoms, and then add H^+ to balance the hydrogen atoms, as shown below:

$$ClO_2^- + 2H_2O \rightarrow ClO_4^- + 4e^- + 4H^+$$
$$MnO_4^- + 3e^- + 4H^+ \rightarrow MnO_2 + 2H_2O$$

Do a quick double-check to confirm that the charges are balanced in each half-reaction.

TIP

If ionic compounds are involved in a reaction, separate the compounds into their component ions before writing half-reactions. When you first write the half-reactions, write only the ions that are actually oxidized or reduced. For example, in the problem shown here, write only the chlorite, perchlorate, and permanganate ions.

③ Balance Electrons and Add the Half-Reactions Now, multiply each half-reaction by a factor that will make the number of electrons the same in both half-reactions. Multiply the oxidation half-reaction by 3 and the reduction half-reaction by 4, as shown below.

$3 \times [ClO_2^- + 2H_2O \rightarrow ClO_4^- + 4e^- + 4H^+]$
$= 3ClO_2^- + 6H_2O \rightarrow 3ClO_4^- + 12e^- + 12H^+$
$4 \times [MnO_4^- + 3e^- + 4H^+ \rightarrow MnO_2 + 2H_2O]$
$= 4MnO_4^- + 12e^- + 16H^+ \rightarrow 4MnO_2 + 8H_2O$

Then, add the half-reactions together and cancel like terms, as shown below:

$$3ClO_2^- + 6\cancel{H_2O} \rightarrow 3ClO_4^- + \cancel{12e^-} + 12H^+$$
$$\underline{4MnO_4^- + \cancel{12e^-} + \overset{4}{\cancel{16}}H^+ \rightarrow 4MnO_2 + \overset{2}{\cancel{8}}H_2O}$$
$$3ClO_2^- + 4MnO_4^- + 4H^+ \rightarrow 3ClO_4^- + 4MnO_2 + 2H_2O$$

Finally, add K^+ ions to balance the original equation, as shown below:

$4HMnO_4 + 3KClO_2 \rightarrow 4MnO_2 + 3KClO_4 + 2H_2O$

A quick double-check confirms that all of the atoms are balanced.

TIP

Remember to double-check that all atoms are balanced in a redox reaction.

Problem Set

1. Hydrogen fluoride (HF) is an ionic compound. It forms according to the following reaction:

   $H_2 + F_2 \rightarrow 2HF$

   Which element is oxidized in this reaction? Which element is reduced?

2. Chlorine gas (Cl_2) can react with hydrogen bromide (HBr) to form bromine (Br_2) and hydrogen chloride (HCl). Identify the oxidation number of each atom in each substance. Which atoms are oxidized in the reaction? Which atoms are reduced?

3. Write the oxidation and reduction half-reactions for the reaction described in Question 2. Use these half-reactions to balance the chemical equation.

4. Water can form from hydrogen gas and oxygen gas according to the equation below:

   $2H_2 + O_2 \rightarrow 2H_2O$

   Which element is oxidized in this reaction? Which element is reduced? Identify the number of electrons involved in the balanced equation.

5. Nitric acid (HNO_3) can react with hydroiodic acid (HI) to produce nitric oxide (NO), iodine (I_2), and water (H_2O). Which atoms are oxidized in the reaction? Which atoms are reduced? (Hint: Calculate oxidation numbers first.)

6. Use oxidation and reduction half-reactions for the reaction described in Question 5 to balance the chemical equation. (Hint: Remember to add water and H^+ to balance oxygen and hydrogen atoms.)

7. **Challenge** Hydroiodic acid (HI) can react with sulfuric acid (H_2SO_4) to form hydrogen sulfide (H_2S) and iodine (I_2). Write an unbalanced chemical equation for this reaction. Identify the oxidation number of each atom in the reaction.

8. **Challenge** Write the oxidation and reduction half-reactions for the reaction described in Question 7. Use those half-reactions to balance the chemical equation. (Hint: Remember to add water and H^+ to balance oxygen and hydrogen atoms.)

9. **Challenge** Potassium dichromate ($K_2Cr_2O_7$) can react with water and sulfur according to the equation below:

   $2K_2Cr_2O_7 + 2H_2O + 3S \rightarrow 4KOH + 2Cr_2O_3 + 3SO_2$

   Which atoms are oxidized in the reaction? Which atoms are reduced? How many electrons are involved in the balanced equation?

Stoichiometry and Its Uses

Stoichiometry helps chemists quantify the amounts of reactants and products in chemical reactions.

Stoichiometry is the branch of chemistry that deals with quantifying the amounts of substances that are involved in reactions. Stoichiometry is important because chemicals react in specific ways. A reaction will proceed to completion only if the reactants are present in the correct ratio. If there is not enough of one reactant, the other reactants will not be completely consumed. Using stoichiometry, chemists can predict the amount of a substance that will be produced in a reaction. They can also use stoichiometry to predict whether a given reactant will be completely consumed during a chemical reaction. Stoichiometry relies on a rule called the *law of multiple proportions*. This law states that elements can combine only in specific ratios of whole integers. For example, hydrogen (H) and oxygen (O) can combine to make water (H_2O) and hydrogen peroxide (H_2O_2), but they cannot combine to form H_3O_4 or $H_{1.5}O_{2.3}$. The subscripts on the atoms in a chemical formula give the number of atoms of each element in one molecule or formula unit of the compound.

OBJECTIVES

- Define *stoichiometry*.
- Demonstrate the law of multiple proportions in formulas.

EXAMPLE 1

Quantify the Ratios of Elements in Compounds

Silver nitrate ($AgNO_3$), a white solid that can stain skin brown, is sometimes used for temporary tattoos. How many atoms of silver, nitrogen, and oxygen would be required to form one formula unit of silver nitrate?

Solution

1. **Recall Relevant Information** The law of multiple proportions states that elements can combine only in specific ratios of whole integers. The subscripts in chemical formulas can be used to calculate these ratios.

2. **Examine the Chemical Formula** The silver (Ag) and nitrogen (N) symbols in $AgNO_3$ have no subscripts. The subscript on the oxygen (O) symbol is 3.

3. **Solve** Forming one formula unit of silver nitrate would require one silver atom, one nitrogen atom, and three oxygen atoms.

REMEMBER

THE LAW OF MULTIPLE PROPORTIONS

- The law of multiple proportions states that elements can combine only in specific ratios of whole integers.

- In chemical formulas, such as H_2O, subscripts represent the numbers of each type of atom in a molecule or formula unit.

- The subscript 1 is never used in chemical formulas. If only one atom of an element is present in a molecule or formula unit, that element's chemical symbol has no subscript in the chemical formula.

EXAMPLE 2

Identify Proportions in Reactions

Table salt, or sodium chloride (NaCl), can be produced by reacting sodium metal (Na) with chlorine gas (Cl_2), as shown in the equation below:

$$2Na + Cl_2 \rightarrow 2NaCl$$

If 100 atoms of sodium react with 48 molecules of chlorine gas (Cl_2), how many formula units of NaCl will be produced?

Solution

1 **Recall Relevant Information**   A reaction consumes all of the reactants only if they are present in the correct ratio. The coefficients in the chemical equation give the ratio of the reactants needed to produce the product.

2 **Examine the Equation**   According to the chemical equation, two atoms of sodium are required to completely react with one molecule of chlorine. The result of this reaction is the formation of two formula units of NaCl.

3 **Solve**   For all 100 atoms of sodium to completely react with chlorine, $100 \div 2 = 50$ molecules of chlorine would be required. Only 48 molecules are present. Therefore, all the chlorine will be consumed, but not all the sodium will be consumed. To react with 48 molecules of chlorine, $48 \times 2 = 96$ atoms of sodium are required. This reaction will produce 96 formula units of sodium chloride, with four atoms of sodium left over.

TIP

If one of the reactants in a reaction is completely consumed but the other reactants are not completely consumed, the reactant that is completely consumed is called the *limiting reactant*. In Example 2, chlorine is the limiting reactant.

Problem Set

1. Ammonia's chemical formula is NH_3. How many atoms of nitrogen (N) and hydrogen (H) are required to form a single molecule of this compound?

2. Hydrogen chloride (HCl) can form from hydrogen gas (H_2) and chlorine gas (Cl_2) according to the equation below:

   $$H_2 + Cl_2 \rightarrow 2HCl$$

   If 500 molecules of H_2 react with 400 molecules of Cl_2, how many formula units of HCl will be produced?

3. Ethyl alcohol has the chemical formula C_2H_5OH. How many atoms of carbon (C), hydrogen (H), and oxygen (O) are in each molecule of ethyl alcohol?

4. Nitrogen gas (N_2) and hydrogen gas (H_2) can react to form ammonia (NH_3) according to the equation below:

   $$3H_2 + N_2 \rightarrow 2NH_3$$

   If 5,400 molecules of H_2 react with 3,000 molecules of N_2, how many molecules of NH_3 will form?

5. **Challenge**   Iron (Fe) can react with oxygen (O_2) to form rust (Fe_2O_3) according to the following equation:

   $$4Fe + 3O_2 \rightarrow 2Fe_2O_3$$

   If 2.5×10^5 atoms of iron react with 3.4×10^5 molecules of oxygen, how many formula units of Fe_2O_3 will form?

6. **Challenge**   Glucose has the chemical formula $C_6H_{12}O_6$. What is the ratio of carbon to hydrogen to oxygen in glucose?

Mole-Number Relationships

You can use Avogadro's number to calculate the number of particles in a given amount of a sample, and the amount of a substance from a given number of particles.

OBJECTIVE

- Use Avogadro's number to convert between moles and numbers of particles.

Atoms and molecules are too small to count by usual means. Even the smallest visible object contains hundreds of billions of atoms. Therefore, chemists use a specific unit, the mole (mol), to describe the numbers of particles in a sample of a substance. The mole is a way of counting any type of particle (atom, molecule, ion, or formula unit). One mole of a substance is defined as the amount of that substance with the same number of particles as there are in 12 grams of carbon-12. That number is 6.02×10^{23}. Just as one dozen doughnuts means 12 doughnuts, one mole of a substance means 6.02×10^{23} particles of that substance. This experimentally determined number of particles in a mole is called *Avogadro's number*. Avogadro's number can be used to convert between the number of moles of a substance and the number of particles in a sample of that substance.

EXAMPLE 1

Calculate the Number of Particles in a Given Amount of a Substance

Caffeine ($C_8H_{10}N_4O_2$) is a drug that is naturally produced in the leaves and seeds of many plants. How many molecules of caffeine are in 2.31 mol of caffeine?

Solution

1 **Strategize** One mole of caffeine consists of 6.02×10^{23} molecules of caffeine. Use a conversion factor to calculate the number of molecules of caffeine in 2.31 mol.

2 **Solve** The calculation is shown below (use a scientific calculator to solve):

$$2.31 \text{ mol caffeine} \times \frac{6.02 \times 10^{23} \text{ molecules caffeine}}{1 \text{ mol caffeine}}$$

$$= 1.39 \times 10^{24} \text{ molecules caffeine}$$

Therefore, 2.31 mol caffeine contains 1.39×10^{24} molecules of caffeine.

REMEMBER

AVOGADRO'S NUMBER

- Avogadro's number is 6.02×10^{23}.

- One mole of a substance contains Avogadro's number of basic particles of the substance.

- The chemical formula for a substance shows the atoms that make up a basic particle of the substance.

- The formula unit is the basic particle of ionic compounds. The molecule is the basic particle of covalent compounds and molecular elements. The atom is the basic particle of nonmolecular elements.

EXAMPLE 2

Calculate the Number of Moles in a Given Number of Particles

Automobile airbags inflate when sodium azide (NaN_3) rapidly decomposes to form sodium (Na) and nitrogen gas (N_2). If a particular sample of NaN_3 contains 9.20×10^{29} formula units of NaN_3, how many moles of NaN_3 are in the sample?

Solution

1 Strategize   One mole of NaN_3 corresponds to 6.02×10^{23} formula units of NaN_3. Use a conversion factor to convert 9.20×10^{29} formula units to moles.

2 Solve   The calculation is shown below (use a scientific calculator to solve):

$$9.20 \times 10^{29} \text{ formula units } NaN_3 \times \frac{1 \text{ mol } NaN_3}{6.02 \times 10^{23} \text{ formula units } NaN_3}$$

$$= 1.53 \times 10^6 \text{ mol } NaN_3$$

Therefore, the sample contains 1.53×10^6 mol NaN_3.

Problem Set

1. Common baking soda has the chemical formula $NaHCO_3$. A particular sample of baking soda contains 12.04×10^{23} formula units of $NaHCO_3$. How many moles of $NaHCO_3$ does the sample contain?

2. A chemical reaction produces 3.81 mol of potassium chloride (KCl). How many formula units of KCl does the reaction produce?

3. Arsenic (As) appears frequently in conventional detective fiction. In fact, ingestion of about 1.50 mol can be dangerous. How many atoms of arsenic are in 1.50 mol of arsenic?

4. A particular chemical reaction produces 0.34 mol sulfuric acid (H_2SO_4). How many formula units of sulfuric acid does the reaction produce?

5. Nitrogen gas (N_2) makes up more than 70 percent of earth's atmosphere. If a sample of nitrogen gas contains 8.62×10^2 molecules of nitrogen gas (N_2), how many moles of nitrogen gas does the sample contain?

6. A sample of N_2O_3 contains 1.00×10^6 molecules of N_2O_3. How many moles of N_2O_3 does the sample contain?

7. **Challenge**   Methane (CH_4) is a colorless, odorless gas. Burning one molecule of methane produces one molecule of carbon dioxide (CO_2) and two molecules of water (H_2O). How many molecules of water are produced when 2.50 mol of methane burns?

8. **Challenge**   Sucrose, or common table sugar, has the chemical formula $C_{12}H_{22}O_{11}$. How many hydrogen atoms are present in 0.50 mol sucrose?

9. **Challenge**   Ozone (O_3) is produced when oxygen gas molecules (O_2) are split into single oxygen atoms (O). These oxygen atoms then combine with oxygen molecules to form ozone. Which contains more molecules, a mole of O_3 or a mole of O_2? Which contains more atoms, 1 mol O_3, 1 mol O_2, or 1 mol O?

Mole-Mass Relationships

You can use the mole to relate the mass of an individual atom or molecule to the mass of a sample of a substance made up of that atom or molecule.

Chemists must often compare quantities of different substances. The same mass of different substances may contain very different numbers of atoms or molecules. Therefore, it is more accurate to use the mole to compare macroscopic quantities of substances. We can calculate the molar mass of a substance—the mass of one mole of the substance—from its chemical formula and the average atomic masses of the elements in it. If we know a substance's molar mass, we can determine the number of moles of the substance in a given sample.

OBJECTIVE

- Use the mole to solve molar mass and sample mass problems.

EXAMPLE 1

Calculate the Molar Mass of a Compound

Oseltamivir ($C_{16}H_{28}N_2O_4$) is a drug for the treatment of influenza infections ("flu"). What is the molar mass of oseltamivir?

Solution

1 Collect   List the molar masses of the elements in the compound.

Element	Average Atomic Mass (amu)
Carbon	12.011
Hydrogen	1.0079
Nitrogen	14.007
Oxygen	15.999

2 Strategize and Calculate   Multiply the average atomic mass of each element by the number of atoms of that element in one molecule of oseltamivir. The mass of the compound is the sum of the total masses.

Total mass of carbon in the molecule $= 16 \times 12.011 = 192.18$ amu
Total mass of hydrogen in the molecule $= 28 \times 1.0079 = 28.221$ amu
Total mass of nitrogen in the molecule $= 2 \times 14.007 = 28.014$ amu
Total mass of oxygen in the molecule $= 4 \times 15.999 = 63.996$ amu

Total mass of one molecule of oseltamivir $= 312.41$ amu

3 Solve   The mass of one molecule of oseltamivir is 312.41 amu, so the molar mass of oseltamivir is 312.41 g/mol.

REMEMBER

THE MOLE

- The mass of one mole of a substance in grams is the same as the mass of one atom or molecule of the substance in atomic mass units.

- One mole of a substance contains 6.023×10^{23} atoms or molecules of that substance.

- The molar mass of a substance is the mass of one mole of the substance. It is given in grams per mole, or g/mol.

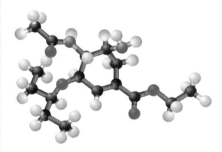

In this model of the chemical structure of oseltamivir, carbon atoms are black, hydrogen atoms are white, nitrogen atoms are blue, and oxygen atoms are red.

EXAMPLE 2

Calculate the Number of Moles of a Substance

Amyl acetate ($CH_3COO(CH_2)_4CH_3$) is used to make products smell like bananas. The molar mass of amyl acetate is 130.2 g/mol. A chemist produces 183.5 g of amyl acetate. How many moles of amyl acetate does the chemist produce?

TIP

If the molar mass of a compound is not given in the problem, you can calculate it. Remember that the subscript on each elemental symbol indicates how many atoms of that element are in one molecule of the compound.

Solution

1   **Set Up the Unit Conversion** $183.5 \text{ g amyl acetate} \times \dfrac{1 \text{ mol amyl acetate}}{130.2 \text{ g amyl acetate}}$

2   **Cancel Similar Units** $183.5 \text{ g amyl acetate} \times \dfrac{1 \text{ mol amyl acetate}}{130.2 \text{ g amyl acetate}}$

3   **Solve** $\dfrac{183.5}{130.2} \text{ mol amyl acetate} = 1.409 \text{ mol amyl acetate}$

Problem Set

1. The formula for sucrose is $C_{12}H_{22}O_{11}$. What is the molar mass of sucrose?

2. A chemical reaction produces 56.2 g of iron sulfide (molar mass 87.92 g/mol). How many moles of iron sulfide does the reaction produce?

3. A student needs 1.52 mol of sodium hydroxide (molar mass 40.00 g/mol). How many grams of sodium hydroxide are required?

4. Chlorophyll allows plants to carry out photosynthesis. There are two forms of chlorophyll: chlorophyll *a* ($C_{55}H_{72}O_5N_4Mg$) and chlorophyll *b* ($C_{55}H_{70}O_6N_4Mg$). What is the difference in molar mass between these two forms?

5. A chemical engineer needs 52.4 mol of acetone (C_3H_6O). How many grams of acetone are needed?

6. A chemist needs 0.035 mol of copper(II) sulfate ($CuSO_4$). The chemist has 785 mg of copper(II) sulfate. How many more grams of copper(II) sulfate does the chemist need?

7. **Challenge** A biologist grows a turmeric plant in an atmosphere containing $^{14}CO_2$, so all the carbon-containing compounds in the plant contain only carbon-14 (^{14}C). What would be the difference in mass between one mole of curcumin ($C_{21}H_{20}O_6$) produced by this plant and one mole of curcumin produced by a plant grown in a normal atmosphere? (Hint: The molar mass of carbon-14 is 14.003 g/mol.)

8. **Challenge** In rocks, the mineral albite ($NaAlSi_3O_8$) can react with carbon dioxide and water to form the mineral kaolinite ($Al_2Si_2O_5(OH)_4$) as well as several other products. Two molecules of albite are required to form each molecule of kaolinite. If 1.49 kg of albite completely reacts with carbon dioxide and water, how many grams of kaolinite will form?

9. **Challenge** One mole of $Pb(NO_3)_2$ can react with two moles of KI to produce one mole of PbI_2 and two moles of KNO_3. How many grams of KI are required to completely react with 45.3 mg of $Pb(NO_3)_2$?

Mole-Volume Relationships

You can use Avogadro's hypothesis to relate the number of moles of a gas to the volume of that gas at standard temperature and pressure.

A vogadro's hypothesis states that equal volumes of gases under equal conditions of temperature and pressure contain equal numbers of molecules. Because the volume of a gas varies with temperature and pressure, chemists generally specify the temperature and pressure conditions under which the volume of a gas is measured. If no temperature or pressure conditions are given in a problem or experimental setup, the problem or experiment is assumed to occur at standard temperature and pressure (STP). Chemists define *standard temperature and pressure* to be 0°C (273 K) and 1 atm (101.3 kPa). At STP, the volume of one mole of any gas is 22.4 L. Therefore, if you know the number of moles of gas in a sample at STP, you can predict the volume of the gas.

OBJECTIVE

- Use Avogadro's hypothesis to solve molar volume problems.

EXAMPLE 1

Calculate the Number of Moles of a Gas at STP

Nitrous oxide (N_2O), also known as laughing gas, is a colorless, almost odorless gas used as a mild anesthetic. It is also used to improve engine performance in racecars. A particular container holds 4.55 L of nitrous oxide at STP. How many moles of nitrous oxide does the container hold?

Solution

1 **Strategize**   At STP, one mole of a gas occupies a volume of 22.4 L. Use this conversion factor to convert liters to moles.

2 **Solve**   The conversion is shown below:

$$4.55 \; \cancel{L} \times \frac{1 \; mol}{22.4 \; \cancel{L}} = 0.203 \; mol$$

So, the container holds 0.203 mol N_2O.

REMEMBER

STANDARD TEMPERATURE AND PRESSURE (STP)

- Standard temperature is 0°C.

- Standard pressure is 101.3 kPa, or 1 atm.

- At STP, one mole of a gas occupies a volume of 22.4 L.

EXAMPLE 2

Calculate the Volume of a Gas at STP

Helium (He) is thought to be the second most abundant element in the universe. A particular container holds 5.22 mol helium gas at STP. What is the volume of the container?

TIP

The volume of one mole of a gas at STP is 22.4 L. This is true for both monatomic gases, such as helium (He), and polyatomic gases, such as oxygen (O_2) and ammonia (NH_3).

Solution

1 **Strategize**   A gas fills the entire volume of its container. Therefore, the volume of the container will equal the volume of the helium gas. So, to solve this problem, use a conversion factor to convert moles of helium to liters of helium.

2 **Solve**   The conversion is shown below:

$$5.22 \text{ mol} \times \frac{22.4 \text{ L}}{1 \text{ mol}} = 117 \text{ L}$$

The volume of helium is 117 L. Therefore, the container must also have a volume of 117 L.

Problem Set

1. Nitrogen (N_2) is the most abundant element in earth's atmosphere. A scientist collected a 3.51 L sample of N_2 at STP. How many moles of N_2 did the scientist collect?

2. A chemical reaction produces 3.52 mol of hydrogen gas (H_2) at STP. How many liters of hydrogen gas does the reaction produce?

3. Propane gas (C_3H_8) is used for cooking in barbecues and portable stoves. If a tank has a volume of 11.2 L, how many moles of propane can it hold at STP?

4. A chemical reaction consumes 0.800 L of oxygen gas (O_2) at STP. How many moles of oxygen gas does the reaction consume?

5. Chlorine gas was first used as a weapon in World War I. It causes irritation to the eyes, skin, and upper and lower respiratory tract. What volume does 2.35 mol of chlorine gas (Cl_2) occupy at STP?

6. A student has a 1.00 L bottle of water. He drinks all the water and leaves the bottle on his desk. If the room the bottle is in is at STP, how many moles of air are in the bottle?

7. **Challenge**   A chemical engineer needs 29.3 L of sulfur trioxide (SO_3) at STP. She has 0.25 mol of SO_3. How many more liters of SO_3 does the chemical engineer need at STP?

8. **Challenge**   Hydrogen (H_2) and oxygen (O_2) can react to produce water according to the following chemical equation:

   $$2H_2 + O_2 \rightarrow 2H_2O$$

   How many moles of O_2 would be required to completely react with 4.00 L of H_2 at STP?

9. **Challenge**   Nitrogen gas (N_2) can react with hydrogen gas (H_2) to produce ammonia (NH_3) according to the equation below:

   $$3H_2 + N_2 \rightarrow 2NH_3$$

   How many liters of hydrogen would be required to completely react with 2.80 mol of nitrogen at STP?

Moles and Chemical Equations

Chemists use balanced chemical equations to make predictions and calculations related to chemical reactions.

In industry, chemical engineers develop methods for producing useful chemicals with a minimum of waste. They use molar quantities of products or reactants to predict yields in chemical reactions. The coefficients of a chemical equation are the basis for interpreting and predicting quantitative relationships in chemical reactions. Calculations using balanced chemical equations are called *stoichiometric calculations*. Stoichiometric relationships are based on the mole concept.

OBJECTIVE

- Interpret balanced chemical equations in terms of interacting moles, particles, and volumes of gases.

EXAMPLE 1

Determine Mole Ratios from a Balanced Chemical Equation

Sodium chloride (NaCl), or common table salt, can be prepared by the reaction of sodium metal with chlorine gas according to the equation below:

$2Na + Cl_2 \rightarrow 2NaCl$

How many moles of NaCl form for each mole of sodium that reacts? How many moles of Cl_2 are consumed for each mole of sodium that reacts? How many moles of NaCl form for each mole of Cl_2 that reacts?

Solution

1 Recall Relevant Information The coefficients in a balanced chemical equation give the number of atoms, ions, molecules, or formula units of each substance involved in the reaction. One mole of a substance contains a specific number of particles, and that number is the same for all substances. Therefore, the coefficients in a balanced chemical equation also give the number of moles of each substance involved in the reaction.

2 Examine the Chemical Equation Sodium (Na) and sodium chloride both have coefficients of 2. Chlorine (Cl_2) has no coefficient. Therefore, two moles of sodium can react with one mole of chlorine to form two moles of sodium chloride.

3 Solve Two moles of sodium react to produce two moles of NaCl, so each mole of sodium can produce one mole of NaCl. One mole of chlorine reacts with two moles of sodium, so $1 \div 2 = 0.5$ mol Cl_2 would be required to react with one mole of sodium. Two moles of NaCl form for each mole of Cl_2 that reacts.

REMEMBER

MOLE RATIOS

- The ratio of the coefficients in a balanced chemical equation is the mole ratio of the substances in the reaction.

- Coefficients (and mole ratios) allow chemists to predict the amounts of different substances involved in a chemical reaction if they know the amount of one of the substances.

- A chemical equation must be balanced before you can use the coefficients to calculate mole ratios.

EXAMPLE 2

Use Mole Ratios to Determine Gas Volumes

Hydrogen chloride gas (HCl) can form from hydrogen gas and chlorine gas according to the equation below:

$$H_{2\,(g)} + Cl_{2\,(g)} \rightarrow 2HCl_{(g)}$$

How many liters of chlorine gas and hydrogen gas would be required to produce 2 mol HCl at STP?

Solution

1 **Recall Relevant Information** At standard temperature and pressure, one mole of a gas occupies a volume of 22.4 L. The coefficients in the chemical equation give the number of moles of reactants and products involved in the reaction.

2 **Solve** The equation shows that one mole of H_2 reacts with one mole of Cl_2 to form two moles of HCl. Therefore, 22.4 L of H_2 and 22.4 L of Cl_2 would be required to produce 2 mol HCl at STP.

TIP

Because all gases have the same molar volume (volume per mole) at STP, the coefficients in a chemical equation also give the ratio of gas volumes involved in a chemical reaction.

Problem Set

1. Hydrogen gas and oxygen gas can react to form water vapor according to the equation below:

$$2H_{2\,(g)} + O_{2\,(g)} \rightarrow 2H_2O_{(g)}$$

How many liters of hydrogen gas are required to produce 2 mol $H_2O_{(g)}$ at STP?

2. Carbonic acid (H_2CO_3) forms when carbon dioxide (CO_2) dissolves in water according to the equation below:

$$CO_2 + H_2O \rightarrow H_2CO_3$$

How many moles of CO_2 must dissolve in water to produce 2 mol H_2CO_3? Answer without doing any calculations.

3. Sodium hydroxide (NaOH), commonly called lye, is used to clear clogged drains because it is very corrosive. Sodium metal (Na) reacts with water to form sodium hydroxide according to the equation shown below:

$$2Na + 2H_2O \rightarrow 2NaOH + H_2$$

Explain why 6.02×10^{23} atoms of sodium would yield 3.01×10^{23} molecules of hydrogen gas (H_2) in this reaction, assuming enough water is present.

4. Ethane (C_2H_6) can burn in oxygen to produce carbon dioxide and water according to the equation below:

$$2C_2H_{6\,(g)} + 7O_{2\,(g)} \rightarrow 4CO_{2\,(g)} + 6H_2O_{(l)}$$

How many liters of oxygen would be required to completely react with 22.4 L of C_2H_6 at STP? How many liters of CO_2 would form?

5. **Challenge** Identify which of the following statements is true at STP for the balanced equation shown below:

$$2H_2S_{(g)} + 3O_{2\,(g)} \rightarrow 2SO_{2\,(g)} + 2H_2O_{(g)}$$

A. When 4 mol H_2S reacts with 6 mol O_2, exactly 2 mol SO_2 is produced.
B. When 1 mol H_2S reacts with 1 mol O_2, 1 mol H_2O is produced.
C. When 44.8 L of H_2S reacts with 67.2 L of O_2, 44.8 L of SO_2 is produced.
D. When 22.4 L of H_2S reacts with 44.8 L of O_2, 67.2 L of SO_2 is produced.

6. **Challenge** Methane (CH_4), ammonia (NH_3), and oxygen can react to form hydrogen cyanide (HCN) and water according to the equation below:

$$2CH_4 + 2NH_3 + 3O_2 \rightarrow 2HCN + 6H_2O$$

How many moles of oxygen are required to produce one mole of HCN? How many moles of water will be produced if three moles of ammonia react completely?

Calculating Yields of Reactions

You can use a balanced chemical equation to predict how much of a product will form from a given amount of reactant.

You can use the coefficients in a balanced chemical equation to determine the molar ratios of reactants and products in a reaction. If you also know the molar masses of the reactants and products, you can use a balanced chemical equation to predict how much product will form from a specific amount of reactant. The amount of a given product that a certain reaction system can produce is called the *yield* of the reaction. Chemists and chemical engineers often calculate yields so that they can determine the amount of reactants needed to produce a certain amount of product.

OBJECTIVE

- Use a balanced chemical equation to determine mass relationships for a chemical reaction.

EXAMPLE 1

Convert Moles of Reactant to Moles of Product

The balanced chemical equation below shows how iron(III) sulfate ($Fe_2(SO_4)_3$) can react with ammonia and water to produce iron(III) hydroxide ($Fe(OH)_3$) and ammonium sulfate (($NH_4)_2SO_4$). If 1.25 mol iron(III) sulfate completely reacts with ammonia and water, how many moles of iron(III) hydroxide and ammonium sulfate will form?

$$Fe_2(SO_4)_3 + 6NH_3 + 6H_2O \rightarrow 2Fe(OH)_3 + 3(NH_4)_2SO_4$$

Solution

1 **Examine the Chemical Equation** The coefficients in the chemical equation indicate the number of molecules or moles of each species required for a balanced reaction. According to this equation, one mole of iron(III) sulfate reacts with six moles of ammonia and six moles of water to form two moles of iron(III) hydroxide and three moles of ammonium sulfate.

2 **Solve** Use the coefficients to set up conversion factors, as shown below:

$$1.25 \text{ mol Fe}_2(SO_4)_3 \times \frac{2 \text{ mol Fe(OH)}_3}{1 \text{ mol Fe}_2(SO_4)_3} = 2.50 \text{ mol Fe(OH)}_3$$

$$1.25 \text{ mol Fe}_2(SO_4)_3 \times \frac{3 \text{ mol (NH}_4)_2SO_4}{1 \text{ mol Fe}_2(SO_4)_3} = 3.75 \text{ mol (NH}_4)_2SO_4$$

So, 1.25 mol iron(III) sulfate can produce 2.50 mol iron(III) hydroxide and 3.75 mol ammonium sulfate.

REMEMBER

REACTION YIELD

- The yield of a chemical reaction is the amount of products produced by the reaction.

- The coefficients in a balanced chemical equation give the relative numbers of moles or particles of each species required to produce a balanced reaction.

- The coefficient 1 is never written in a chemical equation. If no coefficient is present in front of a species, the coefficient is assumed to be 1.

EXAMPLE 2

Convert Mass of Reactant to Mass of Product

A scientist has 34.00 g $Fe_2(SO_4)_3$ and enough ammonia and water to completely react with the $Fe_2(SO_4)_3$. How many grams of $Fe(OH)_3$ can the scientist expect to form if all the $Fe_2(SO_4)_3$ reacts with ammonia and water according to the equation in Example 1? The molar mass of $Fe_2(SO_4)_3$ is 399.86 g/mol. The molar mass of $Fe(OH)_3$ is 106.87 g/mol.

You cannot use the coefficients in a balanced chemical equation to convert between grams of one substance and grams of another. The coefficients refer to moles or particles, not to masses.

Solution

1 **Strategize** The coefficients in the equation can be used to obtain mole ratios of reactants and products. Therefore, to solve this problem, first convert grams of reactant to moles of reactant. Then, use the coefficients to convert moles of reactant to moles of product. Finally, convert moles of product to grams of product. The following information is given in the problem:

mass of $Fe_2(SO_4)_3 = 34.00$ g
molar mass of $Fe_2(SO_4)_3 = 399.86$ g/mol
molar mass of $Fe(OH)_3 = 106.87$ g/mol

2 **Solve** Convert grams of $Fe_2(SO_4)_3$ to moles of $Fe_2(SO_4)_3$, as shown below:

$$34.00 \text{ g } Fe_2(SO_4)_3 \times \frac{1 \text{ mol } Fe_2(SO_4)_3}{399.86 \text{ g } Fe_2(SO_4)_3} = 0.08503 \text{ mol } Fe_2(SO_4)_3$$

Now, convert moles of $Fe_2(SO_4)_3$ to moles of $Fe(OH)_3$, as shown below:

$$0.08503 \text{ mol } Fe_2(SO_4)_3 \times \frac{2 \text{ mol } Fe(OH)_3}{1 \text{ mol } Fe_2(SO_4)_3} = 0.1701 \text{ mol } Fe(OH)_3$$

Finally, convert moles of $Fe(OH)_3$ to grams of $Fe(OH)_3$, as shown below:

$$0.1701 \text{ mol } Fe(OH)_3 \times \frac{106.87 \text{ g } Fe(OH)_3}{1 \text{ mol } Fe(OH)_3} = 18.17 \text{g } Fe(OH)_3$$

So, 34.00 g $Fe_2(SO_4)_3$ will produce 18.17 g $Fe(OH)_3$.

EXAMPLE 3

Determine the Mass of Reactant Required to Complete a Reaction

How many grams of ammonia are required to completely react with 25.00 g $Fe_2(SO_4)_3$ according to the equation in Example 1? The molar mass of $Fe_2(SO_4)_3$ is 399.86 g/mol. The molar mass of NH_3 is 17.03 g/mol.

Solution

1 **Strategize** The coefficients in the equation can be used to obtain mole ratios of reactants and products. Therefore, to solve this problem, first convert grams of $Fe_2(SO_4)_3$ to moles of $Fe_2(SO_4)_3$. Then, use the coefficients to convert moles of $Fe_2(SO_4)_3$ to moles of NH_3. Finally, convert moles of NH_3 to grams of NH_3. The following information is given in the problem:

mass of $Fe_2(SO_4)_3 = 25.00$ g
molar mass of $Fe_2(SO_4)_3 = 399.86$ g/mol
molar mass of $NH_3 = 17.03$ g/mol

2 **Solve**   Convert grams of $Fe_2(SO_4)_3$ to moles of $Fe_2(SO_4)_3$, as shown below:

$$25.00 \text{ g } Fe_2(SO_4)_3 \times \frac{1 \text{ mol } Fe_2(SO_4)_3}{399.86 \text{ g } Fe_2(SO_4)_3} = 0.06252 \text{ mol } Fe_2(SO_4)_3$$

Now, convert moles of $Fe_2(SO_4)_3$ to moles of NH_3, as shown below:

$$0.06252 \text{ mol } Fe_2(SO_4)_3 \times \frac{6 \text{ mol } NH_3}{1 \text{ mol } Fe_2(SO_4)_3} = 0.3751 \text{ mol } NH_3$$

Finally, convert moles of NH_3 to grams of NH_3, as shown below:

$$0.3751 \text{ mol } NH_3 \times \frac{17.03 \text{ g } NH_3}{1 \text{ mol } NH_3} = 6.388 \text{ g } NH_3$$

So, 6.388 g NH_3 is required to completely react with 25.00 g $Fe_2(SO_4)_3$.

TIP

You can use coefficients to convert between amounts of any two species in a chemical reaction. In other words, if you know the mass of only one species in the reaction, you can calculate the masses of all the other species (as long as you know their molar masses).

EXAMPLE 4

Determine the Mass of Reactant Required to Produce a Given Amount of Product

A scientist wants to produce 125.00 g ammonium sulfate. How many grams of water would the scientist require to produce this amount of ammonium sulfate according to the equation in Example 1? The molar mass of H_2O is 18.01 g/mol. The molar mass of $(NH_4)_2SO_4$ is 132.13 g/mol.

TIP

Remember that you can use the periodic table to calculate the molar mass of a compound if you know its chemical formula.

Solution

1 **Strategize**   First, convert grams of $(NH_4)_2SO_4$ to moles of $(NH_4)_2SO_4$. Then, use the coefficients to convert moles of $(NH_4)_2SO_4$ to moles of H_2O. Finally, convert moles of H_2O to grams of H_2O. The following information is given in the problem:

mass of $(NH_4)_2SO_4 = 125.00$ g
molar mass of $(NH_4)_2SO_4 = 132.13$ g/mol
molar mass of $H_2O = 18.01$ g/mol

2 **Solve**   Convert grams of $(NH_4)_2SO_4$ to moles of $(NH_4)_2SO_4$, as shown below:

$$125.00 \text{ g } (NH_4)_2SO_4 \times \frac{1 \text{ mol } (NH_4)_2SO_4}{132.13 \text{ g } (NH_4)_2SO_4} = 0.9460 \text{ mol } (NH_4)_2SO_4$$

Now, convert moles of $(NH_4)_2SO_4$ to moles of H_2O, as shown below:

$$0.9460 \text{ mol } (NH_4)_2SO_4 \times \frac{6 \text{ mol } H_2O}{3 \text{ mol } (NH_4)_2SO_4} = 1.892 \text{ mol } H_2O$$

Finally, convert moles of H_2O to grams of H_2O, as shown below:

$$1.892 \text{ mol } H_2O \times \frac{18.01 \text{ g } H_2O}{1 \text{ mol } H_2O} = 34.07 \text{ g } H_2O$$

So, 34.07 g H_2O is required to completely react with iron(III) sulfate and ammonia to produce 125.00 g $(NH_4)_2SO_4$.

Problem Set

1. Consider the equation below:

$$C + O_2 \rightarrow CO_2$$

If 3.25 mol C completely reacts with O_2, how many moles of CO_2 will form?

2. The equation below shows a reaction that can be used to prepare pure iron from Fe_2O_3, an iron ore:

$$2Fe_2O_3 + 3C \rightarrow 4Fe + 3CO_2$$

How many moles of carbon (C) would be required to completely react with 2.3 mol Fe_2O_3?

3. If 1.68 mol Fe_2O_3 completely reacts with carbon according to the equation in Question 2, how many grams of pure iron will be produced? The molar mass of iron is 55.847 g/mol.

4. The equation below shows how water forms from hydrogen gas and oxygen gas:

$$2H_2 + O_2 \rightarrow 2H_2O$$

How many grams of hydrogen gas (H_2) would be required to produce 100.0 g H_2O? (Hint: Use the periodic table to calculate the molar masses of H_2 and H_2O.)

5. How many grams of oxygen gas (O_2) would be required to completely react with 10.25 g H_2 according to the equation in Question 4? (Hint: Use the periodic table to calculate the molar mass of O_2.)

6. Consider the equation below:

$$3H_2 + N_2 \rightarrow 2NH_3$$

How many grams of ammonia (NH_3) will be produced if 100.5 g H_2 completely reacts with N_2? (Hint: Use the periodic table to calculate the molar masses of H_2 and NH_3.)

7. **Challenge** Sodium metal (Na) and chlorine gas (Cl_2) can react to form sodium chloride (NaCl). How many moles of NaCl would be produced if 3.5 mol Cl_2 completely reacted with sodium metal? (Hint: Write a balanced chemical equation for the reaction first.)

8. **Challenge** The equation below shows the reaction of octane (C_8H_{18}) with oxygen. How many grams of carbon dioxide (CO_2) would be produced if 143.2 g octane completely reacted with oxygen?

$$2C_8H_{18} + 25O_2 \rightarrow 16CO_2 + 18H_2O$$

(Hint: Use the periodic table to calculate the molar masses of CO_2 and octane.)

9. **Challenge** Lead(II) nitrate ($Pb(NO_3)_2$) can react with potassium iodide (KI) to produce lead(II) iodide (PbI_2) and potassium nitrate (KNO_3). How many grams of KI are required to completely react with 45.3 mg $Pb(NO_3)_2$? (Hint: Write a balanced chemical equation for the reaction first.)

Percent Yield

The percent yield of a chemical reaction is equal to 100 times the actual yield of a product divided by the maximum predicted yield.

If you know the amounts of reactants involved in a reaction, you can predict the *yield* of the reaction, or how much of a given product will form. However, the yield calculated in this way is the theoretical, or maximum, yield of the reaction. The yield of a real reaction is generally lower than its theoretical yield. The *percent yield* of a reaction is the percentage of the theoretical yield that is actually obtained. The closer the percent yield of a reaction is to 100, the closer the actual yield of the reaction is to the theoretical yield. The percent yield of a reaction is especially relevant in industrial processes. Many chemical engineers try to develop ways of maximizing the percent yield of industrial processes.

OBJECTIVE

- Calculate the percent yield of a reaction.

EXAMPLE 1

Calculate Percent Yield from Theoretical Yield

The theoretical yield of a particular chemical reaction is 153.6 g methanol (CH_3OH). When a chemist carries out the reaction, she produces 113.5 g methanol. What is the percent yield of the reaction?

Solution

1 Strategize To calculate percent yield, divide the actual yield by the theoretical yield. Then, multiply the result by 100.

2 Solve The percent yield is calculated as shown below:

$$\frac{113.5 \text{ g}}{153.6 \text{ g}} \times 100 = 73.89\%$$

REMEMBER

PERCENT YIELD

- The percent yield of a reaction is a measure of the degree to which the reaction proceeds to completion.

- You can calculate percent yield using masses, moles, or volumes of products. However, make sure you use the same units for actual yield and theoretical yield when calculating percent yield.

EXAMPLE 2

Calculate Percent Yield from a Chemical Equation

When heated to high temperature, calcium carbonate ($CaCO_3$) decomposes to produce calcium oxide (CaO) and carbon dioxide (CO_2), as represented by the equation below:

$$CaCO_{3\,(s)} \rightarrow CaO_{(s)} + CO_{2\,(g)}$$

A geochemist heated 100.1 g $CaCO_3$ and obtained 42.03 g CaO. What was the percent yield of the reaction?

Solution

1 **Collect and Strategize** Calculate the theoretical yield of the reaction. To calculate theoretical yield, you must know the number of moles of reactant ($CaCO_3$). The periodic table shows that the molar mass of $CaCO_3$ is 100.1 g/mol. Therefore, the reaction involved 1.000 mol $CaCO_3$.

2 **Calculate Theoretical Yield** Use the number of moles of $CaCO_3$ in the reaction and the coefficients of the balanced equation to calculate the theoretical yield of CaO, as shown below:

$$1.000 \text{ mol } CaCO_3 \times \frac{1 \text{ mol CaO}}{1 \text{ mol } CaCO_3} = 1.000 \text{ mol CaO}$$

The periodic table shows that the molar mass of CaO is 56.08 g/mol. Therefore, the theoretical yield of the reaction is 56.08 g CaO.

3 **Solve** The percent yield is calculated as shown below:

$$\text{percent yield} = \frac{\text{actual yield}}{\text{theoretical yield}} \times 100 = \frac{42.03 \text{ g}}{56.08 \text{ g}} \times 100 = 74.95\%$$

TIP

When calculating percent yield, check first to see if the equation for the reaction is balanced. Make sure to apply the coefficients of the reactants and products to your calculations.

Problem Set

1. The theoretical yield for a reaction is 55.9 g iron(III) chloride ($FeCl_3$). The actual yield is 24.6 g $FeCl_3$. What is the percent yield of the reaction?

2. The theoretical yield for a reaction is 2.35 mol CO_2. The actual yield is 1.94 mol CO_2. What is the percent yield of the reaction?

3. The theoretical yield for a reaction is 1.53 kg H_2O. The reaction actually produces 930.5 g H_2O. What is the percent yield of the reaction? (Hint: Make sure to check your units.)

4. Ammonia (NH_3) can be produced by the reaction of hydrogen gas with nitrogen gas, as shown in the equation below:

$$3H_2 + N_2 \rightarrow 2NH_3$$

A chemist reacts 2.00 mol H_2 with excess N_2. The reaction yields 0.654 mol NH_3. What is the percent yield of the reaction?

5. The theoretical yield of a reaction is 5.32 mol potassium permanganate ($KMnO_4$). If the reaction actually produces 652.5 g $KMnO_4$, what is the percent yield of the reaction?

6. Boron trifluoride (BF_3) reacts with water to produce boric acid (H_3BO_3) and fluoroboric acid (HBF_4) according to the equation below:

$$4BF_3 + 3H_2O \rightarrow H_3BO_3 + 3HBF_4$$

If the percent yield of the reaction is 15.0%, how many moles of H_3BO_3 will be produced when 4.28 mol BF_3 reacts with excess water?

7. **Challenge** Consider the equation below:

$$MnO_2 + 4HCl \rightarrow MnCl_2 + Cl_2 + 2H_2O$$

If the percent yield is 85.0%, what mass of MnO_2 would be required to produce 53.5 g $MnCl_2$ in the presence of excess HCl?

8. **Challenge** Calcium oxide (CaO) reacts with tetraphosphorus decoxide (P_4O_{10}) to form calcium phosphate ($Ca_3(PO_4)_2$) according to the following equation:

$$6CaO + P_4O_{10} \rightarrow 2Ca_3(PO_4)_2$$

In a particular reaction, 14.2 g P_4O_{10} reacts with excess CaO and produces 24.8 g of $Ca_3(PO_4)_2$. What is the percent yield of the reaction?

9. **Challenge** Methane (CH_4) and oxygen react to form carbon dioxide and water according to the following equation:

$$CH_4 + 2O_2 \rightarrow CO_2 + 2H_2O$$

If the percent yield for the reaction is 90.0%, how many grams of CO_2 and H_2O will be produced when 16.0 g CH_4 reacts with excess O_2?

The Behavior of Gases

The kinetic theory of gases describes the movement of gases. It explains properties such as compressibility, diffusion, pressure, and temperature in terms of the motion and collisions of the particles that make up the gases.

OBJECTIVE

- Explain bulk properties of gases in terms of the spacing, motion, and collisions taking place at the molecular level.

The kinetic theory of gases treats gases as very small particles (atoms and molecules) that are widely spaced, move rapidly and randomly, and collide with one another and with the walls of their container. The kinetic theory explains the compressibility, pressure, and diffusion of gases. Gases are compressible (their volume decreases as pressure increases) because of the distance between the particles. As pressure increases, the particles get closer together. Because there is so much space between gas particles, the volume of a gas can decrease significantly as pressure increases. The collisions of particles with the walls of the container cause the gas to exert pressure on the walls of its container. The rapid motion of the gas particles and the collisions between the particles cause gases to diffuse, or spread, and fill the entire volume of a container.

EXAMPLE 1

Explain Gas Pressure

A scientist places one mole of a gas into each of two containers. The first container's volume is twice that of the second container. Explain why the pressure the gas exerts on the walls of the second container is greater than the pressure it exerts on the walls of the first container.

Solution

1 **Recall Relevant Information** Gas particles have mass and are in constant motion. Gas particles frequently collide with the walls of the container. Colliding objects exert force on each other. Pressure is a measure of force per unit area. The more gas particles strike a given area, the more force is exerted on the area. The greater the force per unit area is, the higher the pressure is.

2 **Solve** In a small container, a given gas particle does not have to travel very far before it hits a wall. Therefore, the gas particles in the smaller container collide with the walls more often than those in the larger container do. The larger number of collisions results in a greater force being exerted on the container walls. The greater force explains the higher pressure in the smaller container.

REMEMBER

THE BEHAVIOR OF GASES

- Many of the properties of gases result from the motions and distribution of the particles in the gases.

- When a gas absorbs heat, its particles move faster. If the volume of the gas container is fixed, the temperature and pressure of the gas will increase. If the pressure on the gas is fixed, its volume will increase and its temperature will remain the same.

EXAMPLE 2

TIP

You can think of gas particles in a container like strangers moving around in a room. In a large room, people will tend to spread out fairly evenly, rather than staying clumped in a corner. Similarly, gas particles in a container tend to move out and fill the whole volume of the container, rather than remaining concentrated in one part of the container.

Explain Diffusion of Gases

The diagram shows two containers filled with two different gases (represented by red and blue dots). The containers are connected by a tube with a closed valve.

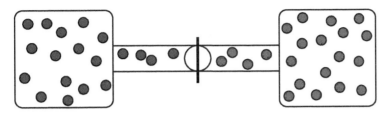

Describe how the particles will be arranged after the valve is left open for one day.

Solution

1 Recall Relevant Information Gas particles are in constant, random motion. Gas particles collide often with each other and with the walls of their container.

2 Apply Because the motions of the particles are random, the angles at which they collide will also be random, and the particles will travel in all possible directions. Because collisions are frequent, each particle will change direction many times in the course of one day.

3 Solve Many particles will collide at an angle that will send them straight through the tube to the other side. The result will be the same as if the particles were all in the same container. Once on the other side, collisions will cause the particles of the two gases to mix randomly. As a result, both containers will have a random mixture of roughly equal numbers of each type of particle.

Problem Set

1. A teacher uses a permanent marker to write on a chart at the front of a classroom. In a few minutes, everyone in the room can smell the odor of the marker. Use the kinetic theory of gases to explain this observation. (Hint: Most odors are carried by gas particles.)

2. Explain why increasing the volume of a container decreases the pressure of the gas in the container, assuming the temperature remains fixed.

3. Most of the gas particles in the air are either nitrogen molecules or oxygen molecules. If you could see the nitrogen and oxygen molecules in a sample of air, how would they probably be distributed? Explain your answer.

4. Container A and container B have the same volume. Container A holds twice as many moles of gas as container B. In which container is the pressure probably highest? Explain your answer.

5. **Challenge** Why does pumping air into a tire increase the pressure inside the tire?

6. **Challenge** Explain why gases can be compressed but solids and liquids cannot.

Boyle's Law

Boyle's law states that the pressure and volume of a gas are inversely proportional when the temperature and the amount of gas are kept constant.

- Use Boyle's law to solve problems involving changes in pressure and volume of gases.

Boyle's law describes the relationship between pressure (P) and volume (V) for a fixed amount of gas at a fixed temperature. According to Boyle's law, if you increase the pressure of a gas, its volume decreases. If you decrease pressure, volume increases. One way to express this relationship mathematically is with the equation $PV = k$, in which k is a constant. However, a more commonly used equation is $P_1V_1 = P_2V_2$. In this equation, P_1 and V_1 represent the pressure and volume of a gas before a change, and P_2 and V_2 represent the pressure and volume of the gas after the change. This equation describes the effects of changing the pressure or volume of a gas.

EXAMPLE 1

Describe the Effects of a Change in Pressure

A 2.0 L balloon has a pressure of 2.0 atm. When the balloon is compressed, the pressure increases to 5.0 atm. What is the volume of the compressed balloon?

Solution

1 **Collect and Strategize** Use the equation $P_1V_1 = P_2V_2$ to solve this problem. The following information is given in the problem:

$V_1 = 2.0$ L
$P_1 = 2.0$ atm
$P_2 = 5.0$ atm

Rearranging the equation to solve for V_2 yields the equation shown below:

$$V_2 = \frac{P_1V_1}{P_2}$$

2 **Solve** Substituting the values given in the problem yields the following:

$$V_2 = \frac{P_1V_1}{P_2} = \frac{(2.0 \text{ atm})(2.0 \text{ L})}{5.0 \text{ atm}} = \frac{4.0 \text{ L}}{5.0} = 0.80 \text{ L}$$

Therefore, the final volume is 0.80 L. This makes sense: According to Boyle's law, as pressure increases, volume decreases proportionally.

REMEMBER

BOYLE'S LAW

- Boyle's law relates the pressure and volume of a gas at a fixed temperature.

- Boyle's law applies only to systems in which neither the amount of gas nor the temperature is changing.

- Although Boyle's law describes the behavior of many gases under common conditions, it does not accurately predict the behavior of all gases under all conditions.

EXAMPLE 2

Describe the Effects of a Change in Volume

A 1.0 L sample of nitrogen gas is at a pressure of 1.0 atm. What will be the pressure of the gas if the volume is reduced to 0.25 L?

Solution

① Collect and Strategize   Use the equation $P_1V_1 = P_2V_2$ to solve this problem. The following information is given in the problem:

$V_1 = 1.0$ L

$P_1 = 1.0$ atm

$V_2 = 0.25$ L

Rearranging the equation to solve for P_2 yields the equation shown below:

$$P_2 = \frac{P_1V_1}{V_2}$$

② Solve   Substituting the values given in the problem yields the following:

$$P_2 = \frac{P_1V_1}{V_2} = \frac{(1.0 \text{ atm})(1.0 \text{ L})}{0.25 \text{ L}} = \frac{1.0 \text{ atm}}{0.25} = 4.0 \text{ atm}$$

Therefore, the final pressure is 4.0 atm. This makes sense: According to Boyle's law, as volume decreases, pressure increases proportionally.

TIP

Remember to check whether the answer you calculate is reasonable. Think about the process that is going on, and ask yourself whether your answer makes sense.

Problem Set

1. The initial pressure and volume of a gas sample are 1.0 atm and 0.50 L, respectively. If the temperature is held constant and the final pressure is 2.0 atm, what is the final volume?

2. Given that $PV = k$, if $k = 2.0$ L · atm for a 4.0 L container of gas, what is the pressure of the gas?

3. The initial pressure of gas inside a 1.0 L container is 2.0 atm. If the container's volume decreases to 0.50 L and the temperature remains constant, what will the final pressure of the gas in the container be?

4. A 3.0 L container holds a sample of oxygen gas at 1.5 atm pressure. If the pressure increases to 2.0 atm and the temperature remains constant, what is the new volume of the container?

5. A container with a volume of 0.50 L contains air at a pressure of 1.0 atm. If the volume is reduced to 0.10 L at constant temperature, what will be the resulting pressure of the air inside?

6. Use the kinetic theory of gases to explain Boyle's law.

7. **Challenge**   When the volume of a container of gas changes by a certain factor at a constant temperature, the pressure doubles. By what factor does the container's volume change? Explain your answer.

8. **Challenge**   The pressure inside a typical 11.0 L scuba tank is about 204 atm at room temperature. How many 2.0 L soda bottles would be required to hold all the air in a scuba tank if you filled each bottle to 1.0 atm pressure at the same temperature?

9. **Challenge**   Sketch a graph of pressure vs. volume for a gas that is decreasing in volume while temperature is held constant.

Charles's Law

Charles's law states that the volume and temperature of a gas are directly proportional when pressure and the amount of gas are kept constant.

Charles's law describes the relationship between temperature (T) and volume (V) for a fixed amount of gas at a fixed pressure. According to Charles's law, if you increase the temperature of a gas, its volume increases. If you decrease the temperature of a gas, its volume decreases. One way to express this relationship mathematically is with the equation $V = kT$, in which k is a constant. However, a more commonly used equation is $\frac{V_1}{T_1} = \frac{V_2}{T_2}$. In this equation, T_1 and V_1 represent the temperature and volume of a gas before a change, and T_2 and V_2 represent the temperature and volume of the gas after the change. This equation describes the effects of changing the temperature or volume of a gas. When using the Charles's law equation, you should always convert temperature to kelvins.

OBJECTIVE

- Use Charles's law to solve problems involving changes in temperature and volume of gases.

EXAMPLE 1

Describe the Effects of a Change in Temperature

A sealed 1.0 L plastic soda bottle contains air at 340 K. The temperature of the air decreases to 260 K. Assuming the pressure inside the bottle does not change, what is the final volume of the bottle (and the gas)?

Solution

1 Collect and Strategize Use the equation $\frac{V_1}{T_1} = \frac{V_2}{T_2}$ to solve this problem. The following information is given:

$V_1 = 1.0$ L
$T_1 = 340$ K
$T_2 = 260$ K

Rearranging the equation to solve for V_2 yields the following:

$$V_2 = \frac{V_1 T_2}{T_1}$$

2 Solve Substituting the values given in the problem yields the following:

$$V_2 = \frac{V_1 T_2}{T_1} = \frac{(1.0 \text{ L})(260 \text{ K})}{(340 \text{ K})} = \frac{260 \text{ L}}{340} = 0.76 \text{ L}$$

So, the final volume of the bottle is 0.76 L. This makes sense: According to Charles's law, as temperature decreases, volume decreases proportionally.

REMEMBER

CHARLES'S LAW

- Charles's law relates the temperature and volume of a gas at fixed pressure.

- Charles's law applies only to systems in which neither the pressure nor the amount of gas is changing.

- Although Charles's law describes the behavior of many gases under common conditions, it does not accurately predict the behavior of all gases under all conditions.

EXAMPLE 2

Describe the Effects of a Change in Volume

A sample of a gas at 225 K is allowed to expand at constant pressure from 1.5 L to 5.00 L. What is the final temperature of the gas?

Solution

1 **Collect and Strategize** Use the equation $\dfrac{V_1}{T_1} = \dfrac{V_2}{T_2}$ to solve this problem. The following information is given:

$V_1 = 1.5$ L

$T_1 = 225$ K

$V_2 = 5.0$ L

Rearranging the equation to solve for T_2 yields the following:

$$T_2 = \frac{V_2 T_1}{V_1}$$

2 **Solve** Substituting the values given in the problem yields the following:

$$T_2 = \frac{V_2 T_1}{V_1} = \frac{(5.0\ \cancel{L})(225\ \text{K})}{(1.5\ \cancel{L})} = \frac{1{,}130\ \text{K}}{1.5} = 750\ \text{K}$$

So, the final temperature of the bottle is 750 K. This makes sense: According to Charles's law, as volume increases, temperature increases proportionally.

TIP

When solving gas problems, always convert temperatures to kelvins. Using kelvins ensures that there are no negative numbers in the equations. It also ensures that the ratios between different temperatures are correct.

Problem Set

1. When an inflated balloon is placed in a freezer, it shrinks. Use Charles's law to explain this observation. (Hint: Assume that the pressure inside the balloon does not change.)

2. A sample of a gas has a volume of 1.5 L at 150 K. If the gas is heated to 235 K at constant pressure, what will its final volume be?

3. A gas at 325 K has a volume of 4.0 L. If the gas's volume changes to 2.0 L at constant pressure, what will be the new temperature?

4. The temperature of a gas rose from 250 K to 350 K. At 350 K, the volume of the gas was 3.0 L. If the pressure did not change, what was the initial volume of the gas?

5. Charles's law can be expressed mathematically as $V = kT$. If the constant k for 6.0 L of a gas is 0.020 L/K (liters per kelvin), what is the temperature of the gas?

6. The temperature of a gas is decreased by a factor of two at constant pressure. Does the gas expand or shrink? Answer **without** doing any calculations. Explain your answer.

7. **Challenge** A scientist triples the temperature of a gas at constant pressure. By what factor does the gas's volume change? Explain your answer.

8. **Challenge** A sample of a gas takes up 2.35 L of space at room temperature (20.0°C). What volume will the gas occupy at –5.00°C? (Hint: Don't forget to convert the temperatures to kelvins.)

9. **Challenge** Sketch a graph of volume vs. temperature for a gas that is heated at constant pressure.

Gay-Lussac's Law

Gay-Lussac's law states that the pressure and temperature of a gas are directly proportional when volume and the amount of gas are kept constant.

OBJECTIVE

- Use Gay-Lussac's law to solve problems involving changes in pressure and temperature of gases.

Gay-Lussac's law describes the relationship between temperature (T) and pressure (P) for a fixed amount of gas at a fixed volume. According to Gay-Lussac's law, if you increase the temperature of a gas, its pressure increases. If you decrease the temperature of a gas, its pressure decreases. This relationship can be expressed mathematically with the equation $P = kT$, in which k is a constant. However, a more commonly used equation is $\frac{P_1}{T_1} = \frac{P_2}{T_2}$. In this equation, T_1 and P_1 represent the temperature and pressure of a gas before a change, and T_2 and P_2 represent the temperature and pressure of the gas after the change. This equation describes the effects of changing the temperature or pressure of a gas. When using the Gay-Lussac's law equation, you should always convert temperatures to kelvins.

EXAMPLE 1

Describe the Effects of a Change in Temperature

The air inside a sealed, rigid container has a temperature of 295 K. At this temperature, the pressure in the container is 1.0 atm. What will the pressure inside the container be if the air is heated to 373 K?

Solution

1 Collect and Strategize Because the container is rigid, its volume must be constant. Use the equation $\frac{P_1}{T_1} = \frac{P_2}{T_2}$ to solve this problem. The following information is given:

$P_1 = 1.0$ atm

$T_1 = 295$ K

$T_2 = 373$ K

Rearranging the equation to solve for P_2 yields the following:

$P_2 = \frac{P_1 T_2}{T_1}$

2 Solve Substituting the values given in the problem yields the following:

$P_2 = \frac{P_1 T_2}{T_1} = \frac{(1.0\ \text{atm})(373\ \cancel{K})}{(295\ \cancel{K})} = \frac{373\ \text{atm}}{295} = 1.3\ \text{atm}$

So, the final pressure in the container is 1.3 atm. This makes sense: According to Gay-Lussac's law, as temperature increases, pressure increases proportionally.

REMEMBER

GAY-LUSSAC'S LAW

- Gay-Lussac's law relates the temperature and pressure of a gas at fixed volume.

- Gay-Lussac's law applies only to systems in which neither the volume nor the amount of gas is changing.

- Although Gay-Lussac's law describes the behavior of many gases under common conditions, it does not accurately predict the behavior of all gases under all conditions.

EXAMPLE 2

Describe the Effects of a Change in Pressure

At 325 K, the pressure inside a gas-filled container is 2.3 atm. If the pressure inside the container decreases to 0.75 atm but the volume of the container does not change, what is the final temperature of the gas?

Solution

1 **Collect and Strategize** Use the equation $\frac{P_1}{T_1} = \frac{P_2}{T_2}$ to solve this problem. The following information is given:

$P_1 = 2.3$ atm

$T_1 = 325$ K

$P_2 = 0.75$ atm

Rearranging the equation to solve for T_2 yields the following:

$$T_2 = \frac{T_1 P_2}{P_1}$$

2 **Solve** Substituting the values given in the problem yields the following:

$$T_2 = \frac{T_1 P_2}{P_1} = \frac{(325 \text{ K})(0.75 \text{ atm})}{(2.3 \text{ atm})} = \frac{240 \text{ K}}{2.3} = 100 \text{ K}$$

So, the final temperature in the container is 100 K. This makes sense: According to Gay-Lussac's law, as pressure decreases, temperature decreases proportionally.

TIP

If two quantities are directly related, an increase in one quantity results in an increase in the other quantity. Similarly, a decrease in one quantity results in a decrease in the other quantity.

Problem Set

1. A sample of gas is enclosed in a rigid container. At 135 K, the pressure of the gas is 1.5 atm. If the temperature increases to 235 K, what will the final pressure inside the container be?

2. The gas inside a rigid container has a pressure of 0.50 atm at 273 K. The pressure of the gas increases to 1.0 atm. What is the final temperature of the gas?

3. A gas has a pressure of 2.0 atm. If the temperature decreases from 250 K to 125 K and the volume remains constant, what will be the resulting pressure?

4. Gay-Lussac's law can be expressed by the equation $P = kT$. If a gas has a temperature of 273 K at 1.0 atm, what are the value and units of the constant k in this equation?

5. A sealed, air-filled, rigid jar is placed in a freezer for an hour. When the jar is removed from the freezer and opened, will air rush into or out of the jar? Explain your answer. (Hint: Air always moves from areas of high pressure to areas of low pressure.)

6. Use the kinetic theory of gases to explain Gay-Lussac's law.

7. **Challenge** A rigid cylinder containing nitrogen gas at a pressure of 10.0 atm was cooled from 100.0°C to 0.0°C. What was the final pressure of the nitrogen? (Hint: Remember to convert temperatures to kelvins.)

8. **Challenge** The pressure of a gas enclosed in a rigid container quadruples. By what factor does its temperature change? Explain your answer.

9. **Challenge** Sketch a graph of pressure vs. temperature for a gas that is heated at constant volume.

Problem Set 56

The Ideal Gas Law

The ideal gas law combines the laws of Charles, Boyle, Gay-Lussac, and Avogadro into one law. This one law relates pressure, volume, temperature, and number of moles of a gas.

Remember that Boyle's law describes the relationship between the pressure and volume of a gas, Charles's law describes the relationship between the temperature and volume of a gas, and Gay-Lussac's law describes the relationship between the temperature and pressure of a gas. However, each of these laws applies only in specific situations. For example, Boyle's law cannot be used to determine the pressure of a gas if both volume and temperature are changing. Scientists use a more complete gas law, the *ideal gas law*, to describe the relationship between temperature, pressure, volume, and number of moles of a gas. The ideal gas law can be written as $PV = nRT$, where P is pressure, V is volume, n is number of moles, T is temperature, and R is a constant called the *gas constant*. Like the other gas laws, the ideal gas law can also be written in a form that allows the calculation of the results of a change in one of these quantities: $\frac{P_1V_1}{n_1T_1} = \frac{P_2V_2}{n_2T_2}$.

OBJECTIVE

- **Use the ideal gas law to solve problems involving changes in pressure, volume, temperature, and number of moles of a gas.**

EXAMPLE 1

Determine the Effects of a Change in Pressure and Volume

A 2.5 mol sample of a gas has a temperature of 729 K, a pressure of 3.00 atm, and a volume of 3.8 L. What will be the new temperature of the gas if its pressure changes to 2.20 atm and its volume changes to 5.4 L? Assume the amount of gas is constant.

Solution

1 Collect and Strategize Use the equation $\frac{P_1V_1}{n_1T_1} = \frac{P_2V_2}{n_2T_2}$ to solve this problem.

The following information is given:

$n_1 = n_2 = 2.5$ mol
$P_1 = 3.00$ atm
$V_1 = 3.8$ L
$T_1 = 729$ K
$P_2 = 2.20$ atm
$V_2 = 5.4$ L

Because $n_1 = n_2$, n_1 and n_2 cancel out of the equation above, leaving $\frac{P_1V_1}{T_1} = \frac{P_2V_2}{T_2}$. This form of the ideal gas law, which applies when the number of moles of gas is constant, is sometimes called the *combined gas law*.

REMEMBER

IDEAL GASES

- An ideal gas is a gas made up of particles that are infinitely small and do not interact with one another. Ideal gases do not exist. However, many real gases behave like ideal gases under common conditions.
- The ideal gas law is an idealized relationship between pressure, volume, temperature, and number of moles of a gas. It gives exactly correct results only for an ideal gas. However, the ideal gas law, like Boyle's law, Charles's law, and Gay-Lussac's law, can give reasonably good results for real gases under conditions in which the real gases behave like ideal gases. All of these gas laws work reasonably well for many real gases under common conditions.
- In general, real gases deviate most from ideal gas behavior at very low temperatures and very high pressures.

Rearranging the combined gas law equation to solve for T_2 yields the following:

$$T_2 = \frac{P_2 V_2 T_1}{P_1 V_1}$$

2 **Solve** Substituting the given values and solving for T_2 yields the following:

$$T_2 = \frac{P_2 V_2 T_1}{P_1 V_1} = \frac{(2.20 \text{ atm}) (5.4 \text{ L}) (729 \text{ K})}{(3.00 \text{ atm})(3.8 \text{ L})} = \frac{8.66 \times 10^3 \text{ K}}{11} = 7.9 \times 10^2 \text{ K}$$

The combined gas law is a combination of Boyle's law, Charles's law, and Gay-Lussac's law. It applies only when the number of moles of gas remains fixed.

EXAMPLE 2

Calculate the Value of the Gas Constant

Use the ideal gas law to calculate the value and units of the gas constant, R.

Solution

1 **Collect and Strategize** The ideal gas law can be written as $PV = nRT$. At STP, 1.00 mol of a gas has a volume of 22.4 L. STP (standard temperature and pressure) is 273 K and 1.00 atm. Use this information to solve for R by rearranging the equation and substituting. Rearranging the equation to solve for R yields the following:

$$R = \frac{PV}{nT}$$

2 **Solve** Substitute the known values and solve, paying close attention to units, as shown below:

$$R = \frac{PV}{nT} = \frac{(1.00 \text{ atm})(22.4 \text{ L})}{(1.00 \text{ mol})(273 \text{ K})} = 0.0821 \text{ L} \cdot \text{atm/mol} \cdot \text{K}$$

EXAMPLE 3

Calculate the Number of Moles of a Gas

A sample of a gas has a temperature of 309 K, a pressure of 1.00 atm, and a volume of 2.05 L. How many moles of gas are in the sample?

Solution

1 **Collect and Strategize** The problem does not describe a change in conditions, so use the $PV = nRT$ form of the ideal gas law to solve this problem. The following information is given in the problem:

$P = 1.00$ atm

$V = 2.05$ L

$T = 309$ K

From Example 2, the value of R is 0.0821 L · atm/mol · K. Rearrange the equation to solve for n, as shown below:

$$n = \frac{PV}{RT}$$

2 **Solve** Substituting the given values and solving yields the following:

$$n = \frac{PV}{RT} = \frac{(1.00 \text{ atm})(2.05 \text{ L})}{(0.0821 \text{ L} \cdot \text{atm/mol} \cdot \text{K})(309 \text{ K})} = 0.0808 \text{ mol}$$

EXAMPLE 4

Calculate the Pressure of a Gas

A tank of oxygen gas contains 32.5 mol. The volume of the tank is 50.0 L. What is the pressure of the oxygen in the tank when the temperature is 294 K?

Solution

1 **Collect and Strategize**   Use the equation $PV = nRT$ to solve this problem. The following information is given in the problem:

$V = 50.0$ L

$n = 32.5$ mol

$T = 294$ K

Rearrange the equation to solve for P, as shown below:

$P = \dfrac{nRT}{V}$

2 **Solve**   Substitute the given values and solve. Remember that $R = 0.0821$ L · atm/mol · K.

$P = \dfrac{nRT}{V} = \dfrac{(32.5 \text{ mol})(0.0821 \text{ L} \cdot \text{atm/mol} \cdot \text{K})(294 \text{ K})}{(50.0 \text{ L})} = 15.7$ atm

TIP

As with all gas law calculations, calculations involving the ideal gas law or the combined gas law must include temperatures in kelvins.

EXAMPLE 5

Determine the Effects of Changing Several Variables

A chemical reaction produces 52 L of Cl_2 gas at STP. What would the volume of this gas be at 155 K and 2.5 atm?

Solution

1 **Collect and Strategize**   Because the number of moles of gas does not change, the combined gas law, $\dfrac{P_1 V_1}{T_1} = \dfrac{P_2 V_2}{T_2}$, can be used to solve this problem. The following information is given (remember that STP is 273 K and 1.0 atm):

$P_1 = 1.0$ atm

$T_1 = 273$ K

$V_1 = 52$ L

$P_2 = 2.5$ atm

$T_2 = 155$ K

Rearrange the equation to solve for V_2, as shown below:

$V_2 = \dfrac{T_2 V_1 P_1}{T_1 P_2}$

2 **Solve**   Substitute the given values and solve, as shown below:

$V_2 = \dfrac{T_2 V_1 P_1}{T_1 P_2} = \dfrac{(155 \text{ K}) (52 \text{ L}) (1.0 \text{ atm})}{(273 \text{ K})(2.5 \text{ atm})} = 12$ L

TIP

In many gas law problems, you will need to use both forms of the ideal gas law equation. You may need to use $PV = nRT$ to calculate the pressure, volume, temperature, or number of moles for a sample of a gas. Then, you may need to use a variation on the equation $\dfrac{P_1 V_1}{n_1 T_1} = \dfrac{P_2 V_2}{n_2 T_2}$ to calculate the effects of changing one or more of the variables.

Problem Set

1. A particular chemical reaction produces 1.4 mol carbon dioxide gas at 1.5 atm and 245 K. What is the volume of the carbon dioxide? ($R = 0.0821$ L · atm/mol · K)

2. At 273 K, 1.5 mol N_2 gas fills a 2.5 L container to a pressure of 13.4 atm. What will the pressure inside the container be if the temperature increases to 355 K and the container shrinks to a volume of 2.3 L?

3. A sample of water vapor has a volume of 11.5 L and a pressure of 0.45 atm at 293 K. How many moles of water vapor are in the sample?

4. A bacterial culture isolated from sewage produces 0.376 L of methane (CH_4) at 304 K and 1.5 atm. What would the volume of the methane be at STP?

5. A particular chemical reaction requires 2.95 mol sulfur dioxide gas (SO_2). A scientist has a 5.2 L tank of SO_2 gas at a pressure of 45.2 atm and a temperature of 293 K. Does the scientist have enough SO_2 to carry out the reaction? If so, how many moles of SO_2 will be left over? If not, how many more moles of SO_2 does the scientist need? Explain your answer.

6. The maximum safe pressure that a 4.00 L vessel can hold is 3.50 atm. If the vessel contains 0.410 mol of helium, what is the maximum temperature to which the vessel can be subjected?

7. **Challenge** A 3.4 L rigid container holds a sample of argon (Ar) gas at a pressure of 1.0 atm and a temperature of 263 K. If a scientist adds 2.5 mol Ar to the container without changing the temperature or volume, what will the new pressure inside the container be? (Hint: First, calculate the number of moles that were in the container originally.)

8. **Challenge** A 34.5 L container holds 25.6 mol O_2 gas at 321 K. By how much would the pressure change if the temperature decreased to 285 K and 4.5 mol O_2 were added to the container? (Hint: Calculate the initial pressure inside the container first.)

9. **Challenge** The pressure on a sample of gas is halved. At the same time, the volume of the container holding the gas is doubled. Will the temperature of the gas change? Explain your answer.

Absolute Zero

Absolute zero, or 0 K, is the temperature at which all atomic and molecular motion stops.

The temperature of a substance is a measure of the average kinetic energy of the particles in the substance. Absolute zero is the temperature at which there is no motion of atoms and molecules—that is, at absolute zero, the kinetic energy of the particles in a substance is zero. The Kelvin temperature scale is based on the kinetic energies of the particles in a substance. Therefore, a substance's temperature in kelvins is directly proportional to the average kinetic energy of its particles, which is why absolute zero is equal to 0 K. As the name implies, absolute zero is the lowest temperature possible. Scientists have never been able to cool any substance to absolute zero, but they have gotten very close using lasers and other kinds of technology.

EXAMPLE 1

Interpret a Graph of Temperature vs. Kinetic Energy

The graph below shows how the temperature of a substance (in kelvins and degrees Celsius) is related to the average kinetic energy of the particles in the substance.

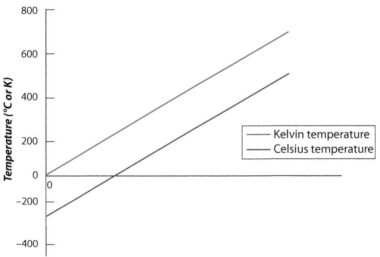

Use the graph to explain why it is correct to say that a substance's temperature in kelvins is directly proportional to the average kinetic energy of its particles, but it is *not* correct to say that a substance's temperature in degrees Celsius is directly proportional to the average kinetic energy of its particles.

REMEMBER

TEMPERATURE AND KINETIC ENERGY

- The temperature of a substance is a measure of the average kinetic energy of the particles in the substance.

- Temperatures on the Kelvin scale are directly proportional to the average kinetic energy of particles. So, for example, if the Kelvin temperature of a substance doubles, the average kinetic energy of its particles also doubles. This is not true of other temperature scales.

- The Kelvin temperature scale is defined based on absolute zero. Absolute zero is 0 K by definition.

Solution

1 Recall Relevant Information For temperature (T) to be directly proportional to kinetic energy (E_k), T and E_k must be related by the equation $T = kE_k$, where k is a constant. On a graph of T vs. E_k like the one on the previous page, this equation would be a straight line. It would intersect the vertical axis at the point (0, 0).

2 Analyze the Graph The blue line shows the graph of Kelvin temperature vs. average kinetic energy. It is a straight line, and it intersects the vertical axis at the point (0, 0). The red line shows the graph of Celsius temperature vs. average kinetic energy. It is also a straight line, but it does not intersect the vertical axis at the point (0, 0).

3 Solve The graph of Kelvin temperature vs. average kinetic energy fulfills the requirements for a direct relationship. Therefore, temperature in kelvins and average kinetic energy are directly proportional. The graph of Celsius temperature vs. average kinetic energy does not fulfill the requirements for a direct relationship. Therefore, temperature in degrees Celsius and average kinetic energy are not directly proportional.

TIP

Remember that the equation for a straight line is $y = mx + b$, where m is the slope of the line and b is the y-intercept of the line.

Problem Set

1. What is absolute zero in degrees Celsius? (Hint: Remember that one Celsius degree is equivalent to one kelvin, and 100°C = 373 K.)

2. Which of the following statements about temperature is true?
   A. Absolute zero is equal to 0°C.
   B. The temperature of a substance is equal to its average kinetic energy.
   C. Absolute zero is the temperature at which the particles in a substance have maximum kinetic energy.
   D. The temperature of a substance is a measure of the average kinetic energy of the particles in the substance.

3. A sample of a substance has a temperature of 150 K. The substance absorbs heat until the average kinetic energy of its particles has doubled. What is the final temperature of the substance? (Hint: Remember that Kelvin temperature is directly proportional to average kinetic energy.)

4. Explain why the particles in a substance at absolute zero are not moving.

5. **Challenge** Substance A has a temperature of 55 K. Substance B has a temperature of 5°C. Which substance's particles have the higher average kinetic energy? Explain your answer.

6. **Challenge** Sketch a graph of average kinetic energy of particles vs. time for a solid that is losing heat.

Dalton's Law of Partial Pressures

Dalton's law of partial pressures relates the partial pressure of each gas in a mixture to the total pressure of the mixture.

More than two centuries ago, chemist John Dalton developed a useful law for figuring out how much pressure each gas in a mixture contributes to the mixture's total pressure. Dalton's law, also known as Dalton's law of partial pressures, states that the total pressure exerted by a mixture of gases is equal to the sum of the partial pressures of the gases. The equation for this law is shown below:

$$P_{total} = P_1 + P_2 + \cdots P_n$$

In this equation, P_{total} is the total pressure of the gas mixture, and P_1, P_2, and P_n represent the partial pressures of each component gas. This law assumes that gases in a mixture do not interact and that all of them behave like ideal gases. Because there is an enormous amount of space between the molecules of each gas, no gas molecules would influence the motion of other gas molecules and change the pressure. Thus, the pressure is the same whether a container holds just one gas or a mixture of gases.

OBJECTIVE

- Use Dalton's law to calculate the total pressure of a mixture of gases and the partial pressure of each gas in a mixture.

EXAMPLE 1

Calculate Partial Pressures with the Ideal Gas Law

A 5.0 L container holds 2.0 mol H_2, 3.0 mol He, and 4.0 mol Ar at 308 K. What is the partial pressure of each gas? What is the total pressure in the container?

Solution

1 Collect and Strategize Use the ideal gas equation, $PV = nRT$, to calculate the partial pressure for each individual gas. Then, add the partial pressures together to calculate the total pressure in the container. The following information is given:

$V = 5.0$ L
$n_{H_2} = 2.0$ mol
$n_{He} = 3.0$ mol
$n_{Ar} = 4.0$ mol
$T = 308$ K

The gas constant, R, is equal to 0.0821 L · atm/mol · K. Rearranging the equation to solve for P yields the following:

$$P = \frac{nRT}{V}$$

REMEMBER

PARTIAL PRESSURES

- Dalton's law states that the total pressure of a mixture of gases is the sum of the partial pressures of the component gases.

- The partial pressure of a gas in a mixture is equal to the mole fraction of the gas multiplied by the total pressure of the mixture.

- The mole fraction of a gas is equal to the number of moles of the gas in a mixture divided by the total number of moles of gas in the mixture.

2 **Solve**   Solve the equation for P for each gas. For H_2, the calculation is as shown below:

$$P = \frac{nRT}{V} = \frac{(2.0 \text{ mol}) (0.0821 \text{ L} \cdot \text{atm/mol} \cdot \text{K})(308 \text{ K})}{5.0 \text{ L}} = 10 \text{ atm}$$

For He, the calculation is shown below:

$$P = \frac{nRT}{V} = \frac{(3.0 \text{ mol}) (0.0821 \text{ L} \cdot \text{atm/mol} \cdot \text{K})(308 \text{ K})}{5.0 \text{ L}} = 15 \text{ atm}$$

For Ar, the calculation is shown below:

$$P = \frac{nRT}{V} = \frac{(4.0 \text{ mol}) (0.0821 \text{ L} \cdot \text{atm/mol} \cdot \text{K})(308 \text{ K})}{5.0 \text{ L}} = 20 \text{ atm}$$

Now, add the partial pressures together to determine the total pressure. The total pressure is $10 + 15 + 20 = 45$ atm.

Problem Set

1. A 3.0 L container holds 3.0 mol N_2, 2.0 mol F_2, and 1.0 mol H_2 at 297 K. What is the partial pressure of each gas? What is the total pressure in the container? ($R = 0.0821$ L · atm/mol · K)

2. A 4.0 L container holds 2.0 mol O_2, 3.0 mol Ar, and 1.0 mol He at 300.0 K. What is the partial pressure of each gas? What is the total pressure in the container?

3. A mixture of O_2, Ar, and He exerts a total pressure of 5.6 atm. The partial pressure of O_2 is 1.5 atm. The partial pressure of Ar is 0.75 atm. What is the partial pressure of He in the mixture?

4. An 11.5 L container holds 20.179 g Ne, 79.896 g Ar, and 6.0039 g He at a temperature of 155 K. What is the partial pressure of each gas? What is the total pressure in the container? (Hint: Convert grams to moles.)

5. A mixture of gases contains 1.0 mol CO_2 and 2.0 mol O_2. Which gas has the higher partial pressure? Explain your answer.

6. A 4.0 L container holds 31.998 g O_2 and 28.014 g N_2 at 298 K. What is the partial pressure of each gas? What is the total pressure of the mixture? (Hint: Convert grams to moles.)

7. **Challenge**   A 4.2 L container holds a mixture of water vapor (H_2O), oxygen gas (O_2), and nitrogen gas (N_2) at 298 K. The total pressure in the container is 12.5 atm. If there are 0.50 mol H_2O and 0.75 mol O_2 in the container, what is the partial pressure of the N_2 gas?

8. **Challenge**   A mixture of gases contains 3.0 mol H_2, 4.0 mol O_2, and 3.0 mol N_2. If the total pressure is 20.0 atm, calculate the partial pressure of each gas. (Hint: The partial pressure of each gas is equal to its mole fraction times the total pressure of the mixture. The mole fraction of a gas is the number of moles of that gas divided by the total number of moles of gas in the mixture.)

9. **Challenge**   A mixture of Ar, Xe, and Ne has a total pressure of 22.4 atm. The partial pressure of Ar is 5.6 atm. The partial pressure of Xe is 8.4 atm. If the mixture contains a total of 20.0 mol gas, how many moles of neon (Ne) are there in the mixture?

Graham's Law of Effusion

Graham's law describes the relationship between the molar mass of a gas and the speed at which its particles move.

The process in which a gas escapes from a container through a small hole in the container is called *effusion*. Effusion is different from diffusion. *Diffusion* is the process in which a gas moves from an area of higher concentration to an area of lower concentration. Diffusion is responsible for the scent of a permanent marker or a drop of perfume spreading throughout a large room. Although effusion and diffusion are different processes, they do have one thing in common: The speed at which they occur is inversely proportional to the square root of the molar mass of the gas involved. This relationship is known as *Graham's law*. Graham's law states that gases with large molar masses will effuse and diffuse more slowly than gases with small molar masses. Graham's law applies to conditions of constant temperature and pressure.

OBJECTIVE

- Use Graham's law to compare the rates of effusion or diffusion of different gases.

EXAMPLE 1

Derive an Equation Relating Effusion Rate to Molar Mass

The molar mass of gas A is M_A, and its effusion rate is r_A. The molar mass of gas B is M_B, and its effusion rate is r_B. Derive an equation relating M_A and M_B to the ratio of r_A to r_B for the same experimental conditions.

Solution

1 **Recall Relevant Information**   According to Graham's law, the rate of effusion of a gas is inversely proportional to the molar mass of the gas. Mathematically, this can be expressed as $r = \dfrac{k}{\sqrt{M}}$, where r is the rate of effusion, k is a constant, and M is the molar mass of the gas. The value of the constant k depends on the conditions of the experiment. Therefore, $r_A = \dfrac{k}{\sqrt{M_A}}$, and $r_B = \dfrac{k}{\sqrt{M_B}}$. The experimental conditions are the same, so the value of k is the same in both equations.

2 **Solve**   Divide the two equations above to give the final equation, as shown below:

$$\frac{r_A}{r_B} = \frac{\dfrac{k}{\sqrt{M_A}}}{\dfrac{k}{\sqrt{M_B}}} = \frac{\sqrt{M_B}}{\sqrt{M_A}}$$

REMEMBER

EFFUSION AND DIFFUSION

- Effusion is the process in which a gas passes out through a hole in its container.

- Diffusion is the process in which gas molecules move from an area of higher concentration to an area of lower concentration.

- The effusion rate or diffusion rate of a gas is proportional to the inverse of the square root of the molar mass of the gas.

- The lower the molar mass of a gas is, the higher its effusion rate or diffusion rate is.

EXAMPLE 2

Compare the Diffusion Rates of Two Gases

Compare the diffusion rates of carbon dioxide (CO_2) and sulfur dioxide (SO_2) under the same experimental conditions.

Solution

1 **Collect and Strategize**   The equation derived in Example 1 gives the relationship between the effusion (or diffusion) rates of two gases and the molar masses of the gases. Therefore, to solve this problem, first calculate the molar mass of each gas, and then use the equation from Example 1 to solve.

2 **Solve**   The periodic table shows that the molar mass of CO_2 is 44.009 g/mol, and the molar mass of SO_2 is 64.06 g/mol. Substituting these values into the equation yields the following:

$$\frac{r_{CO_2}}{r_{SO_2}} = \frac{\sqrt{M_{SO_2}}}{\sqrt{M_{CO_2}}} = \frac{\sqrt{64.06}}{\sqrt{44.009}} = \frac{8.004}{6.6339} = 1.207$$

The rate of diffusion of CO_2 is therefore 1.207 times faster than the rate of diffusion of SO_2. This makes sense: Carbon dioxide's molar mass is smaller than sulfur dioxide's molar mass, so according to Graham's law, carbon dioxide should diffuse faster than sulfur dioxide.

> **TIP**
>
> You cannot use the Graham's law equation in Example 1 to compare diffusion or effusion rates for gases under different experimental conditions.

Problem Set

1. One of the diagrams below shows diffusion. The other shows effusion. Identify which diagram shows which process, and explain your answer.

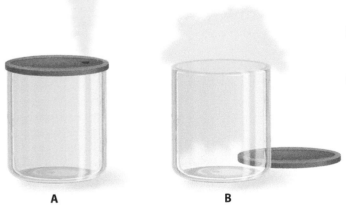

A   B

2. The three main gases in air are nitrogen (N_2), oxygen (O_2), and argon (Ar). Under identical experimental conditions, which of these gases will diffuse fastest? Which will diffuse slowest? Explain your answer.

3. Compare the effusion rates of carbon dioxide (CO_2) and oxygen (O_2) under the same experimental conditions.

4. Which will diffuse more quickly, ethane (C_2H_6) or propanol (C_3H_7OH)? Explain your answer.

5. **Challenge**   What is the molar mass of a gas that effuses 1.86 times faster than xenon (Xe)?

6. **Challenge**   A given volume of N_2 required 68.3 s to effuse from a hole in a chamber. An equal volume of a second gas required 85.6 s to effuse under the same conditions. Which of these could be the molar mass of the unknown gas?
   A. 6.6335 g/mol   **B.**   17.905 g/mol
   C. 28.014 g/mol   **D.**   44.003 g/mol

Phase Diagrams

A phase diagram shows the conditions under which a substance exists as a solid, a liquid, or a gas.

Substances exist as solids, liquids, or gases. For example, H_2O can be solid ice, liquid water, or gaseous water vapor. The temperature of a substance and the pressure on the substance determine which phase it exists in. Therefore, on a graph of pressure vs. temperature, each phase of a substance is represented by a specific region. This kind of graph is called a *phase diagram*. Chemists use lines on phase diagrams to show the temperature and pressure conditions at which a substance changes from one phase to another. Along each line, a substance is in equilibrium between two phases. The place on the diagram where the three lines meet is called the *triple point*. At the triple point, all three phases are in equilibrium: Solid, liquid, and gas are coexisting at the same time in the same system.

EXAMPLE 1

Interpret a Phase Diagram

The phase diagram for substance X is shown below:

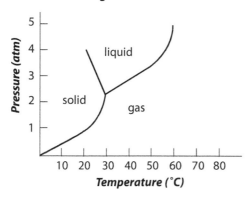

Phase Diagram for Substance X

Under what conditions do the solid, liquid, and gaseous phases of substance X coexist? At 2 atm and 60°C, is substance X a solid, a liquid, or a gas? What is the melting point of substance X at 3.5 atm?

Solution

1 **Recall Relevant Information** A phase diagram is a graph that shows the temperature and pressure conditions under which a substance exists in different phases. The lines on a phase diagram represent conditions at which a substance changes from one phase to another. The triple point is the set of pressure and temperature conditions at which all three phases of a substance coexist.

2 **Examine the Graph**   The lines on the graph form a shape that looks a bit like the capital letter *Y*. On the far left, at low temperatures, substance X exists as a solid. On the far right, at high temperatures, and on the bottom, at low pressures, substance X exists as a gas. In the upper central region, at moderate temperatures and pressures, substance X exists as a liquid.

3 **Solve**   The point at which the three lines on the graph intersect is the triple point. At this point, the solid, liquid, and gaseous phases coexist. For substance X, the triple point occurs at approximately 30°C and 2.75 atm. The conditions of 2 atm and 60°C fall within the "gas" region of the diagram, so substance X is a gas under these conditions. The melting point of a substance is the temperature at which it changes from a solid to a liquid. The line between the "solid" region on the diagram and the "liquid" region shows the conditions under which substance X changes from a solid to a liquid. Therefore, to find the melting point of substance X at 3.5 atm, draw a horizontal line at 3.5 atm and find the point where it intersects the line between liquid and solid. The intersection point is at approximately 28°C, so the melting point of substance X at 3.5 atm is approximately 28°C.

TIP

The phase diagrams for many pure substances resemble the phase diagram for substance X that is shown here—that is, they have the shape of a capital letter *Y*.

Problem Set

Use the carbon dioxide phase diagram below to answer Questions 1–6.

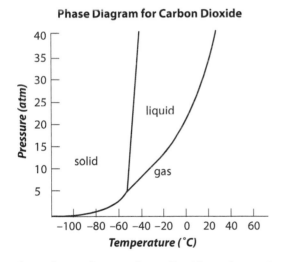

Phase Diagram for Carbon Dioxide

1. In what phase does carbon dioxide exist at 1 atm and 0°C?

2. What are the approximate temperature and pressure conditions of the triple point of carbon dioxide?

3. A sample of carbon dioxide is a gas at –20°C and 1 atm. How much pressure would be needed at this temperature to change the carbon dioxide completely into a liquid?

4. Identify a pressure and temperature at which liquid carbon dioxide and solid carbon dioxide are in equilibrium. (Hint: There is more than one correct answer.)

5. **Challenge**   A scientist raises the temperature of a sample of carbon dioxide from –80°C to 0°C at a constant pressure of 30 atm. What happens to the carbon dioxide as the temperature increases? Explain your answer.

6. **Challenge**   Above what temperature at 10 atm pressure can solid carbon dioxide **not** exist? Explain your answer.

Problem Set 61

Some Properties of Liquids

Intermolecular forces can explain many of the differences in properties between liquids and solids.

Liquids have a definite volume, but no definite shape. In other words, a liquid takes the shape of its container. It cannot shrink or expand to completely fill its container. These properties differentiate liquids from solids and gases. The unique properties of liquids are the result of intermolecular forces—the attractions and repulsions that occur between atoms or molecules in a liquid. The particles in liquids have more energy than those in solids, so liquid particles can move around more. These motions of particles in a liquid overcome some of the intermolecular attractions that make solids rigid, which is why liquids remain fluid. However, some intermolecular attractions do remain and pull liquid molecules together, so liquids aren't quite as free-moving as gases. Intermolecular forces also explain some other properties of liquids. Remember that the higher the molar mass of a substance is, the larger the intermolecular attractions are. Therefore, liquids with higher molar masses tend to be more viscous, or resistant to flow. Liquids with higher molar masses also tend to have higher boiling points, because more energy is needed to overcome the high intermolecular forces and allow liquids to become gases.

OBJECTIVES

- Explain how the properties of liquids depend on intermolecular forces.

- Contrast the intermolecular forces of liquids with those of solids.

EXAMPLE 1

Contrast Intermolecular Forces in Solids and Liquids

Acetic acid (CH_3COOH), which is the acid in vinegar, has a freezing point of 17°C. In terms of intermolecular forces, explain what happens to the acetic acid molecules as liquid acetic acid freezes and becomes solid.

Solution

1 **Recall Relevant Information** Molecules in liquids have more energy than those in solids, so liquid molecules move around more. These motions overcome some of the intermolecular attractions that make solids rigid, so liquids remain fluid. The opposite is true for solids.

2 **Solve** When acetic acid freezes and becomes solid, its molecules lose energy and move more slowly. These slower movements allow the molecules to come in closer contact with each other, and intermolecular attractions pull the molecules into rigid structures. When all of the molecules are locked into specific positions, the liquid becomes completely solid.

REMEMBER

INTERMOLECULAR FORCES IN LIQUIDS

- Molecules in liquids move around more than those in solids, overcoming some of the intermolecular attractions that lock solids into rigid shapes.

- The greater the molar mass of a substance is, the stronger the intermolecular attractions are. This means that liquids with high molar masses generally have higher boiling points and viscosities than liquids with lower molar masses.

EXAMPLE 2

Use Molecular Weights to Predict Properties

The molar mass of liquid bromine (Br_2) is almost five times greater than that of liquid nitrogen (N_2). According to this information, which liquid is likely to be more viscous?

TIP

Remember that you can use the periodic table to calculate the molar mass of a substance.

Solution

1 **Recall Relevant Information**   The higher the molar mass of a substance is, the larger its intermolecular attractions tend to be. Therefore, liquids with higher molar masses tend to be more viscous than those with lower molar masses. Molecules in liquids with higher molar masses are more attracted to each other than those in liquids with lower molar masses, so liquids with higher molar masses are more resistant to flow.

2 **Solve**   Liquid bromine has a significantly larger molar mass than liquid nitrogen, so bromine is likely to be more viscous than nitrogen.

Problem Set

1. Explain what happens in terms of intermolecular forces when a solid melts and becomes a liquid.

2. The molar mass of liquid carbon tetrachloride (CCl_4) is more than three times greater than that of liquid carbon dioxide (CO_2). Which liquid is probably more viscous? Explain your answer.

3. Explain what happens in terms of intermolecular forces when a liquid boils and becomes a gas.

4. Explain why liquids take the shapes of their containers, but solids do not.

5. **Challenge**   Explain why the temperature of a solid does not increase as it melts to form a liquid. (Hint: Temperature is a measure of the average kinetic energy of the particles in a substance.)

6. **Challenge**   Water forms special intermolecular attractions called *hydrogen bonds*, which are stronger than most other types of intermolecular forces. How do hydrogen bonds affect water's boiling point? Explain how water's hydrogen bonds affect its viscosity.

Some Properties of Solids

The forces between the particles in solids explain many of the unique properties of solids.

Unlike liquids, solids are rigid and have a definite shape. The rigidity of solids is due primarily to the forces between the particles in the solid. The particles in a solid have less energy than those in a liquid or gas. As a result, the forces between the particles hold the particles in fixed positions. The particles cannot slide past one another, so the solid's shape remains fixed. In some solids, the particles do not form neatly ordered structures. These solids are known as *amorphous solids*. However, in most solids, the particles are arranged in specific, repeating patterns. These solids are known as *crystalline solids* because their particles form crystals. The pattern that the particles form determines the shape of the crystal. The nature of the substance and the bonds between and within its particles determine many of the properties of the solid, such as its melting point and hardness.

EXAMPLE 1

Explain the Shape of a Crystalline Solid

The illustrations below show the crystal shapes of two common minerals, halite (NaCl) and calcite ($CaCO_3$).

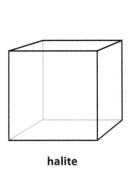

halite

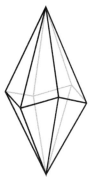

calcite

Both of these substances are ionic compounds. What do the shapes of the crystals tell you about the arrangement of ions in the crystals?

Solution

1 **Recall Relevant Information** Ionic compounds are made of positive and negative ions held together by ionic bonds. The positive and negative ions are arranged in a regular, repeating pattern. This pattern results in the formation of a crystal.

2 **Solve** The pattern formed by the ions in a crystal determines the shape of the crystal. Because the two crystals have different shapes, the ions in the crystals must be arranged differently.

EXAMPLE 2

Predict the Properties of a Solid

Which solid probably has the higher melting point, sucrose ($C_{12}H_{22}O_{11}$) or magnesium chloride ($MgCl_2$)?

Solution

1 **Recall Relevant Information** The strength of the forces between the particles in a solid affect its melting point. Sucrose is a covalently bonded solid. Magnesium chloride is an ionic solid.

2 **Solve** The ionic bonds between the magnesium ions (Mg^{2+}) and the chloride ions (Cl^-) in magnesium chloride are much stronger than the intermolecular forces between sucrose molecules in solid sucrose. Therefore, more energy is required to break the ionic bonds in magnesium chloride than to overcome the intermolecular forces in sucrose. Magnesium chloride probably has a higher melting point than sucrose.

TIP

Ionic compounds generally have much higher melting points than covalent compounds. Ionic compounds are also generally much harder than covalent compounds.

Problem Set

1. Explain why a liquid can take the shape of its container, but a solid cannot.

2. The mineral fluorite (CaF_2) is an ionic compound. The compound glucose ($C_6H_{12}O_6$) is a covalent compound. Which substance probably has the higher melting point? Explain your answer.

3. Which of the following statements about solids is true?
   A. Only ionic compounds can form crystals.
   B. The ions in an ionic crystalline solid are arranged randomly.
   C. The particles in an amorphous solid are not arranged in a specific pattern.
   D. Covalently bonded solids tend to have higher melting points than ionically bonded solids.

4. Which probably has a higher melting point, solid gold (Au) or solid aluminum (Al)? Explain your answer. (Hint: Remember that intermolecular forces get stronger as molar mass increases.)

5. **Challenge** Magnesium bromide ($MgBr_2$) is an ionic solid. Does magnesium bromide more likely form amorphous solids or crystalline solids? Explain your answer.

6. **Challenge** Which probably has the higher melting point, solid iodine (I_2) or solid potassium iodide (KI)? Explain your answer.

Solutions

A solution is a homogeneous mixture that consists of a solvent and one or more solutes.

Solutions play important roles in many everyday processes. They are vital to the survival of living things. Solutions are found inside each of your cells, and in the cells of all living things. Blood, lymph, and other bodily fluids are solutions. Ocean water, the water in freshwater bodies, and even tap water are all solutions. A solution is a homogeneous mixture. In most solutions, one or more substances are dissolved in a single substance. The substances that are dissolved are called *solutes*. The substance they are dissolved in is called the *solvent*. In general, the solutes in a solution are present in relatively small amounts compared to the solvent. For example, when common table salt (NaCl) dissolves in water, it forms a solution of salt water. In this solution, salt is the solute and water is the solvent. Most common solutions consist of one or more solid solutes dissolved in a liquid solvent. However, a solution can be a mixture of any combination of physical states.

OBJECTIVES

- Define *solute*, *solvent*, and *solution*.
- Explain what a saturated solution is.

REMEMBER

SOLUTIONS

- When a solution forms, the components of the solution do not react with one another. Like the components of all mixtures, the components of a solution retain their own chemical identities.

- The concentration of a solution is a description of the amount of solute dissolved in a given amount of solvent. For example, the concentration of a salt solution can be described in terms of moles of salt per liter or kilogram of water.

- The higher the concentration of a solution, the more solute it contains in a given volume or mass.

- A saturated solution is a solution in which no more solute can be dissolved.

- The amount of solute that will dissolve in a solvent depends in part on the temperature of the solvent. The greater the temperature of the solvent is, the more solute will dissolve.

EXAMPLE 1

Identify the Components of a Solution

Identify the solvent and the solute(s) in sweetened iced tea.

Solution

1 **Recall Relevant Information**   In a solution, the substance that is dissolved is the solute, and the substance that the solute is dissolved in is the solvent. To identify the solvent and solute(s) in a solution, it can be helpful to imagine how the solution might be prepared. To make iced tea, hot water is poured over tea leaves, and then the tea is cooled. To sweeten the tea, sugar or another sweetener is added.

2 **Solve**   Sweetened iced tea is a solution of a sweetener and various compounds from tea leaves dissolved in water. The sweetener and the compounds from the tea leaves are the solutes. The water is the solvent. In other words, iced tea is an *aqueous solution*, or a solution in which the solvent is water.

EXAMPLE 2

Compare Saturated and Unsaturated Solutions

A student stirs some table salt into a cup of cool water. Some of the salt dissolves, but some of it remains at the bottom of the cup. When the student heats the water, the remaining salt dissolves. Explain these observations.

TIP

A solution in which more solute can still be dissolved is called an *unsaturated* or *undersaturated* solution.

Solution

1 **Recall Relevant Information**   It's not possible to dissolve an infinite amount of solute in a solvent. At any given temperature, a specific amount of solvent can dissolve only a certain amount of solute. A solution in which the solvent cannot dissolve any more of a solute is a *saturated* solution. In general, a warm liquid solvent can dissolve more solid solute than a cooler liquid solvent.

2 **Solve**   When the student added the salt to the cool water and stirred, some of the salt dissolved in the water. The rest of the salt would not dissolve because the solution was saturated. The water could not dissolve any more salt at that temperature. When the student heated the water, the water's ability to dissolve the salt increased. That is why the rest of the salt dissolved when the water was heated.

Problem Set

1. Which of the following statements correctly describes the relationship between a solute, a solvent, and a solution?
    A. The solvent is dissolved in the solute to form the solution.
    B. The solute is dissolved in the solvent to form the solution.
    C. The solvent and the solute are dissolved in the solution.
    D. The solution is dissolved in the solute to form the solvent.

2. A scientist makes a saturated solution of potassium iodide (KI) in water. What could the scientist do to the solution to allow more KI to dissolve in it?

3. A cup of hot coffee can be made sweeter than a cup of iced coffee can. Explain this observation.

4. Identify the solute(s) and solvent in ocean water.

5. **Challenge**   A chemist has two calcium chloride ($CaCl_2$) solutions. Solution A has 0.25 mol $CaCl_2$ dissolved in 2 L of water. Solution B has 0.25 mol $CaCl_2$ dissolved in 1 L of water. Which solution has the higher concentration?

6. **Challenge**   Household ammonia is a solution that is produced by passing ammonia gas (NH_3) through water. What is the solvent in this solution? What is the solute?

The Dissolving Process

Many factors influence the dissolving process. Knowing these factors allows chemists to prepare solutions effectively.

Many solutions are prepared by dissolving a solid in a liquid. Dissolution occurs as a result of random molecular motions. The particles in matter are in constant, random motion. Over time, these random motions cause the solute and the solvent to become evenly mixed. Intermolecular forces can also cause dissolution. Anything that increases the motions of the solute and solvent particles, or increases the number of solute particles exposed to solvent particles, increases the rate of dissolution and the amount of solute that can dissolve in a given amount of solvent. Therefore, heating a solution, stirring a solution, or breaking a solid solute into smaller pieces can all increase the rate at which the solute dissolves. Heating the solution also increases the solubility of the solute. The solubility of a solute is the maximum amount of solute that can dissolve in a given amount of solvent at a given temperature.

OBJECTIVES

- **Describe how dissolution occurs.**
- **Define** *solubility* **and explain how it is measured.**
- **Describe the factors that affect solubility and dissolving rate.**

EXAMPLE 1

Interpret a Solubility Curve

A student performed a laboratory experiment to create a solubility curve for solid potassium nitrate (KNO_3). A solubility curve shows the mass of a solute that can dissolve in a solvent at different temperatures. Use the student's graph of temperature vs. solubility, shown below, to determine the number of grams of potassium nitrate that can dissolve in 100 g of water at 50°C.

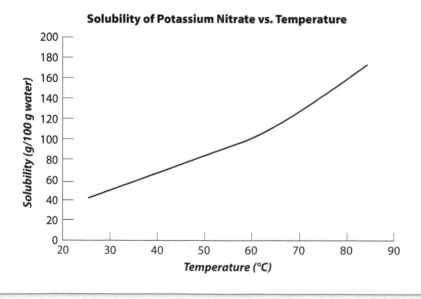

REMEMBER

SOLUBILITY

- A solubility curve shows the effect of varying temperatures on the amount of a solute that can dissolve in a given amount of solvent.

- The solubility of a substance is the amount of a substance that can dissolve in a given amount of solvent. Solubility is generally expressed in units of grams of solute per 100 grams of solvent (g solute/100 g solvent).

Solution

1. Study the Graph To solve the problem, first find the 50°C mark on the x-axis of the graph. Draw a vertical line from that point up, until it crosses the solubility curve. Then, draw a horizontal line through the intersection point all the way to the y-axis. The point where that line crosses the y-axis gives the mass of KNO_3 that will dissolve.

TIP

The solubility of most solids in most liquids increases as temperature increases.

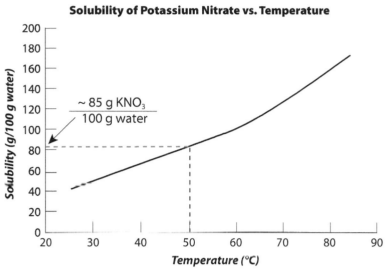

Solubility of Potassium Nitrate vs. Temperature

~ 85 g KNO_3 / 100 g water

2. Solve The graph shows that approximately 85 g KNO_3 can dissolve in 100 g of water at 50°C.

Problem Set

1. Copper(II) sulfate ($CuSO_4$) is a bluish solid at room temperature. A student adds some copper(II) sulfate to water. Describe two ways the student could get the copper(II) sulfate to dissolve more quickly.

2. Explain how the graph in Example 1 shows that increasing temperature increases the solubility of a solid in water.

3. Explain the difference between solubility and dissolving rate.

4. Substance A has a solubility in water of 3.4 g/100 g water. How many grams of substance A would be required to make a saturated solution in 1 kg of water?

5. **Challenge** Explain why heating or stirring a solution can increase the rate at which the solute dissolves in the solvent.

6. **Challenge** The graph below is a solubility curve for carbon dioxide gas. Compare this curve to the one in Example 1. Use these curves to draw a conclusion about the effects of heating on the solubility of solids and gases in liquids.

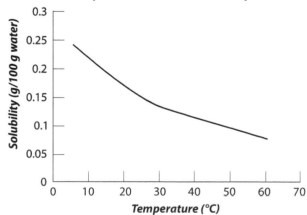

Solubility of Carbon Dioxide vs. Temperature

Molarity and Mole Fraction

Molarity and mole fraction are two ways of expressing the concentration of a solution.

Many important chemical reactions occur in solution. The amount of various solutes in a given amount of solution has a significant effect on the rate at which those reactions occur. The amount of solute in a given amount of solution is the solute's *concentration* in the solution. Chemists express concentration in several ways. The most common way of expressing concentration is as molarity. The *molarity* of a solute in solution is the number of moles (mol) of the solute in one liter (L) of solution. The symbol for the molarity of a solution is *M*. Another common way of expressing concentration, especially for mixtures of gases, is as mole fraction. The *mole fraction* of a substance in a mixture is the ratio of the number of moles of that substance to the total number of moles of all substances in the mixture. Because mole fraction is a ratio, it has no units.

EXAMPLE 1

Calculate Molarity from Moles

A student dissolves 0.080 mol NaCl and 0.025 mol $CuSO_4$ in enough water to form 3.50 L of solution. What is the molarity of each solute in the solution?

Solution

1. **Collect and Strategize** Molarity is defined as the number of moles of solute per liter of solution. Therefore, to calculate the molarity of this solution, divide the number of moles of each solute by the number of liters of solution to calculate the molarity. The following information is given:

   amount of NaCl = 0.080 mol

   amount of $CuSO_4$ = 0.025 mol

   volume of solution = 3.50 L

2. **Solve** The molarity can be calculated as shown below:

$$\frac{0.080 \text{ mol NaCl}}{3.50 \text{ L solution}} = \frac{0.023 \text{ mol NaCl}}{1 \text{ L solution}} = 0.023\ M \text{ NaCl}$$

$$\frac{0.025 \text{ mol CuSO}_4}{3.50 \text{ L solution}} = \frac{0.0071 \text{ mol CuSO}_4}{1 \text{ L solution}} = 0.0071\ M \text{ CuSO}_4$$

   So, the concentration of NaCl in the solution is 0.023 *M*, and the concentration of $CuSO_4$ in the solution is 0.0071 *M*. Another way to express this is to say that the solution is 0.023 *M* in NaCl and 0.0071 *M* in $CuSO_4$.

OBJECTIVES

- **Define *molarity* and *mole fraction*.**
- **Perform calculations involving molarity and mole fraction.**

REMEMBER

MOLARITY AND MOLE FRACTION

- The molarity of a solute in a solution *(M)* is the number of moles of the solute that are dissolved in one liter of solution.
- Molarity is generally used to describe the concentrations of solutions in which the solvent is a liquid.
- The mole fraction of a substance in a mixture is the ratio of the number of moles of the substance in the mixture to the total number of moles of all substances in the mixture.
- Mole fraction is represented by the symbol *X*.
- Mole fraction is most often used to express the proportions of components in mixtures in which all the components are in the same phase. For example, mole fraction is often used to describe the compositions of mixtures of gases or mixtures of liquids.

EXAMPLE 2

Calculate Molarity from Grams

A mass of 80.0 g of calcium bromide ($CaBr_2$) is dissolved in enough water to form 2.00 L of solution. What is the molarity of the solution?

Solution

1 **Collect and Strategize** First, calculate the number of moles of $CaBr_2$. Then, divide the number of moles by the number of liters of solution to calculate the molarity. The example gives the following information:

mass of $CaBr_2$ = 80.0 g

volume of solution = 2.00 L

The periodic table shows that the molar mass of $CaBr_2$ is 199.9 g/mol.

2 **Solve** Use a conversion factor to convert the mass of $CaBr_2$ given to number of moles of $CaBr_2$, as shown below:

$$80.0 \text{ g } CaBr_2 \times \frac{1 \text{ mol } CaBr_2}{199.9 \text{ g } CaBr_2} = 0.400 \text{ mol } CaBr_2$$

The molarity can be calculated as shown below:

$$\frac{0.400 \text{ mol } CaBr_2}{2.00 \text{ L solution}} = \frac{0.200 \text{ mol } CaBr_2}{1 \text{ L solution}} = 0.200 \text{ } M$$

Therefore, this is a 0.200 M solution of $CaBr_2$.

TIP

Molarity must always be expressed in moles per liter, not grams per liter. Always convert grams to moles before calculating molarity.

TIP

The *1 L solution* in the molarity conversion factor is considered to be an exact unit. Therefore, it does not affect the number of significant figures in the answer.

EXAMPLE 3

Calculate Mass from Volume and Molarity

How many grams of silver nitrate ($AgNO_3$) are in 500.0 mL of a 0.10 M $AgNO_3$ solution?

Solution

1 **Collect and Strategize** To solve this problem, first use the molarity and volume of the solution to calculate the number of moles of $AgNO_3$. Then, use the molar mass of $AgNO_3$ to convert moles to grams. The example gives the following information:

volume of solution = 500.0 mL

molarity of solution = 0.10 M

The periodic table shows that the molar mass of $AgNO_3$ is 169.9 g/mol.

2 **Convert Volume to Moles** The molarity of the solution is 0.10 M. Therefore, 1 L of solution contains 0.10 mol $AgNO_3$. Use this concentration as a conversion factor to calculate the number of moles of $AgNO_3$ in 500.0 mL of solution, as shown below. Remember to convert milliliters to liters.

$$500.0 \text{ mL solution} \times \frac{1 \text{ L}}{1,000 \text{ mL}} \times \frac{0.10 \text{ mol } AgNO_3}{1 \text{ L solution}} = 0.050 \text{ mol } AgNO_3$$

TIP

In a solution with only one solute, the phrase *the molarity of the solution* is used to refer to the concentration of that solute in the solution. In a solution with more than one solute, it is more correct to refer to the molarity of a particular solute in solution.

3 Solve Now, use the molar mass of $AgNO_3$ as a conversion factor to calculate the mass of $AgNO_3$ in the solution, as shown below:

$$0.050 \; \cancel{mol \; AgNO_3} \times \frac{169.9 \text{ g } AgNO_3}{1 \; \cancel{mol \; AgNO_3}} = 8.5 \text{ g } AgNO_3$$

EXAMPLE 4

Calculate Mole Fraction from Moles

A particular sample of air contains 2.694 mol N_2 (nitrogen gas), 0.725 mol O_2 (oxygen gas), and 0.0320 mol Ar (argon gas). What is the mole fraction of each gas in this sample of air?

Solution

1 Collect and Strategize To calculate mole fraction, first find the total number of moles of all substances in the sample. The problem gives the following information:

amount of N_2 = 2.694 mol

amount of O_2 = 0.725 mol

amount of Ar = 0.0320 mol

2 Solve First, calculate the total number of moles of gas in the sample: $2.694 + 0.725 + 0.0320 = 3.451$ mol. Now, find the mole fraction (X) of each gas using division, as shown below:

$$X_{N_2} = \frac{2.694 \; \cancel{mol}}{3.451 \; \cancel{mol}} = 0.7806$$

$$X_{O_2} = \frac{0.725 \; \cancel{mol}}{3.451 \; \cancel{mol}} = 0.210$$

$$X_{Ar} = \frac{0.0320 \; \cancel{mol}}{3.451 \; \cancel{mol}} = 0.00927$$

To double-check, add the calculated mole fractions together: $0.7806 + 0.210 + 0.00927 = 1.000$, so the calculations are correct.

TIP

The subscript on the X identifies the mole fraction being calculated. For example, X_{Ar} is the mole fraction of Ar (argon) in the mixture.

EXAMPLE 5

Calculate Mole Fraction from Mass

A scientist makes a solution of ethanol (CH_3CH_2OH) and water (H_2O) by combining 36.9 g of ethanol and 21.6 g of water. What are the mole fractions of ethanol and water in the solution?

Solution

1 **Collect** To calculate mole fraction, you must know the number of moles of each substance. From the periodic table, the molar mass of ethanol is 46.068 g/mol, and the molar mass of water is 18.015 g/mol. The example gives the following information:

mass of ethanol = 36.9 g

mass of water = 21.6 g

2 **Solve** Use the molar masses as conversion factors to convert grams to moles, as shown below:

$$36.9 \text{ g ethanol} \times \frac{1 \text{ mol ethanol}}{46.068 \text{ g ethanol}} = 0.801 \text{ mol ethanol}$$

$$21.6 \text{ g water} \times \frac{1 \text{ mol water}}{18.015 \text{ g water}} = 1.20 \text{ mol water}$$

The total number of moles of water and ethanol in the solution is 1.20 + 0.801 = 2.00 mol. Therefore, the mole fraction (X) of each substance is calculated as shown below:

$$X_{ethanol} = \frac{0.801 \text{ mol}}{2.00 \text{ mol}} = 0.401$$

$$X_{water} = \frac{1.20 \text{ mol}}{2.00 \text{ mol}} = 0.600$$

Mole fractions should always add up to 1. Therefore, to check the calculations, add the mole fractions together: 0.401 + 0.600 = 1.001. This is within rounding error of 1, so the calculations are correct.

TIP

Remember that the molar mass of a compound is equal to the sum of the average atomic masses of all the atoms in one molecule or formula unit of the compound. Average atomic masses can be found on the periodic table at the back of the book.

Problem Set

1. A student dissolves 0.112 mol sucrose in enough water to make 4.0 L of solution. What is the molarity of the solution?

2. How many moles of sodium hydroxide (NaOH) are in 1.5 L of 0.20 M NaOH solution?

3. A scientist mixes 5.23 mol water, 1.14 mol methanol, and 0.893 mol ethanol. What is the mole fraction of each substance in the solution?

4. A student prepares a solution by dissolving 20.0 g of aluminum chloride ($AlCl_3$) in enough water to produce 500 mL of solution. What is the molarity of the solution?

5. A scientist makes a solution of methanol (CH_3OH) and water (H_2O) by mixing 64.0 g of methanol with 144 g of water. What is the mole fraction of each component in this solution?

6. A chemist needs to prepare 75 mL of a 0.25 M solution of sodium sulfate (Na_2SO_4). What mass of sodium sulfate should the chemist use to prepare the solution?

7. **Challenge** The molarity of a solution can change when the temperature of the solution changes. However, mole fraction is independent of temperature. Explain this observation. (Hint: Remember that most substances expand when they are heated.)

8. **Challenge** How many grams of water (H_2O) would have to be added to 2.00 mol of acetone (CH_3COCH_3) to prepare a solution in which the mole fraction of acetone is 0.200?

9. **Challenge** A student prepared 1.00 L of a 1.00 M H_2SO_4 solution. How much water would the student have to add to dilute the solution from 1.00 M to 0.0500 M?

Molality and Mass Percent

Molality and mass percent are two ways to express the concentration of a solution.

Remember that molarity (M) and mole fraction (X) are two ways of expressing the concentration of a solution. Another common way to express solution concentration is *molality*, which is represented by the symbol m. The molality of a solute in a solution is equal to the number of moles (mol) of the solute in one kilogram (kg) of solvent. The main advantage of using molality instead of molarity is that molality is temperature independent. Two other ways to express the concentration of a solution are mass percent and volume percent. The mass percent of any component in a mixture is equal to 100 times the mass of that component divided by the total mass of the mixture. Similarly, the volume percent of a component in a solution is equal to 100 times the volume of that component divided by the total volume of the mixture. Mass percent and volume percent, like mole fraction, have no units.

OBJECTIVE

- Use molality, mass percent, and volume percent to express the concentration of a solution.

REMEMBER

MOLALITY AND MASS PERCENT

- The molality of a solute in solution is the number of moles of solute that are dissolved in one kilogram of solvent.

- The denominator in a molality calculation is kilograms of *solvent*, not kilograms of *solution*.

- The molality of a solution does not change with temperature.

- The mass percent of one component in a mixture is 100 times the ratio of the mass of that component in the mixture to the total mass of the mixture.

- The volume percent of one component in a mixture is 100 times the ratio of the volume of that component in the mixture to the total mass of the mixture.

- Volume percent is most often used to describe the concentration of a mixture of liquids.

EXAMPLE 1

Calculate the Molality of a Solution

What is the molality of a solution made by dissolving 2.50 g of table sugar (sucrose, $C_{12}H_{22}O_{11}$) in 50.0 mL of water at 4°C? The density of water at 4°C is 1.00 g/mL.

Solution

1 **Collect and Strategize**   To calculate the molality of a solution, you must know the number of moles of solute and the mass of the solvent. Therefore, to solve this problem, first convert grams of sucrose to moles of sucrose, and milliliters of water to kilograms of water. The periodic table shows that the molar mass of sucrose is 342.30 g/mol. Use molar mass as a conversion factor to convert grams to moles, as shown below:

$$2.50 \, g \times \frac{1 \, mol}{342.30 \, g} = 7.30 \times 10^{-3} \, mol$$

Next, use density as a conversion factor to convert milliliters to kilograms, as shown below:

$$50.0 \, mL \times \frac{1.00 \, g}{1 \, mL} \times \frac{1 \, kg}{1,000 \, g} = 0.0500 \, kg$$

2 **Solve**   The molality of the solution is found by dividing the number of moles of solute (sugar) by the number of kilograms of solvent (water), as shown below:

$$m = \frac{mol \, solute}{kg \, solvent} = \frac{7.30 \times 10^{-3} \, mol}{0.0500 \, kg} = 0.146 \, m$$

EXAMPLE 2

Calculate Mass Percent

A student dissolves 0.655 mol sucrose in 1.00 L H_2O at 4°C. What is the mass percent of sucrose in the solution? The density of water at 4°C is 1.00 g/mL.

Solution

1 **Collect and Strategize** Use molar mass to convert moles to grams and use density to convert liters to grams. The molar mass of sucrose is 342.30 g/mol, so the mass of sucrose in the solution can be calculated as shown below:

$$0.655 \ \text{mol} \times \frac{342.30 \ \text{g}}{1 \ \text{mol}} = 224 \ \text{g}$$

The mass of water can be calculated as shown below:

$$1.00 \ \text{L} \times \frac{1,000 \ \text{mL}}{1 \ \text{L}} = \frac{1.00 \ \text{g}}{1 \ \text{mL}} = 1.00 \times 10^3 \ \text{g}$$

2 **Solve** The total mass of the solution is $(1.00 \times 10^3) + 224 = 1,224$ g. Therefore, the mass percent of sucrose can be calculated by dividing the mass of the solute (sucrose) by the total mass of the solution and multiplying by 100, as shown below:

$$\text{mass percent sucrose} = \frac{224 \ \text{g}}{1,224 \ \text{g}} \times 100 = 18.3\%$$

TIP

When calculating mass percent or volume percent, make sure to double-check your units. The units in the numerator and the denominator must be the same. For example, to calculate mass percent, you must divide grams by grams or kilograms by kilograms, not grams by kilograms.

Problem Set

1. A student dissolves 0.250 mol NaCl in 2.05 kg H_2O. What is the molality of the resulting solution?

2. A chemist dissolves 15.53 g NaOH in 0.750 kg H_2O. What is the mass percent of each component in the mixture? (Hint: Make sure to check your units.)

3. What is the mass percent of NaCl in a solution prepared by dissolving 1.00 mol NaCl in 3.45 kg H_2O? (Hint: Calculate the molar mass of NaCl.)

4. Describe the difference between molarity and molality. Explain why the molarity of a solution may change as temperature changes, but the molality of a solution does not change as temperature changes. (Hint: Remember that most substances expand when they are heated.)

5. What is the mass percent of each component in a solution prepared by dissolving 0.0250 mol cholesterol ($C_{27}H_{46}O$) in 50.00 g chloroform ($CHCl_3$)?

6. A student dissolves 1.57 g silver nitrate ($AgNO_3$) in 1.00 L H_2O at 40°C. What is the molality of the resulting solution? The density of water at 40°C is 0.9922 g/mL.

7. **Challenge** A student dissolves 10.439 g citric acid ($C_6H_8O_7$) in 60.00 mol H_2O. What is the molality of the solution?

8. **Challenge** A chemist has a solution that is 6.50 mass percent $BaCl_2$ in water. What is the molality of the solution?

9. **Challenge** What volume of acetone is contained in 5.05 L of a solution that is 35.0% acetone by volume? (Hint: Volume percent is calculated in a manner similar to mass percent.)

Colligative Properties

Substances dissolved in a solvent will affect the physical properties of the solvent.

When a solute is dissolved in a solvent, the solution will have a different freezing point, melting point, boiling point, and vapor pressure than the pure solvent itself. How much the physical properties of the solvent change depends on the solvent and on the number of solute particles present. It does not depend on the chemical nature of the solute itself. The more solute particles present in the solution, the greater the change is in the solvent's properties. Therefore, the difference between the colligative properties of a solution and those of the pure solvent can be used to determine both the amount and the identity of the solute dissolved in the solvent. Note that the word *colligative* means "tied together," referring to the relationship between the solute and the solvent.

OBJECTIVE

- Describe the effects of solutes on boiling point, freezing point, and vapor pressure of solvents.

EXAMPLE 1

Calculate Freezing-Point Depression

An increase in the number of solute particles will depress the freezing point of a solution or solvent. A student dissolves 1.50 g NaCl in 0.100 kg pure water. The freezing point of pure water is 0°C. What will the freezing point of the solution be? The freezing-point depression constant for water is −1.86°C/*m*.

Solution

① Collect The equation used to calculate the freezing-point depression of a solvent due to the presence of a solute is shown below:

$$\Delta T_f = K_f m$$

In this equation, ΔT_f is the change in the freezing-point temperature, K_f is the freezing-point depression constant for the solvent, and m is the molality of the solution. The following information is given in the problem:

mass of NaCl = 1.50 g

mass of water = 0.100 kg

freezing point of water = 0°C

K_f for water = −1.86°C/*m*

② Gather Required Information First, calculate the molality of the solution. The molar mass of NaCl is 58.443 g/mol. To calculate the molality of the solution, first calculate the number of moles of NaCl in solution, and then divide by the mass of solvent. NaCl dissociates in water to form Na^+ and Cl^- ions, so remember to multiply the number of moles of NaCl by two to determine the total concentration of particles in solution, as shown on the next page:

REMEMBER

COLLIGATIVE PROPERTIES

- Colligative properties include freezing point, boiling point, and vapor pressure.

- The change in the colligative properties of a solvent depends only on the solvent and on the concentration of solute particles. It does not depend on the identity of the solute particles.

- Every solvent has its own freezing-point depression constant and boiling-point elevation constant. For water, the freezing-point depression constant (K_f) is −1.86°C/*m*, and the boiling-point elevation constant (K_b) is 0.512°C/*m*.

$$m_{sol} = \frac{\text{mol solute}}{\text{kg solvent}}$$

The number of moles of NaCl in the solution can be calculated as shown below:

$$\text{mol NaCl} = 1.50 \text{ g NaCl} \times \frac{1 \text{ mol NaCl}}{58.443 \text{ g NaCl}} = 0.0257 \text{ mol NaCl}$$

The molality of the solution is calculated as shown below:

$$m_{sol} = \frac{0.0257 \text{ mol NaCl}}{0.100 \text{ kg H}_2\text{O}} \times \frac{2 \text{ mol particles}}{1 \text{ mol NaCl}} = 0.514 \, m$$

3 Solve To solve, substitute the required information into the equation, as shown below:

$$\Delta T_f = -(1.86°C/m)(0.514 \, m) = -0.956°C$$

So, the freezing point of the solvent will decrease by 0.956°C. The freezing point of pure water is 0°C, so the freezing point of the solution will be $0°C - 0.956°C = -0.956°C$.

Remember that the freezing-point depression, boiling-point elevation, and vapor-pressure change equations yield the *change* in freezing point, boiling point, or vapor pressure when a solute is present. To find the actual freezing point, boiling point, or vapor pressure of the solution, you must add or subtract the change in the property to the value of the property for the pure solvent.

EXAMPLE 2

Determine the Molality of a Solution

A scientist wants to make a solution of ethanol (CH_3CH_2OH) and water that will remain liquid at a temperature of $-20°C$. How many grams of ethanol must the scientist add to 1.00 kg of pure water to make the required solution?

Solution

1 Strategize and Collect Solve the equation $\Delta T_f = K_f m$ for m. Determine the required molality for the solution and then use the molar mass of ethanol to determine the number of grams of ethanol required. The following information is given in the problem:

$$\Delta T_f = -20°C$$

mass of water = 1.00 kg

2 Gather Required Information The molar mass of ethanol is 46.068 g/mol. The freezing point of pure water is 0°C, so the required freezing-point depression is $-20°C$. Solving the equation for m yields the following:

$$\Delta T_f = K_f m$$

$$m = \frac{\Delta T_f}{K_f} = \frac{-20.0°C}{-1.86°C/m} = 10.8 \, m$$

3 Solve Use the required molality of the solution to calculate the mass of ethanol required in the solution, as shown below:

$$\text{mass of ethanol} = \frac{10.8 \text{ mol ethanol}}{1.00 \text{ kg H}_2\text{O}} \times \frac{46.068 \text{ g ethanol}}{1 \text{ mol ethanol}} \times 1.00 \text{ kg H}_2\text{O}$$

mass of ethanol = 498 g ethanol

Problem Set 67 Colligative Properties **149**

EXAMPLE 3

Determine the Effects of Solutes on Solvent Properties

A student prepares three solutions by dissolving NaCl, BaCl$_2$, and C$_6$H$_{12}$O$_6$ (glucose) in pure water, as shown below. Which solution will have the highest boiling point?

Solute	Amount of Solute (mol)	Amount of Solvent (kg)
NaCl	1.0	1.0
BaCl$_2$	0.5	1.0
C$_6$H$_{12}$O$_6$	1.5	1.0

Solution

1 **Strategize**   Remember that it is the concentration of solute particles that determines the boiling-point elevation of a solution. Therefore, the solution with the greatest concentration of solute particles will have the highest boiling point. Because the amount of solvent is the same in each case, to solve this problem, simply compare the number of solute particles that are present in each case.

2 **Solve**   As shown to the right, glucose does not ionize in water, so the glucose solution will contain 1.5 mol solute particles. Each mole of NaCl will produce two moles of ions when dissolved in water, so the NaCl solution will contain 2.0 mol solute particles. Each mole of BaCl$_2$ will produce three moles of ions when dissolved in water, so the BaCl$_2$ solution will contain 1.5 mol solute particles. Therefore, the NaCl solution will have the highest boiling point.

$$NaCl_{(s)} \longrightarrow Na^+_{(aq)} + Cl^-_{(aq)}$$

$$BaCl_{2\,(s)} \longrightarrow Na^{2+}_{(aq)} + 2Cl^-_{(aq)}$$

$$C_6H_{12}O_{6\,(s)} \longrightarrow C_6H_{12}O_{6\,(aq)}$$

Each solute behaves differently in aqueous solution.

EXAMPLE 4

Determine Vapor-Pressure Lowering for a Solution

A scientist mixes 1.00 mol sucrose with 4.00 mol pure water at 20°C. How much will the vapor pressure of the solution decrease? The vapor pressure of pure water at 20°C is 2.33 kPa.

Solution

1 **Collect Information**   Use the equation below to calculate the change in vapor pressure of a solution containing a single, nonvolatile nonelectrolyte (that is, a substance that does not dissociate in solution, such as sucrose):

$$\Delta P_{sol} = P_A^\circ X_B$$

In this equation, X_B is the mole fraction of the solute in the solution, ΔP_{sol} is the change in vapor pressure of the solution, and P_A° is the vapor pressure of the pure solvent. The following information is given in the problem:

amount of sucrose = 1.00 mol

amount of water = 4.00 mol

vapor pressure of pure water at 20°C = 2.33 kPa

TIP

Raoult's law describes the vapor pressure of a solution containing a single, nonvolatile solvent, as shown below:

$$P_{sol} = P_A^\circ X_A$$

In this equation, P_{sol} is the vapor pressure of the solution, P_A° is the vapor pressure of the pure solvent, and X_A is the mole fraction of the solvent in the solution. The equation in Example 4 is a variation on Raoult's law.

2 Gather Required Information First, calculate the mole fraction of sucrose in the solution. Calculate this mole fraction as shown below:

$$X_{sucrose} = \frac{\text{moles of sucrose}}{\text{total moles of solution}}$$

$$X_{sucrose} = \frac{1.00 \text{ mol sucrose}}{5.00 \text{ mol solution}} = 0.200$$

3 Solve Substituting the values above into the equation yields the following:

$$\Delta P_{sol} = P_A^\circ X_B = (2.33 \text{ kPa})(0.200) = 0.466 \text{ kPa}$$

So, the vapor pressure of the solution will be 0.466 kPa lower than that of pure water.

The graph to the right shows the vapor pressure curve for pure water and the curve for an aqueous solution of a nonvolatile substance. This curve shows why the boiling point of a solution is higher than that of the pure solvent, but the freezing point is lower.

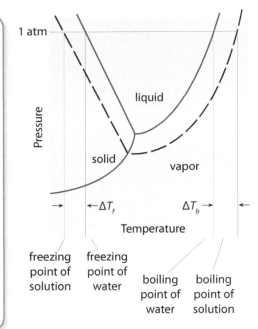

Problem Set

1. Methanol (CH_3OH) does not dissociate in water, whereas $CaCl_2$ will dissociate into one Ca^+ and two Cl^- ions. If methanol and $CaCl_2$ sell at the same price per mole, which would be cheaper to use to keep an aqueous solution from freezing? Explain your answer.

2. A student makes a $0.87\,m$ solution of methanol (CH_3OH) in water. What is the boiling point of the solution? The boiling-point elevation constant for water is $0.512°C/m$.

3. Salt is often used to melt ice on roads and sidewalks in the winter time. When salt is spread on snow-covered sidewalks at 0°C, the snow melts. When the same amount of salt is spread on the same sidewalks at –30°C, nothing happens. Explain.

4. A student dissolves 2.40 mol each of KCl and NaCl in separate but equal volumes of water. Compare the freezing and boiling points of the two solutions. Explain your answer. (KCl dissociates to form one K^+ ion and one Cl^- ion. NaCl dissociates to form one Na^+ and one Cl^- ion.)

5. An aqueous solution boils at 100.50°C. What is the freezing point of the solution? The boiling-point elevation constant for water is $0.512°C/m$. The freezing-point depression constant for water is $-1.86°C/m$.

6. A student dissolves 15.6 g ammonium chloride (NH_4Cl) in enough water to make 1.00 kg of solution. What are the boiling and freezing points of the solution? Ammonium chloride dissociates to form one $NH4^+$ ion and one Cl^- ion.

7. **Challenge** How much would the freezing point of 12.0 L of water be lowered by the addition of 5.00 kg of ethylene glycol ($C_2H_4(OH)_2$)? How many kilograms of methanol (CH_3OH) would be required to produce the same result? Neither substance dissociates in water.

8. **Challenge** A scientist is trying to identify an unknown substance. She thinks it is potassium bromide (KBr). She dissolves 35.00 g of the substance in 2.00 kg of water. The boiling point of the water increases by 1.5°C. Is the substance potassium bromide? Explain your answer.

9. **Challenge** Pure liquid A has a vapor pressure of 0.90 atm. A student dissolves substance B, which is a nonvolatile nonelectrolyte, in liquid A. The vapor pressure of the solution is 0.60 atm. What is the mole fraction of substance B in the solution?

Separating Solutions

Substances can be separated by taking advantage of their molecular properties.

Chemists must often separate the components of a mixture. To do this, they take advantage of the differences in the chemical or physical properties of the different substances. Chemists use differences in boiling point, electrical charge, solubility, and adsorption to surfaces to separate the components of a mixture. These differences occur because of the three-dimensional shape, ionization, size, and type of bonding found in molecules.

OBJECTIVE

- Describe how distillation and chromatography can be used to separate mixtures.

EXAMPLE 1

Describe Distillation of a Mixture

A scientist wants to separate the components of a mixture using distillation. The table below shows the boiling point of each component of the mixture. Identify the order in which the components will be removed from the mixture during the distillation.

Component	Boiling Point (°C)
A	178
B	45
C	225
D	332

Solution

1 Recall Relevant Information   During distillation, heat is added to a mixture. As the mixture's temperature increases, the components of the mixture begin to boil. As each component in the mixture reaches its boiling point, it boils to form vapor. The vapor rises through the distillation apparatus and enters the cooling chamber, which is at a lower temperature than the rest of the apparatus. The lower temperature causes the vapor to condense back into a liquid, which is then collected. As each component in the mixture reaches its boiling point, it will evaporate, cool, condense, and flow into the collection chambers.

2 Solve   The component with the lowest boiling point, component B, will be removed first. Component A will be next, followed by component C, and then component D.

REMEMBER

CHEMICAL SEPARATIONS

- Distillation and chromatography are two separation processes that take advantage of molecular differences.

- During distillation, heat is added to a mixture of substances to cause them to boil. There are different kinds of distillation. The type of distillation used in a given situation depends on the type of mixture being separated.

- During chromatography, a mixture is separated based on the affinity of the different components for another phase, such as a liquid or a substrate. There are different types of chromatography, and each type is used in different situations.

EXAMPLE 2

Identify Mixtures That Can Be Separated Using Chromatography

In column chromatography, a hollow, vertical glass tube that is narrow at one end is filled with beads or particles of a solid material called a *substrate*. A mixture to be separated is added to the top (wide) end of the tube. Then, a liquid, the solvent, is poured through the column. The substrate is generally more polar than the solvent. As the solvent flows down the column, the solvent carries the mixture along with it. Components that are more attracted to the substrate move through the column more slowly than those that are less attracted to the substrate. Would column chromatography be more useful for separating two nonpolar compounds or for separating a nonpolar compound and a polar compound?

Solution

① Recall Relevant Information   Column chromatography relies on the interactions between polar molecules and nonpolar molecules to separate the components of a mixture. Because the substrate is more polar than the solvent, polar molecules are more attracted to the substrate, and nonpolar substances tend to remain in the solvent.

② Solve   Because column chromatography relies on polarity to separate solutions, it would be most useful for separating a mixture of a polar compound and a nonpolar compound.

Always remember to think at the molecular level. It is molecular structure and interactions within and between molecules that give substances their bulk properties (the properties that we observe, such as boiling point).

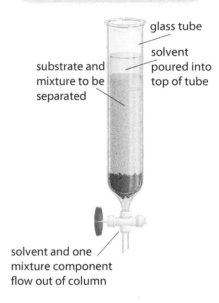

glass tube

solvent

substrate and mixture to be separated

solvent poured into top of tube

solvent and one mixture component flow out of column

Problem Set

1. Why is distillation more useful for separating substances with very different boiling points than for separating substances with similar boiling points?

2. A student marks a line of black ink near the bottom of a strip of coffee filter. The student places the bottom of the strip in a container of water. As the water rises through the filter, lines of different colors appear on the filter. Explain why that happens.

3. Explain how a coastal area with limited freshwater could use distillation to produce freshwater from seawater.

4. Why would it be unlikely that a chromatography setup would use a nonpolar substrate and a nonpolar solvent?

5. **Challenge**   Refineries use fractional distillation to separate the compounds in crude oil. In fractional distillation, a mixture is heated until it completely evaporates. The vapor is allowed to rise through a column that is hotter at the bottom than it is at the top. As the vapor rises, each component condenses at a different temperature (height in the column). Diesel fuel is separated from the column at a lower height than kerosene, which is separated at a lower height than gasoline. Which compound has the highest boiling point? Which has the lowest boiling point? Explain your answer.

6. **Challenge**   A scientist uses column chromatography to separate a mixture of three liquids. Explain why the scientist may need to use three different solvents to separate the mixture.

Properties of Acids and Bases

Acids, bases, and salts are three classes of compounds that, when added to water, will form ions and conduct an electric current.

Substances that taste sour, change litmus paper from blue to red, conduct an electric current in water, react with bases to form salts and water, and produce hydrogen gas when they react with metals are called *acids* (from *acere*, the Latin word for "sour"). Substances that taste bitter, feel slippery or soapy, turn red litmus paper blue, conduct an electric current in water, and react with acids to form salts and water are called *bases*. Strong acids and strong bases both dissociate completely in water. Salts form when an acid and a base are combined in a neutralization reaction. Salts are composed of cations (positively charged ions) that are ionically bound to anions (negatively charged ions). The ions in a salt come from the acid and base that reacted to form it. Salts are soluble in water, and a solution of a salt in water will conduct an electric current.

EXAMPLE 1

Identify Properties of Acids and Bases

A student dissolves a substance in water. The solution conducts an electric current. Based on this information, the student concludes that the substance is an acid. Explain what is wrong with the student's conclusion, and what the student could do to more accurately determine whether the substance is an acid or a base.

Solution

1 **Recall Relevant Information**   Remember that acids, bases, and salts will all conduct electricity when dissolved in water. Acids will turn blue litmus paper red, and bases turn red litmus paper blue.

2 **Solve**   Because acids, bases, and salts all conduct electricity when dissolved in water, just knowing that the substance forms a conducting solution is not enough information for the student to conclude that the substance is an acid. To learn whether the substance is an acid or a base, the student could apply it to red and blue litmus paper. If it is an acid, it will turn blue litmus paper red. If it is a base, it will turn red litmus paper blue.

OBJECTIVE

- Identify the properties of acids, bases, and salts.

REMEMBER

PROPERTIES OF ACIDS AND BASES

- Acids taste sour, change litmus paper from blue to red, and produce hydrogen gas when they react with metals.

- Bases taste bitter, change litmus paper from red to blue, and feel slippery or soapy.

- Salts are formed from neutralization reactions between acids and bases.

- Acids, bases, and salts ionize in water, so aqueous solutions of these substances can conduct electricity.

TIP

NEVER taste or touch a chemical unless your teacher or lab manual instructs you to.

EXAMPLE 2

Identify Properties of Salt Solutions

Hydrochloric acid (HCl) and sodium hydroxide (NaOH) react to produce sodium chloride (NaCl) and water. A student mixes HCl and NaOH in equal molar amounts, so that they completely react with one another. Which of the following characteristics does the resulting solution most likely have?

A. It feels slippery.

B. It conducts electricity.

C. It turns red litmus paper blue.

D. It reacts with metals to produce hydrogen gas.

Solution

1 **Recall Relevant Information**   A salt produced by the reaction of a strong acid with a weak base will produce a slightly acidic solution when dissolved in water. A salt produced by the reaction of a strong base with a weak acid will produce a slightly basic solution when dissolved in water. A salt produced by the reaction of a strong acid with a strong base will produce a solution that is neither acidic nor basic. Hydrochloric acid is a strong acid, and sodium hydroxide is a strong base. Therefore, the resulting solution of NaCl in water should be neither acidic nor basic.

2 **Solve**   A slippery feel and the ability to turn red litmus paper blue are properties of bases, so choices A and C are incorrect. Production of hydrogen gas upon reaction with a metal is a property of an acid, so choice D is incorrect. All salt solutions conduct electricity, so choice B is the correct answer.

TIP

The cation in a salt comes from the parent base. The anion comes from the parent acid.

Common Acids and Bases	
Acids	**Bases**
Hydrochloric acid (HCl)	Sodium hydroxide (NaOH)
Sulfuric acid (H_2SO_4)	Potassium hydroxide (KOH)
Acetic (ethanoic) acid (CH_3COOH)	Calcium hydroxide ($Ca(OH)_2$)
Nitric acid (HNO_3)	Ammonia (NH_3)

Problem Set

1. Household ammonia is a dilute solution of ammonia, a base, in water. Identify two properties of household ammonia that you could use to confirm that it is a base.

2. Vinegar is a dilute solution of acetic acid. Identify two properties of vinegar that you could use to confirm that it is an acid.

3. Aspirin tastes sour if you allow it to dissolve on your tongue slightly. If you dissolved some aspirin in water, how would the solution affect red and blue litmus paper? Explain your answer.

4. Potassium hydroxide is a strong base. Phosphoric acid is a weak acid. When they react, they produce the salt potassium phosphate. Describe two likely characteristics of a solution of potassium phosphate in water.

5. **Challenge** Which salt would result if sodium hydroxide, NaOH, were neutralized by nitric acid, HNO_3?

6. **Challenge**   The liquid in your stomach is very acidic. People may take antacids to neutralize stomach acid when they have heartburn. What type of material is probably found in antacids? Explain your answer.

Arrhenius Acids and Bases

Svante Arrhenius was one of the first chemists to propose a formal definition of *acid* and *base*.

- Define acids and bases according to the Arrhenius method of classification.

Acids and bases play important roles in many chemical processes. There are many different ways to define *acid* and *base*. One of the most common definitions is the Arrhenius definition. According to the Arrhenius definition of acids and bases, an acid is a substance that dissociates to produce hydrogen ions (H^+) when dissolved in water. According to the Arrhenius definition, bases are substances that dissociate to produce hydroxide ions (OH^-) when dissolved in water. When an Arrhenius acid reacts with an Arrhenius base, they produce a solution of a salt in water.

EXAMPLE 1

Identify Arrhenius Acids and Bases

Which of these gives the chemical formula for an Arrhenius acid and an Arrhenius base?

- **A.** HNO_3, NH_3
- **B.** H_2SO_4, KOH
- **C.** CH_4, $NaOH$
- **D.** H_3PO_4, Na_2CO_3

REMEMBER

ARRHENIUS ACIDS AND BASES

- Arrhenius acids contain H^+ ions and produce H^+ ions when dissolved in water.

- Arrhenius bases contain OH^- ions and produce OH^- ions when dissolved in water.

Solution

1 Recall Definitions An Arrhenius acid must ionize to produce H^+ ions. An Arrhenius base must ionize to produce OH^- ions.

2 Apply Definitions HNO_3, H_2SO_4, and H_3PO_4 all release hydrogen ions in water, so they are all Arrhenius acids. KOH and $NaOH$ release hydroxide ions in water, so they are Arrhenius bases. Although NH_3 and Na_2CO_3 will increase the number of hydroxide ions in solution when they dissolve in water, they do not dissociate to produce hydroxide ions, so they are not Arrhenius bases. Although CH_4 contains hydrogen atoms, it will not dissociate in water, so it is not an Arrhenius acid.

3 Solve The only answer choice that contains an Arrhenius acid and an Arrhenius base is choice B. Sulfuric acid, H_2SO_4, dissociates to form H^+ ions in water according to the following equations:

$$H_2SO_4 \rightarrow H^+ + HSO_4^-$$
$$HSO_4^- \rightleftharpoons H^+ + SO_4^{2-}$$

Potassium hydroxide (KOH) dissociates to form OH^- ions in water according to the following equation:

$$KOH \rightarrow K^+ + OH^-$$

EXAMPLE 2

Describe the Formation of a Salt Solution from an Arrhenius Acid and Base

Write the chemical equation for the reaction between nitric acid (HNO_3) and any Arrhenius base. Identify the salt that forms during the reaction.

Solution

1 Identify Reactants   The formula for nitric acid is given, but we need to choose an Arrhenius base for the nitric acid to react with. A commonly used Arrhenius base is sodium hydroxide (NaOH). Therefore, the reactant side of our chemical equation will be the following:

$$HNO_3 + NaOH \rightarrow$$

2 Identify Products   To make it easier to identify the products of this reaction, write the reactants in their ionic forms, as shown below:

$$H^+_{(aq)} + NO^-_{3\ (aq)} + Na^+_{(aq)} + OH^-_{(aq)}$$

The hydrogen ion will react with the hydroxide ion to form water, leaving the Na^+ and NO_3^- ions in solution. Therefore, the products of the reaction will be H_2O, Na^+, and NO_3^-.

3 Solve   The balanced chemical equation for this reaction is shown below:

$$HNO_3 + NaOH \rightarrow H_2O + Na^+_{(aq)} + NO^-_{3\ (aq)}$$

Sodium nitrate, $NaNO_3$, will be the salt formed during this reaction.

Not all compounds that contain hydrogen atoms are Arrhenius acids. A substance is an Arrhenius acid only if it will *dissociate* to produce hydrogen ions when it is dissolved in water. For example, ethane (C_2H_6) contains six hydrogen atoms, but it is not an Arrhenius acid because it does not dissociate in water.

Problem Set

1. Which of the following substances are Arrhenius acids? Which are Arrhenius bases?
   - $HClO_4$
   - $NaCH_3COO$
   - HF
   - $Ca(OH)_2$
   - K_2CO_3
   - $Mg(OH)_2$

2. Write chemical equations to illustrate why HCl is considered an Arrhenius acid and KOH is considered an Arrhenius base.

3. Write the balanced chemical equation for the reaction between HBr and $Cu(OH)_2$. Name and write the formula for the salt formed during the reaction.

4. Write the chemical equation for the reaction of lithium hydroxide (LiOH) with an Arrhenius acid of your choosing. Name and write the formula for the salt formed during the reaction.

5. **Challenge**   Write chemical formulas for the Arrhenius acids that would produce each of the following salts when reacted with NaOH:
   - Na_3PO_4
   - $NaClO_4$
   - $Na_2C_2O_4$

6. **Challenge**   Water (H_2O) can be considered both an Arrhenius acid and an Arrhenius base. Write chemical equations to illustrate why this is so.

Brønsted-Lowry and Lewis Acids and Bases

The Arrhenius definitions of acid and base are not the only definitions used in chemistry. Two other commonly used definitions are the Brønsted-Lowry definition and the Lewis definition.

OBJECTIVE

- Identify and describe the Brønsted-Lowry and Lewis definitions of acids and bases.

According to the Brønsted-Lowry definition of acids and bases, an acid is a substance that can donate a proton (hydrogen ion) to another substance, and a base is a substance that can accept a proton from another substance. The Brønsted-Lowry acid-base definition leads to the concept of conjugate acids and conjugate bases. A conjugate acid is the species formed when a base accepts a proton. A conjugate base is the species formed when an acid donates a proton. The Lewis definition of acids and bases provides a more general definition compared to the other classification systems. A Lewis acid can form a covalent bond by accepting an electron pair from another species. A Lewis base can form a covalent bond by donating an electron pair to another chemical species.

EXAMPLE 1

Identify Brønsted-Lowry and Lewis Acids and Bases

Write a chemical equation to illustrate why ammonia (NH_3) is considered both a Brønsted-Lowry base and a Lewis base when it is dissolved in water. Identify the acid in the dissolution reaction.

Solution

1 Recall Definitions   According to the Brønsted-Lowry definition of acids and bases, a base is a species that accepts a proton, and an acid is a species that donates a proton. According to the Lewis definition of acids and bases, an acid is an electron-pair acceptor, and a base is an electron-pair donor.

2 Write the Chemical Equation   The reactants are ammonia and water. The products are ammonium ion and hydroxide ion. The balanced chemical reaction is shown below:

$$NH_3 + H_2O \rightarrow NH_4^+ + OH^-$$

3 Solve   In the reaction above, ammonia accepts a proton from water. Therefore, ammonia is a Brønsted-Lowry base, and water is a Brønsted-Lowry acid. When the ammonia accepts the proton from water, a covalent bond forms between the ammonia and the proton. The nitrogen in the ammonia donates an electron pair to the proton. Therefore, ammonia acts as a Lewis base, and the proton acts as a Lewis acid.

REMEMBER

BRØNSTED-LOWRY AND LEWIS ACIDS AND BASES

- In aqueous solution, Brønsted-Lowry acids and bases react with water molecules. The water molecules act as either acids or bases (accepting or donating protons).

- The Lewis definition of acids and bases is the most generalized. The Arrhenius and Brønsted-Lowry definitions generally apply only to aqueous solutions, situations in which ionization can occur, and situations in which hydrogen ions are present. The Lewis definition can also be applied to solids, gases, and nonaqueous solutions.

EXAMPLE 2

Identify Conjugate Acids and Bases

Identify whether each of the following species is a Brønsted-Lowry acid or base, and identify its conjugate base or acid: acetate ion (CH_3COO^-) carbonate ion (CO_3^{2-}) and bicarbonate ion (HCO_3^{2-}).

TIP

Conjugate acid-base pairs differ by the presence of a proton. The formula for the conjugate base of an acid is the formula for the acid minus a proton. The formula for the conjugate acid of a base is the formula for the base plus a proton.

Solution

1 Recall Definitions   According to the Brønsted-Lowry definition of acids and bases, a base is a species that accepts a proton, and an acid is a species that donates a proton. A base's conjugate acid is the species formed when the base accepts a proton. An acid's conjugate base is the species formed when the acid donates a proton.

2 Apply Definitions   All three ions are anions, so they could accept one (or more) protons to form neutral compounds. Neither acetate nor carbonate have any protons to donate, but bicarbonate contains one "free" proton.

3 Solve   Because all three species can accept a proton, they are all considered Brønsted-Lowry bases. The acetate ion's conjugate acid is acetic acid (CH_3COOH). The carbonate ion's conjugate acid is bicarbonate ion, (HCO_3^-). The bicarbonate ion's conjugate acid is carbonic acid (H_2CO_3). Because bicarbonate can donate a proton, it is also considered a Brønsted-Lowry acid. Its conjugate base is the carbonate ion. In other words, bicarbonate ion is both an acid and a base under the Brønsted-Lowry definitions. Scientists use the term *amphoteric* to describe compounds of this kind.

Problem Set

1. Give the conjugate base for each of the following acids: $H_2PO_4^-$, H_2Se, HNO_2, and $HAsO_4^{2-}$.

2. Explain why all Arrhenius acids can be considered Brønsted-Lowry acids.

3. Identify each of the following species as either a Brønsted-Lowry acid or base, and identify its conjugate base or acid: $HClO$, AsH_3, $H_2PO_4^-$, H_2O, and TeO_3^-.

4. For each of the following reactions, identify the reactant acting as the acid, the reactant acting as the base, and their respective conjugate bases and acids:

$$H_2S + CN^- \rightarrow HS^- + HCN$$
$$F^- + HSO_4^- \rightarrow HF + SO_4^{2-}$$

5. **Challenge**   Identify the Lewis acid and Lewis base in the following chemical reaction in aqueous solution, and draw Lewis dot structures of the reactants and products to support your answer:

$$BF_3 + F^- \rightarrow BF_4^-$$

(Hint: Draw the Lewis dot structures first.)

6. **Challenge**   Explain why NH_3 can act as a Lewis base, but NH_4^+ cannot. Explain why H_2O can act as a Brønsted-Lowry acid, but not as a Lewis acid.

Measuring Acids and Bases

Scientists use the pH scale to describe the acidity or alkalinity of solutions.

There are many different ways to define *acid* and *base*. The Arrhenius, Brønsted-Lowry, and Lewis definitions of acids and bases apply to specific chemical substances. In many cases, however, the question is whether a particular *solution*, rather than a particular chemical, is acidic or basic. One way to define an acidic or basic solution is by its reaction with litmus paper: Acidic solutions turn blue litmus paper red, and basic solutions turn red litmus paper blue. However, in most cases, a more quantitative method of determining the acidity or alkalinity of a solution is needed. Scientists use the pH scale to define quantitatively how acidic or basic a solution is. Solutions with pH values between 0 and 7 are said to be acidic. Solutions with pH values between 7 and 14 are said to be basic. Solutions with a pH value of 7 are said to be neutral.

EXAMPLE 1

Identify Acids, Bases, and Neutral Substances

Use the pH scale shown below to identify three acidic solutions, three basic solutions, and three solutions that are neutral or very close to neutral.

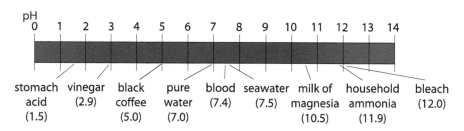

Solution

1 **Recall Definitions** A solution with a pH between 0 and 7 is acidic. A solution with a pH between 7 and 14 is basic. A solution with a pH of 7 is neutral.

2 **Solve** Stomach acid, vinegar, and black coffee have pH values of less than 7, so they are all acids. Milk of magnesia, household ammonia, and bleach have pH values of greater than 7, so they are all bases. Seawater, pure water, and blood have pH values very close to 7, so they are neutral or nearly neutral.

REMEMBER

MEASURING ACIDS AND BASES

- When an acid dissolves in water, it produces hydronium ions, (H_3O^+). For simplicity, these ions are often abbreviated as hydrogen ions, (H^+). However, it is important to remember that true H^+ ions do not exist in aqueous solution.

- Acidic substances have pH < 7, basic substances have pH > 7, and neutral substances have pH $= 7$.

- Water autoionizes according to the equation below: $2H_2O \rightleftharpoons H_3O^+ + OH^-$. In pure water, $[H_3O^+] = [OH^-] = 1 \times 10^{-7} M$. Therefore, the pH of pure water is 7, and a pH of 7 is defined as neutral.

EXAMPLE 2

Calculate pH from Hydronium Ion Concentration

On average, carbonated water has a hydronium ion concentration of about 1×10^{-4} M. (Remember that M is molarity, the number of moles of solute per liter of solution.) In contrast, a 0.1 M solution of sodium bicarbonate (baking soda, $NaHCO_3$) has a hydronium ion concentration of about 3.98×10^{-9} M. Calculate the pH of each solution, and identify whether it is acidic or basic.

Solution

1 **Recall Definitions**   By definition, the pH of a solution is equal to -1 times the base-10 logarithm of the hydronium ion concentration, as shown below:

$$pH = -\log[H_3O^+]$$

2 **Set Up Equations**   Substitute the given hydronium ion concentrations into the equation above. For carbonated water, the equation is as follows:

$$pH = -\log(1 \times 10^{-4})$$

For the sodium bicarbonate solution, the equation is $pH = -\log(3.98 \times 10^{-9})$. You will need a scientific calculator to calculate this, though you can estimate that the resulting pH will be less than 9.

3 **Solve**   The pH of carbonated water is $-\log(1 \times 10^{-4}) = -(-4) = 4$. The pH of the sodium bicarbonate solution is $-\log(3.98 \times 10^{-9}) = -(-8.4) = 8.4$. Therefore, the carbonated water is acidic, and the sodium bicarbonate solution is basic.

TIP

When the hydronium ion concentration of a solution is equal to one multiplied by a power of ten, the pH of the solution is equal to the negative of the power of ten. For example, the pH of a solution with a hydronium ion concentration of 1×10^{-9} M is 9.

EXAMPLE 3

Calculate Hydronium Ion Concentration from pH

A student measures the pH of pure water and finds it to be 7. The student adds some nitric acid (HNO_3) to the water, and the pH drops to 0.82. Calculate the hydronium ion concentration of the pure water and of the HNO_3 solution.

Solution

1 **Identify Equations**   Rearrange the equation describing pH to solve for the hydronium ion concentration, as shown below:

$$pH = -\log[H_3O^+]$$
$$-pH = \log[H_3O^+]$$
$$10^{-pH} = 10^{\log[H_3O^+]} = [H_3O^+]$$

2 **Solve**   Substitute the given pH values into the equation above. For pure water, the equation is as follows:

$$[H_3O^+] = 10^{-7} = 1 \times 10^{-7}\ M$$

For the nitric acid solution, the equation is as shown below:

$$[H_3O^+] = 10^{-0.82} = 1.5 \times 10^{-1}\ M$$

TIP

Always check to make sure your calculated answers are reasonable. For example, a solution of an acid should have a pH less than 7 and a hydronium ion concentration less than 1×10^{-7} M.

EXAMPLE 4

Calculate pH from Hydroxide Ion Concentration

A scientist makes a solution by dissolving 1.54×10^{-3} mol KOH in 1 L of pure water. The resulting solution has a hydroxide ion concentration of 1.54×10^{-3} M. Calculate the pH of the solution.

Solution

1 **Identify Relevant Concepts** To calculate the pH of the solution, you must know the hydronium ion concentration. Therefore, to solve this problem, you need a way to relate hydroxide ion concentration $[OH^-]$, to hydronium ion concentration $[H_3O^+]$. In aqueous solution at 25°C, this relationship is given by the equation below:

$$[OH^-][H_3O^+] = 1 \times 10^{-14}$$

Solve this equation for the hydronium ion concentration, as shown below:

$$[H_3O^+] = \frac{1 \times 10^{-14}}{[OH^-]}$$

Note that in this equation, the quantity 1×10^{-14} is defined to be exact.

2 **Calculate Hydronium Ion Concentration** Substitute the given hydroxide ion concentration into the equation above.

$$[H_3O^+] = \frac{1 \times 10^{-14}}{1.54 \times 10^{-3}} = 6.49 \times 10^{-12}$$

3 **Solve** Finally, calculate the pH of the solution using a scientific calculator.

$$pH = -\log[H_3O^+] = -\log(6.49 \times 10^{-12}) = -(-11.2) = 11.2$$

KOH is a strong base, so it makes sense that a solution of KOH would have a high pH.

The pH of a solution is always calculated from the hydronium ion concentration, even for solutions with very low concentrations of hydronium ions.

EXAMPLE 5

Interpret Graphs of Acids and Bases

A student progressively diluted a solution of HCl by adding water to it. The graph on the next page shows how the hydronium ion concentration of the solution changed as the student added the water. How did the pH of the solution change as the student diluted it? The final hydronium ion concentration of the solution was 1.94×10^{-5} M. What was the final pH of the solution?

Solution

1 **Strategize** To solve this problem, consider the relationship between pH and hydronium ion concentration. Then, use the pH equation to calculate the final pH of the solution.

You can use mathematical rules to estimate pH or hydronium ion concentration. For example, a solution with a pH between 3 and 4 must have a hydronium ion concentration between 10^{-4} and 10^{-3}. A solution with a hydronium ion concentration between 10^{-11} and 10^{-10} must have a pH between 10 and 11.

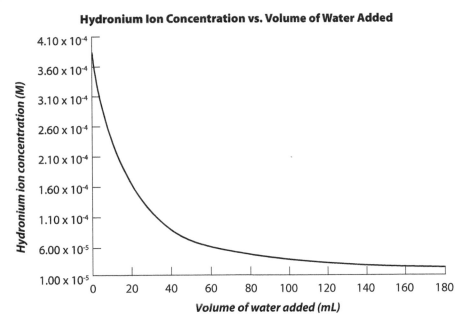

Hydronium Ion Concentration vs. Volume of Water Added

Volume of water added (mL)

TIP

Remember that negative powers of ten get smaller as the exponent gets more negative. For example, 10^{-3} is smaller than 10^{-2}.

2 **Solve** As the solution was diluted, the hydronium ion concentration decreased. The relationship between pH and hydronium ion concentration is an inverse one: As $[H_3O^+]$ decreases, pH increases. Therefore, as the student diluted the solution, its pH increased. The final hydronium ion concentration was $1.94 \times 10^{-5}\ M$, so you can estimate from the molarity above that the final pH is less than 5 but greater than 4. Use a scientific calculator to find that the final pH was $-\log(1.94 \times 10^{-5}) = -(-4.71) = 4.71$.

Problem Set

1. A solution of acetic acid has a hydronium ion concentration of $3.6 \times 10^{-6}\ M$. What is the pH of the solution?

2. The hydronium ion concentration of a solution of sodium sulfate (Na_2SO_4) is $3.61 \times 10^{-8}\ M$. State whether the solution is acidic or basic, **without** calculating its pH.

3. Typical cola soft drinks have pH values of about 2.8–3.4. What is the range of hydronium ion concentrations for cola soft drinks?

4. Assume that the pH of household bleach is 12. What is the hydronium ion concentration in household bleach? What is its hydroxide ion concentration?

5. Milk of magnesia, a common antacid, has a pH of 10.5. What is the hydroxide ion concentration in milk of magnesia?

6. A student has 100 mL of a 0.1 M solution of HCl. Its pH is 1. The student adds pure water, 100 mL at a time, until the volume of the solution is 2 L. Make a graph of pH vs. volume of water added for the solution.

7. **Challenge** A solution of hydrochloric acid has a pH of 2.5. The solution is diluted with water. Its final volume is 10 times greater than its initial volume. What is its final hydronium ion concentration?

8. **Challenge** For aqueous solutions at 25°C, pH + pOH = 14. What is the hydronium ion concentration of a solution with a pOH of 5.6 at 25°C?

9. **Challenge** Which is more acidic, a solution with a hydroxide ion concentration of $3.4 \times 10^{-3}\ M$ or one with a hydroxide ion concentration of $5.6 \times 10^{-8}\ M$? Answer without calculating the pH of either solution.

Titration

The concentration of an unknown acid or base solution can be determined by titration with a base or acid of known concentration.

A cid-base titration is a volumetric procedure for determining the amount of an acid or base present in a solution. A volumetric procedure is one in which the volumes of the different components are precisely measured. Acid-base titrations are most commonly used to determine the concentration of an acid or base solution. For example, you could titrate a solution of HCl of unknown concentration with a solution of NaOH of known concentration, adding the NaOH drop by drop. If you know exactly how much of the NaOH solution to add to the HCl solution to completely neutralize it, and you know the initial volume of the HCl solution, you can calculate the concentration of the HCl solution.

OBJECTIVE

- Describe how to use an acid-base titration to determine the concentration of an unknown solution.

EXAMPLE 1

Interpret a Titration Graph

The graph below shows how the pH of a solution of nitric acid (HNO_3) changed as NaOH was added to it drop by drop. At what point had the sodium hydroxide completely neutralized the nitric acid?

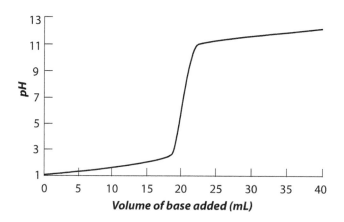

pH vs. Volume of Base Added

Solution

1 Recall Definitions   The acid is completely neutralized when all the hydronium ions have reacted with hydroxide ions to produce water—that is, when there are no excess hydronium or hydroxide ions in solution. By definition, this occurs at a pH of 7.

2 Solve   The pH of the solution reached 7 when 20 mL of base had been added, so that was the point at which all of the acid had been neutralized. After that point, the base that was added caused the pH to increase past 7.

REMEMBER

TITRATION

- An acid-base titration is a form of volumetric analysis.

- When performing a titration, you must know the concentration and chemical formula for the acid or base that is used as the titrant. It is also important to know the formula for the acid and base of unknown concentration.

- At the equivalence point of an acid-base titration, the number of moles of hydronium ions originally present is equal to the number of moles of hydroxide ions added.

- When titrating strong acids and bases, the pH at the equivalence point will be 7.

EXAMPLE 2

Calculate the Concentration of an Unknown Solution

A scientist has a solution of KOH of unknown concentration. She puts 25.0 mL of the KOH solution in a flask. She titrates the KOH solution with 0.0100 M HCl solution. It takes 13.6 mL of the HCl solution to reach the endpoint. What was the initial concentration of the KOH solution? Both chemicals dissociate completely.

Solution

1 Calculate Moles of Acid Added

$$13.6 \text{ mL HCl} \times \frac{0.0100 \text{ mol HCl}}{1 \text{ L HCl}} \times \frac{1 \text{ L}}{1,000 \text{ mL}} = 1.36 \times 10^{-4} \text{ mol HCl}$$

2 Calculate Moles of Base Present Every mole of KOH present in the solution will require one mole of HCl to neutralize it. Therefore, if the KOH solution required 1.36×10^{-4} mol HCl to neutralize it, there must have been 1.36×10^{-4} mol KOH in the solution to begin with.

3 Solve The concentration of the KOH solution is equal to the number of moles of KOH divided by the initial volume of the solution.

$$\frac{1.36 \times 10^{-4} \text{ mol KOH}}{25.0 \text{ mL}} \times \frac{1,000 \text{ mL}}{1 \text{ L}} = 5.44 \times 10^{-3} \text{ M KOH}$$

TIP

Always write out a chemical equation for the neutralization reaction that takes place during a titration, especially if you are dealing with an acid that has more than one proton. Take that into account in any calculations. For the example here, the neutralization reaction is the one shown below:

$$KOH + HCl \rightarrow KCl + H_2O$$

Problem Set

1. Sketch a graph of pH against volume of acid added for the titration of a solution of NaOH of unknown concentration with drops of HCl of known concentration.

2. A sample of 60.0 mL of 0.15 M HNO$_3$ is titrated with 0.500 M NaOH. What volume of NaOH is required to reach the equivalence point? Both chemicals dissociate completely in water.

3. If 22.4 mL of 0.0100 M HCl are required to completely react with 15.0 mL NaOH, what was the initial molarity of the NaOH solution?

4. Calculate the volume of 0.0500 M H$_2$SO$_4$ solution required to completely react with 20.0 mL of 1.00×10^{-3} M NaOH.

5. A student forgets to measure the volume of unknown solution she starts with during an acid-base titration. How will this affect her results?

6. If 15.6 mL of 0.100 M NaOH are required to reach the equivalence point with an HCl solution, what mass of HCl was present in the initial solution? (Hint: Calculate the molar mass of HCl.)

7. **Challenge** A student adds 0.05 M NaOH to a solution of HNO$_3$ of unknown concentration. He accidentally records too small a volume of NaOH. How will this affect his results?

8. **Challenge** If 12.8 mL of 0.100 M HCl are required to completely react with 30.0 mL of an NaOH solution, what was the pH of the solution after 5.00 mL of HCl had been added?

9. **Challenge** Determine the volume of 0.750 M HNO$_3$ required to completely react with all the NaOH in a solution prepared by dissolving 1.75 g of NaOH in 350 mL of water.

Strengths of Acids and Bases

An acid is considered to be strong or weak depending on its degree of dissociation in aqueous solution.

Strong acids and bases completely dissociate, or split into ions, in aqueous solution. In other words, 100 percent of the acid or base formula units that are placed in an aqueous solution will dissociate into their component ions. In contrast, a weak acid or base does not completely dissociate in water. Weak acids and bases are in dynamic equilibrium in aqueous solution. This means that, at any given time, only a certain percentage of the formula units are dissociated. It also means that the ions associate and dissociate constantly over time (this is why the equilibrium is called *dynamic*). Each weak acid and base has a unique dissociation constant (K_a for acids, K_b for bases), which tells the extent of dissociation for that particular acid or base in water. (K_a is called the *acid dissociation constant*, and K_b is called the *base dissociation constant*.) The larger a substance's K_a or K_b, the more the substance dissociates in aqueous solution.

OBJECTIVE

- Compare strong and weak acids and bases.

EXAMPLE 1

Compare Weak Acids

The K_a value for acetic acid (CH_3COOH) is 1.8×10^{-5}. The K_a value for hydrocyanic acid (HCN) is 6.2×10^{-10}. Which is the stronger acid?

Solution

1 **Write Chemical Equations**   First, write the chemical equation for the dissociation of each acid. These equations are shown below:

$$CH_3COOH_{(aq)} + H_2O_{(l)} \rightleftharpoons CH_3COO^-_{(aq)} + H_3O^+_{(aq)}$$

$$HCN_{(aq)} + H_2O_{(l)} \rightleftharpoons CN^-_{(aq)} + H_3O^+_{(aq)}$$

2 **Apply Formulas**   For the dissociation of a generic weak acid, HA, in water, the following equation gives the value of K_a for the acid:

$$K_a = \frac{[H_3O^+][A^-]}{[HA]}$$

This equation shows that acids with larger K_a values will produce higher concentrations of H_3O^+ when they dissolve in water. Therefore, acids with larger K_a values will produce greater reductions in pH than acids with smaller K_a values. This means that the larger an acid's K_a value is, the stronger the acid is.

3 **Solve**   Acetic acid's K_a value is much larger than hydrocyanic acid's K_a value. This means that acetic acid will dissociate more than hydrocyanic acid in water. Acetic acid is therefore a stronger acid than hydrocyanic acid.

REMEMBER

STRENGTHS OF ACIDS AND BASES

- Strong acids and bases dissociate completely in aqueous solution.

- Weak acids and bases do not dissociate completely in aqueous solution.

- The acid or base ionization constant (sometimes termed the *dissociation constant* or *equilibrium constant*) tells the degree of dissociation of a weak acid or base in water.

- The larger the K_a or K_b value, the stronger the weak acid or base and the greater its degree of dissociation in water.

TIP

The dissociation of a generic acid, HA, in water is represented by the chemical equation shown below:

$$HA + H_2O \rightleftharpoons A^- + H_3O^+$$

EXAMPLE 2

Compare Strong and Weak Bases

Ammonia (NH_3) is a weak base. Sodium hydroxide (NaOH) is a strong base. Write chemical equations for the dissolution of each base in water, and predict the relative sizes of their K_b and pK_b values.

Solution

1 **Recall Relevant Information** In a chemical equation, a single-headed arrow indicates a reaction that proceeds only in one direction, and a double-headed arrow indicates a reaction that is in equilibrium. The pK_b value of a base is equal to -1 times the base-ten logarithm of the base's K_b value, as shown in the equation below:

$$pK_b = -\log(K_b)$$

The larger the K_b of a given base, the smaller its pK_b value will be.

2 **Solve** Ammonia will partially dissociate in water, so the chemical equation describing its dissolution will include a double-headed arrow, as shown below:

$$NH_{3\,(g)} + H_2O_{(l)} \rightleftharpoons NH^+_{4\,(aq)} + OH^-_{(aq)}$$

In contrast, sodium hydroxide will dissociate completely in water to yield hydroxide ions and sodium ions, as shown below:

$$NaOH_{(s)} \rightarrow Na^+_{(aq)} + OH^-_{(aq)}$$

Sodium hydroxide is a strong base, and ammonia is a weak base. Therefore, sodium hydroxide's K_b value will be much larger than ammonia's, and sodium hydroxide's pK_b value will be much smaller than ammonia's.

TIP

In the same way that you can calculate a pK_b value for a weak base, you can calculate a pK_a value for a weak acid:

$$pK_a = -\log(K_a)$$

Problem Set

1. Put the following weak acids in order from strongest to weakest: benzoic acid ($K_a = 6.3 \times 10^{-5}$), methanoic acid ($K_a = 1.8 \times 10^{-4}$), hypochlorous acid ($K_a = 2.9 \times 10^{-8}$).

2. Write chemical equations for the dissociation of the strong acid HCl and the weak acid HOCl in water.

3. A student makes $1\,M$ solutions of nitric acid (HNO_3), which is a strong acid, and nitrous acid (HNO_2), which is a weak acid. Which solution will have the lowest pH? Explain your answer.

4. The pK_a of HN_3 is 4.7. What is its K_a? Use a scientific calculator.

5. Use a scientific calculator to calculate the pK_a of acetic acid and the pK_b of methylamine (CH_3NH_2). Acetic acid's K_a is 1.8×10^{-5}. Methylamine's K_a is 4.2×10^{-4}.

6. Put the following weak bases in order from strongest to weakest: ammonia ($pK_b = 4.74$), urea ($pK_b = 13.8$), dimethylamine ($pK_b = 3.23$).

7. **Challenge** Strong acids are sometimes said to have K_a values that approach infinity. Use a chemical equation and the equation for K_a to explain why this is true.

8. **Challenge** Polyprotic acids, such as phosphoric acid (H_3PO_4), can undergo multiple dissociations in water, so they have more than one K_a. Predict whether H_3PO_4 or $H_2PO_4^-$ has the larger K_a. Explain your answer.

9. **Challenge** A solution of the weak acid isocyanic acid (HOCN) has a pH of 5.2. What is the concentration of OCN^- ions in the solution?

The Conservation of Energy

Energy can change forms and be transferred from one system to another, but it can never be created or destroyed.

According to the first law of thermodynamics, it is impossible to create or destroy energy. This is known as the law of conservation of energy. However, energy can be transferred or transformed. In other words, energy can move from one place to another, or it can change from one form to another. The transfer and transformation of energy drives all chemical reactions, physical changes, and other processes in the universe.

EXAMPLE 1

Identify Endothermic and Exothermic Processes

Identify which of the following processes are exothermic and which are endothermic:

- When NaOH pellets dissolve in a beaker full of water, the beaker becomes warm.
- When barium chloride ($BaCl_2$) and ammonium nitrate (NH_4NO_3) are mixed together in a beaker, the beaker gets cold.
- A piece of ice melts when it is placed in a warm room.
- A piece of wood burns in a campfire.

Solution

1 Recall Relevant Information During an exothermic process, heat is released to the surroundings. During an endothermic process, heat is absorbed from the surroundings. Therefore, during an exothermic process, the system loses heat, and the surroundings gain heat and become warmer. During an endothermic process, the system gains heat, and the surroundings lose heat and become cooler.

2 Apply In the first and fourth processes, the surroundings become warmer. In the second and third processes, the surroundings become cooler.

3 Solve The first and fourth processes release heat, so they are exothermic. The second and third processes absorb heat, so they are endothermic.

OBJECTIVE

- Compare endothermic and exothermic processes.

REMEMBER

THE CONSERVATION OF ENERGY

- Energy released from chemical bonds can be stored in other chemical bonds, used to do physical work, or released to the environment as heat.

- The energy released from chemical bonds can be transferred to other systems in different forms, but the total energy found in the different forms will never be more than the original amount released.

- If a given chemical reaction is exothermic, the reverse reaction is endothermic, and vice versa.

TIP

In general, if the surroundings become warmer as a process occurs, the process is exothermic, and if they become cooler, the process is endothermic. However, the actual substances undergoing the process may not change in temperature as the process occurs. For example, the temperature of ice does not change as it melts.

EXAMPLE 2

Describe Energy Changes During Chemical Reactions

The following chemical reaction is exothermic:

$$CH_4 + 2O_2 \rightarrow CO_2 + 2H_2O$$

Which contain more energy, the reactants or the products? What happens to that energy during the reaction?

TIP

If a reaction is exothermic, the reactants contain more energy than the products. If a reaction is endothermic, the products contain more energy than the reactants.

Solution

1 **Recall Relevant Information** An exothermic reaction is one that releases heat. Compounds store energy in chemical bonds. During this reaction, C–H bonds and O–O bonds break, and C–O and H–O bonds form.

2 **Solve** Because an exothermic reaction releases heat, the reactants must have more energy than the products. Both reactants and products store energy in the form of chemical bonds. For the reaction to release energy, the total energy stored in the C–H and O–O bonds in the reactants must be greater than the total energy stored in the C–O and H–O bonds in the products. So, during the reaction, some of the energy stored in the bonds in the reactants is released, and the rest of it is stored in the bonds in the products.

Problem Set

1. Is evaporation an endothermic process or an exothermic process? Explain your answer.

2. A student places a piece of magnesium metal in a test tube containing a small amount of hydrochloric acid. As the magnesium reacts with the acid, the test tube becomes very hot. Is this an endothermic reaction or an exothermic reaction? Explain your answer.

3. What does the law of conservation of energy imply about the total amount of energy in the universe? Explain your answer.

4. The bonds in the reactants of a chemical reaction store 673 kJ of potential energy. The bonds in the products of the reaction store 872 kJ of potential energy. Is the reaction endothermic or exothermic? Explain your answer.

5. **Challenge** During the process of photosynthesis, plants convert carbon dioxide and water into sugar and oxygen. When sugar reacts with oxygen to produce carbon dioxide and water, the reaction releases a great deal of heat. Is photosynthesis an endothermic process or an exothermic process? Explain your answer.

6. **Challenge** The following chemical reaction releases 180.50 kJ of energy:

$$N_{2\,(g)} + O_{2\,(g)} \rightarrow 2NO_{(g)}$$

How many kilojoules of energy are required to convert 4 mol $NO_{(g)}$ into $N_{2\,(g)}$ and $O_{2\,(g)}$?

Measuring the Flow of Heat

Heat is energy that flows from one object to another because of a difference in temperature between the two objects.

When a substance releases heat and cools down, its atoms or molecules slow down. When a substance absorbs heat and warms up, its atoms or molecules move more quickly. Heat flows only from warmer objects or regions to cooler objects or regions. It can never flow from cooler areas to warmer areas. Because heat is a form of energy, scientists use the joule (J), the SI unit of energy, to describe quantities of heat. Scientists also sometimes use the unit the calorie (cal) to describe quantities of heat. One calorie is the amount of energy required to increase the temperature of one gram of liquid water by one degree Celsius. One calorie is equal to 4.186 J.

OBJECTIVE

• Understand that heat is a form of energy that can be transferred between objects.

EXAMPLE 1

Describe Heat Transfer

A student places a metal cube with a temperature of 95°C into a beaker of water with a temperature of 20°C. Describe the heat transfer that will occur, and describe what will happen to the metal atoms and the water molecules as a result.

Solution

1 **Recall Relevant Information**   Heat moves only from warmer objects to cooler ones. When atoms or molecules absorb heat, they move more quickly. When they lose heat, they move more slowly.

2 **Solve**   The metal is warmer than the water, so heat will move from the metal to the water. As the metal loses heat, its temperature will decrease, and the atoms in it will move more slowly. As the water absorbs heat, its temperature will rise, and the molecules in it will move more quickly. The pictures below show the relative motions of the metal atoms and the water molecules before and after the heat transfer has occurred.

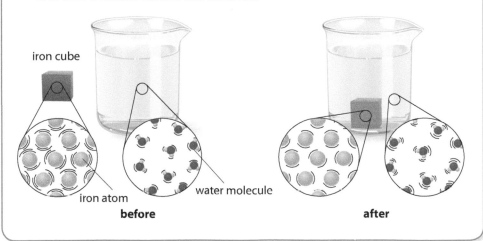

iron cube

iron atom

water molecule

before

after

REMEMBER

HEAT FLOW

• Heat is one form of energy. Light, mechanical, electrical, and chemical energy are other forms of energy.

• Heat manifests itself in substances through molecular motion.

• Heat naturally flows from a warmer object to a cooler one.

TIP

Mechanical devices can move heat from cooler areas to warmer areas. For example, a refrigerator moves heat from within the refrigerator to the room in which the refrigerator is located. However, these devices must use energy to move heat from a cooler area to a warmer one.

EXAMPLE 2

Describe Molecular Motion Caused by Heat Flow

A solid piece of iron absorbs heat until it melts at 1,535°C. The liquid iron continues to absorb heat until it boils and becomes a gas at 2,750°C. Describe how the motions of the iron atoms change as the iron absorbs heat.

Solution

1 **Recall Relevant Information**   At any temperature above absolute zero, the atoms in matter are moving. In a solid, the atoms can only vibrate in place. In a liquid, they can slide past one another. In a gas, they are free to move in any direction. When matter absorbs heat, its atoms move more quickly.

2 **Solve**   As the solid iron absorbs heat, the iron atoms begin to vibrate more quickly. Eventually, they have absorbed enough heat to break the metallic bonding holding them in place, and they begin to move past one another. When this occurs, the iron melts. As the liquid iron absorbs more heat, the iron atoms begin to move even more quickly. Eventually, they gain enough energy to escape from the liquid. At that point, the iron begins to boil, and it becomes a gas.

TIP

The atoms or molecules in a liquid have enough energy to break the bonds that are holding them in fixed positions, but not enough energy to break completely free of the electrostatic attractions between them. Therefore, they are free to move around, but only within a certain area. That is why a liquid has a fixed volume, but not a fixed shape.

Problem Set

1. A student places a sphere of plastic with a temperature of –15°C into a flask of oil with a temperature of 60°C. Describe the heat transfer that will occur, and describe what will happen to the plastic and oil molecules as a result.

2. Describe how the motions of the molecules in liquid water change as the water is cooled to below the freezing point.

3. A student places a metal sphere with a temperature of 98°C into a container of water with a temperature of 50°C. The container is perfectly insulated, and there is no other source of energy in the system. Which of these is most likely the temperature of the water after the sphere and the water have reached thermal equilibrium?
   A. 40°C   **B.** 50°C
   C. 70°C   **D.** 100°C

4. A scientist combines two chemicals in a flask, and then places the flask into a beaker of water. The chemicals undergo an endothermic reaction within the flask. The water does not interact directly with the chemicals in the flask. Describe what will happen to the water. Explain your answer.

5. **Challenge**   A student places a drop of rubbing alcohol on her arm. As the alcohol evaporates, her skin begins to feel cooler. Explain this observation in terms of heat flow.

6. **Challenge**   Explain why water droplets form on the outside of a sealed container of ice placed in a warm room.

Specific Heat

The specific heat of a substance is a measure of the amount of heat necessary to raise the temperature of a sample of the substance.

Specific heat (C_p), also called specific heat capacity, is defined as the quantity of heat that is required to raise the temperature of one gram of a substance by one degree Celsius at a specific pressure. The specific heat of liquid water is relatively high compared to that of many other substances. This high specific heat is one of the reasons that earth's climate is relatively moderate. Earth's oceans absorb and store a great deal of heat from the sun during the day. They release it slowly at night, keeping temperatures relatively stable.

OBJECTIVE

- Perform calculations involving specific heat and heat transfer.

EXAMPLE 1

Calculate the Initial Temperature of a Substance

A student dropped a 25.0 g cylinder of aluminum into a foam cup containing 100.0 g of water at 25.0°C. The final temperature of the water and aluminium was 28.0°C. What was the initial temperature of the aluminum cylinder? The specific heat of aluminum is 0.90 J/g · °C. The specific heat of water is 4.186 J/g · °C.

Solution

❶ **Collect and Strategize** First, calculate the amount of heat the water gained. Then, use that information to determine what the initial temperature of the aluminum must have been. The following information is given:

temperature change of water = 28.0°C − 25.0°C = 3.0°C

mass of aluminum = 25.0 g

mass of water = 100.0 g

The equation relating heat (q), specific heat (C_p), mass (m), and temperature change (ΔT) is shown below:

$$q = mC_p \Delta T$$

First, calculate the heat gained by the water.

$$q_{water} = (100.0\,g)(4.18\,J/g \cdot °C)(3.0\,°C) = 1.3 \times 10^3\,J$$

❷ **Solve** The water gained 1.3×10^3 J of energy, so the aluminum must have lost the same amount of energy. Now, solve the specific heat equation for ΔT. Remember that, because the aluminum lost heat, the value for q in the equation must be negative.

$$q_{Al} = m_{Al}C_{P,Al}\Delta T_{Al}$$

$$\Delta T_{Al} = \frac{q_{Al}}{m_{Al}C_{P,Al}} = \frac{-1.3 \times 10^3\,J}{(25.0\,g)(0.90\,J/g \cdot °C)} = -58°C$$

The aluminum's temperature decreased by 58°C, so its initial temperature must have been 28°C + 58°C = 86°C.

REMEMBER

SPECIFIC HEAT

- The specific heat of a substance is a characteristic property of that substance, and it does not depend on the amount of the substance.

- The larger the specific heat of a substance is, the more energy must be added to raise the temperature of a given amount of that substance, and the more heat a given amount of that substance can store.

- In general, metals have fairly low specific heats. Water has a relatively high specific heat.

TIP

Remember that heat cannot be created or destroyed. Therefore, in a closed system any heat lost by one object or substance must be gained by another object or substance: $-q_{lost} = q_{gained}$.

EXAMPLE 2

Determine the Specific Heat for a Substance

When a 10.0 g cube of an unknown metal gains 25.0 J of heat, the temperature of the metal cube increases by 5.57°C. What is the identity of the metal?

Substance	Specific Heat (J/g · °C)
Aluminum	0.90
Copper	0.39
Iron	0.46
Silver	0.24
Methyl alcohol	2.47

Solution

1 Collect and Strategize Use the equation relating heat, specific heat, mass, and temperature change to calculate the specific heat of the substance. Then, compare the specific heat with the values in the table of specific heats shown to the right. The following information is given in the problem:

mass of metal = 10.0 g

heat gained = 25.0 J

temperature change = 5.57°C

2 Solve First, solve the equation for C_p, the specific heat of the metal.

$$q = mC_p\Delta T$$

$$C_p = \frac{q}{m\Delta T}$$

Now, substitute the given values and solve for C_p.

$$C_p = \frac{25.0\ J}{(10.0\ g)(5.57°C)} = 0.449\ J/g \cdot °C$$

Compare this value to those in the table. Only iron has a specific heat near this value. Therefore, the metal must be iron.

Problem Set

1. A student drops a 15.2 g sphere of copper into a beaker containing 150.0 g of water. The initial temperature of the water is 23.00°C. The final temperature of the water and copper is 23.60°C. If the container is perfectly insulated, how much heat (in joules) does the copper lose?

2. A scientist adds 46.3 J of heat to a 13.4 g sample of an unknown substance. The temperature increases by 1.40°C. What is the specific heat of the substance? From the table on this page, determine what the substance is.

3. A cook uses an aluminum fork with a mass of 25.0 g to stir a pot of boiling water. The fork's temperature increases by 3.00°C. How much heat does the fork absorb?

4. An iron sphere with a mass of 80.0 g and an initial temperature of 5.00°C is placed into water at 80.0°C. The final temperature of the system is 78.0°C. If the system is perfectly insulated, what is the mass of the water?

5. A scientist adds the same amount of heat to 50.0 g of water and 10.0 g of silver. Which material's temperature will increase the most? Use the table above. Explain your answer.

6. A scientist suspects that an unknown liquid is water. She adds 100.0 J of heat to 50.0 g of the liquid, and its temperature increases by 2.5°C. Is the liquid water? Explain your answer.

7. **Challenge** A 45.0 g sample of silver has an initial temperature of 80.0°C. It is placed in 80.4 g of water at 15.0°C. If the system is perfectly insulated, what will its equilibrium temperature be?

8. **Challenge** An 85.0 g cube of iron at 150.0°C is enclosed in 45.0 g of copper at 200.0°C. If the system is perfectly insulated, what will its final temperature be?

9. **Challenge** Why is it important to specify whether a system is perfectly insulated when performing specific heat calculations?

Changes in Enthalpy

The enthalpy change of a reaction is the difference between the heat content of the products and that of the reactants.

All chemical reactions either absorb or release heat. The heat gained or lost during a chemical reaction is the difference in heat content, or enthalpy, of the products and the reactants. Scientists use the symbol H to represent enthalpy. There's no way to directly measure the enthalpy of a substance. Instead, scientists generally study changes in enthalpy, represented by the symbol ΔH. The enthalpy change for a process is the amount of heat absorbed or released during the process. Processes that release heat (exothermic processes) have negative ΔH values, and processes that absorb heat (endothermic processes) have positive ΔH values.

OBJECTIVE
- Identify the change in enthalpy in a system during a chemical or physical change.

EXAMPLE 1

Interpret a Diagram in Terms of Enthalpy Changes

The graph below shows how the temperature of a pure substance changes as heat is added to it:

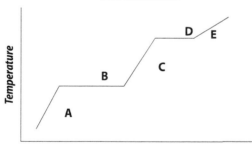

Temperature vs. Amount of Heat Added to a Substance

Describe what is happening and identify the sign of the enthalpy change in each part of the graph as the amount of heat added increases.

Solution

1 **Recall Relevant Information** Reactions in which ΔH is positive are endothermic, and reactions in which ΔH is negative are exothermic. An endothermic reaction is one in which heat energy must enter the system in order for the reaction to proceed. An exothermic reaction releases energy. Melting and boiling are both endothermic processes. During a phase change, the temperature of a substance does not change, even though that substance is gaining or losing heat.

REMEMBER

CHANGES IN ENTHALPY
- Every reaction has associated with it a value for the change in enthalpy (ΔH).
- The ΔH value for a reaction is positive if the reaction is endothermic (absorbs heat from its surroundings). It is negative if the reaction is exothermic (releases heat to its surroundings).

TIP

Remember to put yourself "in the system" when thinking about the direction of heat flow. In an endothermic reaction, heat is coming into the system. In an exothermic reaction, heat is leaving the system.

② **Analyze the Graph**   In segments A, C, and E, the temperature of the substance is increasing as heat is added. In segments B and D, the temperature of the substance does not change, even though heat is being added.

③ **Solve**   In segment B, the substance is changing from a solid to a liquid (that is, it is melting). In segment D, the substance is boiling and changing from a liquid to a gas. During the entire process, the substance is absorbing heat, so the ΔH must be positive for each segment of the graph.

Problem Set

1. Which one of the following statements most likely describes a process with a positive ΔH value?
   A. Water in a pot on a stove begins to boil.
   B. Solid lithium explodes and burns when it is placed in water.
   C. Lava erupts at earth's surface and freezes to a solid almost immediately.
   D. Concentrated sulfuric acid is mixed with water and the container becomes warm.

2. Predict the sign of ΔH for the condensation of water vapor (a gas) to liquid water. Explain your answer.

3. The diagram below represents a chemical reaction. What is the sign of ΔH for this reaction? Explain your answer.

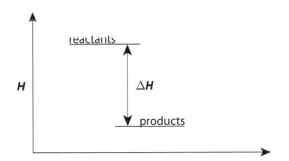

4. Explain why exothermic processes have negative ΔH values, but endothermic processes have positive ΔH values. (Hint: Remember that the change in a quantity is defined as the final value of the quantity minus the initial value of the quantity.)

5. **Challenge**   When hydrogen gas combusts (burns) in oxygen gas, water forms. The reaction is very exothermic, as shown below:

   $$2H_{2\,(g)} + O_{2\,(g)} \rightarrow 2H_2O_{(l)} \qquad \Delta H = -571.6 \text{ kJ}$$

   Predict the value (with correct sign) of ΔH for the formation of 1 mol H_2 and 0.5 mol O_2 from 1 mol H_2O. Explain your answer.

6. **Challenge**   The ecosystems on land and in the upper parts of the oceans are based on organisms that carry out photosynthesis, using energy from the sun to convert oxygen and carbon dioxide to sugar and water. In areas deep below the ocean surface, entire ecosystems are based on chemosynthetic organisms. There is no light deep below the ocean surface, so the organisms at the base of these food chains use energy from chemical reactions to produce food. Do photosynthesis and chemosynthesis have positive or negative ΔH values? Explain your answer.

Writing Thermochemical Equations

Thermochemical equations provide all the necessary information for determining the amount and direction of heat flow during a chemical reaction.

A thermochemical equation is a chemical equation that shows the enthalpy change (ΔH) for the reaction. The change in enthalpy is written after the written chemical equation. The sign of ΔH tells you if the reaction is endothermic or exothermic. You can use thermochemical equations to predict the amount of heat that will be lost or absorbed during chemical reactions.

OBJECTIVE

- Use thermochemical equations to describe heat flow during chemical reactions.

EXAMPLE 1

Calculate ΔH for a Net Reaction

The reaction between hydrogen gas and oxygen gas can be written in the following way:

$$2H_{2\,(g)} + O_{2\,(g)} \rightarrow 2H_2O_{(l)} \qquad \Delta H_{rxn} = -571.6 \text{ kJ}$$

This reaction actually occurs in two steps, as shown by the equations below:

equation 1: $2H_{2\,(g)} + O_{2\,(g)} \rightarrow 2H_2O_{(g)}$ $\qquad \Delta H_1 = -483.6 \text{ kJ}$

equation 2: $\qquad 2H_2O_{(g)} \rightarrow 2H_2O_{(l)}$ $\qquad \Delta H_2 = ? \text{ kJ}$

What is the enthalpy of reaction for the condensation of water vapor in this reaction?

Solution

1 **Collect and Strategize** When added together, the two component equations yield the net equation, as shown below:

$$\begin{array}{r} 2H_{2\,(g)} + O_{2\,(g)} \rightarrow \cancel{2H_2O_{(g)}} \\ + \qquad \cancel{2H_2O_{(g)}} \rightarrow 2H_2O_{(l)} \\ \hline 2H_{2\,(g)} + O_{2\,(g)} \rightarrow 2H_2O_{(l)} \end{array}$$

The total enthalpy change for the sum of two or more chemical reactions is equal to the sum of the enthalpy changes for the component reactions. Therefore, $\Delta H_1 + \Delta H_2 = \Delta H_{rxn}$, where ΔH_{rxn} is the enthalpy of the overall reaction, and $\Delta H_2 = \Delta H_{rxn} - \Delta H_1$.

2 **Solve** Substituting the values given above into the equation for ΔH_2 yields the following:

$$\Delta H_2 = \Delta H_{rxn} - \Delta H_1$$

$$\Delta H_2 = -571.6 \text{ kJ} - (-483.6 \text{ kJ})$$

$$\Delta H_2 = -88.0 \text{ kJ}$$

REMEMBER

WRITING THERMOCHEMICAL EQUATIONS

- A thermochemical equation is based on the reaction of a given number of moles of substance. The ΔH for a reaction is specific to the number of moles of reactant shown in the thermochemical equation. For example, if you double the number of moles that react, you also double the ΔH.

- The physical states of substances are important in thermochemical equations. Changing the state of either reactants or products will change the value and possibly even the sign of ΔH for the reaction.

- If a reaction is reversed, the sign of ΔH for the reaction is also reversed.

EXAMPLE 2

Predict ΔH for a Reaction

Consider the reaction shown below:

$$2Na_{(s)} + 2H_2O_{(l)} \rightarrow 2NaOH_{(aq)} + H_{2\ (g)} \qquad \Delta H = -367.5 \text{ kJ}$$

Calculate the ΔH value for the reaction between 4 mol $NaOH_{(aq)}$ and 2 mol $H_{2\ (g)}$. Will heat be absorbed or released during the reaction?

Solution

1 **Recall Relevant Information** Reversing the direction of a reaction requires reversal of the sign of ΔH, and changing the amount of reactants requires a modification of the given value of ΔH.

2 **Apply** The reaction between NaOH and H_2 is the reverse of the equation above, as shown below:

$$2NaOH_{(aq)} + H_{2\ (g)} \rightarrow 2Na_{(s)} + 2H_2O_{(l)} \qquad -\Delta H = 367.5 \text{ kJ}$$

The ΔH value above is for a reaction that consumes 2 mol NaOH. You must double the ΔH value for a reaction consuming 4 mol NaOH.

3 **Solve** Doubling the ΔH value of the reaction in Step 2 yields 367.5 kJ $\times$ 2 = 735.0 kJ, so the ΔH value for the reaction of 4 mol NaOH with 2 mol H_2 is 735.0 kJ. This is a positive ΔH value, so heat will be absorbed during the reaction.

Remember that the ΔH value for a reaction is always the ΔH for the reaction *as written*. Any changes to the chemical reaction will affect the value of ΔH.

Problem Set

1. The reaction of 1 mol of iron metal with 3 mol aqueous HCl produces 1.5 mol H_2 gas, 1 mol aqueous $FeCl_3$, and 87.9 kJ of heat. Write a thermochemical equation for this reaction.

2. A chemist must add 3,352 kJ of heat to 2 mol solid Al_2O_3 to cause it to break down to form 4 mol solid Al and 3 mol gaseous O_2. Write the thermochemical equation for this reaction.

3. Consider the reaction below:
   $$N_{2\ (g)} + O_{2\ (g)} \rightarrow 2NO_{(g)} \qquad \Delta H = 180.5 \text{ kJ}$$
   How much heat would be required to produce 1.300 mol $NO_{(g)}$?

4. One mol $CH_{4\ (g)}$ reacts with 2 mol $O_{2\ (g)}$ to produce 1 mol $CO_{2\ (g)}$, 2 mol $H_2O_{(l)}$, and 890 kJ of heat. Write a thermochemical equation for the reaction of 3 mol $CH_{4\ (g)}$ with $O_{2\ (g)}$.

5. Consider the reaction below:
   $$C_6H_{6\ (l)} \rightarrow C_6H_{6\ (s)} \qquad \Delta H = -9.87 \text{ kJ}$$
   How much energy is required to melt 3.5 mol $C_6H_{6\ (s)}$?

6. A chemist produces PCl_3 according to the following reaction:
   $$2P_{(s)} + 3Cl_{2\ (g)} \rightarrow 2PCl_{3\ (g)} \qquad \Delta H = -574 \text{ kJ}$$
   How many moles of phosphorus are required to produce 156 kJ of heat?

7. **Challenge** Given the following chemical equation, calculate the amount of heat absorbed when 36.0 g $H_2O_{(s)}$ melts:
   $$H_2O_{(l)} \rightarrow H_2O_{(s)} \qquad \Delta H = -6.01 \text{ kJ}$$

8. **Challenge** Consider the following chemical reactions:
   $$C_{(s)} + 2S_{(s)} \rightarrow CS_{2\ (l)}$$
   $$C_{(s)} + 2S_{(s)} \rightarrow CS_{2\ (s)}$$
   Which reaction will have the larger ΔH value? Explain your answer.

9. **Challenge** Consider the reaction below:
   $$2NaHCO_{3\ (s)} \rightarrow Na_2CO_{3\ (s)} + H_2O_{(g)} + CO_{2\ (g)}$$
   $$\Delta H = 129 \text{ kJ}$$
   Would this reaction be more spontaneous in a warm room or a supercooled freezer? Explain your answer.

Heat During Changes of State

During a change in state, a substance absorbs or releases heat, but its temperature does not change.

Because a change in phase requires a change in the internal energy of a chemical system, heat must either be given off or absorbed for the state change to occur. When a substance goes from a more organized state to a more disorganized state (for example, from ice to liquid water), the system must take in energy. In contrast, when a substance goes from a more disorganized state to a more organized state, the substance releases heat. The temperature of a substance does not change during a phase change because all the heat it is absorbing or releasing goes into the act of changing its state, rather than increasing its temperature. The heat of fusion (ΔH_{fus}) for a substance is the amount of heat required to change one mole of the substance from a solid to a liquid. The heat of vaporization (ΔH_{vap}) for a substance is the amount of heat required to change one mole of the substance from a liquid to a gas.

EXAMPLE 1

Calculate Heat Flow During Freezing

How much heat is released when 2.40 mol $H_2O_{(l)}$ freezes? ΔH_{fus} for H_2O is 6.01 kJ/mol.

Solution

1 Collect and Strategize First, write the chemical equation for the reaction.

$$2.40H_2O_{(l)} \rightarrow 2.40H_2O_{(s)} \qquad \Delta H = ?$$

The heat of fusion of water, which is the ΔH for the following reaction, is given:

$$H_2O_{(s)} \rightarrow H_2O_{(l)} \qquad \Delta H_{fus} = 6.01 \text{ kJ}$$

To calculate the unknown ΔH, first convert the heat of fusion of water into a heat of reaction for the freezing of one mole of liquid water. Then, use that ΔH value to calculate the heat released by the freezing of 2.40 mol H_2O.

2 Solve Freezing is the opposite of melting, so the heat of reaction for freezing will be the negative of the heat of fusion for ice.

$$H_2O_{(l)} \rightarrow H_2O_{(s)} \qquad \Delta H_{fus} = -6.01 \text{ kJ}$$

So, freezing 1 mol H_2O releases 6.01 kJ of heat. Therefore, freezing 2.40 mol H_2O will release 2.40×6.01 kJ = 14.4 kJ.

EXAMPLE 2

Calculate ΔH for a State Change

How much heat must be added to 8.92 g of water to cause it to evaporate completely? ΔH_{vap} for water is 40.7 kJ/mol.

TIP

The molar mass of a compound is equal to the sum of the molar masses of its constituent elements.

Solution

1. **Collect and Strategize** The heat of vaporization is the ΔH for the reaction below:

   $$H_2O_{(l)} \rightarrow H_2O_{(g)} \qquad \Delta H_{vap} = 40.7 \text{ kJ}$$

   The heat of vaporization is given for one mole of water. First, convert the given mass of water to moles of water. Then, use ΔH_{vap} for water to calculate the heat necessary for the state change. The molar mass of water is 18.015 g/mol.

2. **Solve** Use a conversion factor to convert grams to moles.

   $$8.92 \text{ g} \times \frac{1 \text{ mol}}{18.015 \text{ g}} = 0.495 \text{ mol}$$

   Now, set up an equality to calculate ΔH.

   $$\frac{0.495 \text{ mol}}{1 \text{ mol}} = \frac{x}{40.7 \text{ kJ}}$$

   $$x = (0.495)(40.7 \text{ kJ}) = 20.1 \text{ kJ}$$

Problem Set

1. The heat of fusion for ammonia is 5.65 kJ/mol. How much heat is released when 1.5 mol of ammonia freezes?

2. The heat of vaporization for O_2 is 6.82 kJ/mol. How much heat is required to convert 45.2 g of O_2 from a liquid to a gas?

3. Methanol's heat of fusion is 3.16 kJ/mol, and its heat of vaporization is 35.3 kJ/mol. Which would require more energy, melting 2.4 mol of solid methanol or boiling 2.4 mol of liquid methanol? Explain your answer.

4. How much heat must be removed from 3.94 g of gaseous ammonia (NH_3) to cause it to condense? Ammonia's heat of vaporization is 23.4 kJ/mol.

5. Which requires more energy, melting 2 mol solid oxygen or boiling 2 mol liquid methanol? Oxygen's heat of fusion is 0.44 kJ/mol, and methanol's heat of vaporization is 35.3 kJ/mol.

6. Calculate the amount of heat necessary to completely melt 45.2 g of solid ethanol (C_2H_5OH). Ethanol's heat of fusion is 4.60 kJ/mol.

7. **Challenge** The specific heat of liquid water is 4.18 J/g·°C. The heat of vaporization of water is 40.7 kJ/mol. How much heat is required to completely evaporate 15.3 g of liquid water that starts at a temperature of 60.0°C?

8. **Challenge** Consider the equation below, which describes the burning of acetylene:

   $$2C_2H_2 \text{ }_{(g)} + 5O_2 \text{ }_{(g)} \rightarrow 4CO_2 \text{ }_{(g)} + 2H_2O_{(l)}$$

   $$\Delta H = -2{,}600 \text{ kJ}$$

   How many grams of ice could be melted with the heat produced by the burning of 1 mol C_2H_2 (acetylene)? The heat of fusion of water is 6.01 kJ/mol. Look at the moles of acetylene carefully.

9. **Challenge** Consider the equation below, which describes the burning of carbon:

   $$C_{(s)} + O_2 \text{ }_{(g)} \rightarrow CO_2 \text{ }_{(g)} \qquad \Delta H = -394 \text{ kJ}$$

   How many moles of water vapor must condense to release the amount of energy produced when 2 mol $C_{(s)}$ burns? ΔH_{cond} for water is –40.7 kJ/mol.

Hess's Law

You can use Hess's law to determine the enthalpy change for a reaction that is difficult to determine by direct experiment.

Hess's law of heat summation states that the enthalpy change for an overall reaction can be calculated by summing the enthalpies for the individual steps in the reaction. Chemists often use Hess's law to calculate the enthalpy changes for reactions that are difficult to measure directly. You can use Hess's law to calculate the ΔH for a reaction if you can split the reaction into several other reactions for which you know the ΔH values. You can also use Hess's law to calculate the ΔH for one step in a multistep reaction.

OBJECTIVE

- Use Hess's law to find the enthalpy change of a reaction that occurs in several steps.

EXAMPLE 1

Calculate ΔH for One Step in a Reaction

The Haber process is a commonly used process for making ammonia (NH_3) on a large scale. The chemical equation for the overall reaction for this process is the following:

$3H_{2\ (g)} + N_{2\ (g)} \rightarrow 2NH_{3\ (g)}$ $\qquad \Delta H_{rxn} = -92.2\ kJ$

This reaction proceeds in two steps, as shown below:

equation 1: $3H_{2\ (g)} + N_{2\ (g)} \rightarrow H_{2\ (g)} + N_2H_{4\ (g)}$ $\qquad \Delta H_1 = 95.4\ kJ$

equation 2: $H_{2\ (g)} + N_2H_{4\ (g)} \rightarrow 2NH_{3\ (g)}$ $\qquad \Delta H_2 = ?$

Use Hess's law to calculate ΔH_2.

Solution

1 **Recall Relevant Information** Hess's law states that the overall enthalpy change for a reaction is equal to the sum of the enthalpy changes for the individual steps in the reaction. Therefore, for the Haber process reaction, $\Delta H_{rxn} = \Delta H_1 + \Delta H_2$.

2 **Solve** If $\Delta H_{rxn} = \Delta H_1 + \Delta H_2$, then $\Delta H_2 = \Delta H_{rxn} - \Delta H_1$. (Make sure to keep the signs correct.) Substituting the given values and solving yields the following:

$\Delta H_2 = \Delta H_{rxn} - \Delta H_1$

$\Delta H_2 = -92.2\ kJ - 95.4\ kJ = -187.6\ kJ$

So, the second reaction step (equation 2) is exothermic, with a ΔH of $-187.6\ kJ$.

REMEMBER

HESS'S LAW

- Hess's law can be used to determine the enthalpy change for a reaction that is difficult to carry out in the lab.

- Hess's law allows for the addition of individual chemical equations and enthalpy values to determine the enthalpy change for an overall reaction.

- When you reverse a reaction, the sign on the enthalpy value changes. When you multiply a reaction by a given value, the magnitude of the enthalpy change will change by that same amount.

EXAMPLE 2

Use Hess's Law to Calculate ΔH for a Reaction

The water-gas reaction produces carbon monoxide and hydrogen gas, which can be used as fuel. The overall equation for the direct reaction looks like this:

$$C_{(s)} + H_2O_{(g)} \rightarrow CO_{(g)} + H_{2\,(g)} \qquad \Delta H_{rxn} = ?$$

Use the following information to calculate ΔH for the water-gas reaction:

equation 1: $C_{(s)} + O_{2\,(g)} \rightarrow CO_{2\,(g)}$ $\Delta H_1 = -393.5$ kJ

equation 2: $2CO_{(g)} + O_{2\,(g)} \rightarrow 2CO_{2\,(g)}$ $\Delta H_2 = -566.0$ kJ

equation 3: $2H_{2\,(g)} + O_{2\,(g)} \rightarrow 2H_2O_{(g)}$ $\Delta H_3 = -483.6$ kJ

Solution

1   **Strategize**   The idea is to find a combination of equations 1, 2, and 3 that will add to give the overall equation. It may be necessary to reverse some of the individual equations and cancel substances from both sides of the arrow to get the three equations to add up to the overall equation for the water-gas reaction.

2   **Examine the Reactions**   In the water-gas reaction, $C_{(s)}$ and $H_2O_{(g)}$ are the reactants, and $CO_{(g)}$ and $H_{2\,(g)}$ are the products. Figure out a way to combine equations 1, 2, and 3 so that their sum has the correct reactants and products. $C_{(s)}$ is a reactant in equation 1, and it does not appear in any of the other equations. Therefore, equation 1 must be included in the final calculations exactly as it is written. Equation 3 as written has $H_2O_{(g)}$ as a product. This equation will need to be reversed, so that $H_2O_{(g)}$ is a reactant. Reversing equation 3 will also give $H_{2\,(g)}$ on the products side, as it is in the overall water-gas equation. In equation 2, $CO_{(g)}$ is a reactant. Therefore, equation 2 will need to be reversed as well. Making these changes yields the following:

equation 1: $C_{(s)} + O_{2\,(g)} \rightarrow CO_{2\,(g)}$ $\Delta H_1 = -393.5$ kJ

equation 2: $2CO_{2\,(g)} \rightarrow 2CO_{(g)} + O_{2\,(g)}$ $-\Delta H_2 = 566.0$ kJ

equation 3: $2H_2O_{(g)} \rightarrow 2H_{2\,(g)} + O_{2\,(g)}$ $-\Delta H_3 = 483.6$ kJ

3   **Balance Products and Reactants**   Examine the equations in Step 2. Notice that the $CO_{2\,(g)}$ entries in equations 1 and 2 do not cancel out. In equation 2, there are 2 mol $CO_{2\,(g)}$, but in equation 1, there is only 1 mol $CO_{2\,(g)}$. Also notice that if the equations were added together as written, the result would be $2H_2O_{(g)}$ on the reactants side and $2CO_{(g)}$ and $2H_{2\,(g)}$ on the products side. In the overall water-gas equation, the coefficients on each species are 1, not 2. Therefore, the equations must be altered further to balance the reactants and products. The coefficients on the $CO_{2\,(g)}$, $CO_{(g)}$, and $H_{2\,(g)}$ must be decreased by one-half, so multiply equations 2 and 3 (in their reversed forms) by one-half, as shown below:

equation 2: $\frac{1}{2}[2CO_{2\,(g)} \rightarrow 2CO_{(g)} + O_{2\,(g)}]$ $-\Delta H_2 = \frac{1}{2} \times 566.0$ kJ

           $CO_{2\,(g)} \rightarrow CO_{(g)} + \frac{1}{2}O_{2\,(g)}$ $-\Delta H_2 = 283.0$ kJ

equation 3: $\frac{1}{2}[2H_2O_{(g)} \rightarrow 2H_{2\,(g)} + O_{2\,(g)}]$ $-\Delta H_3 = \frac{1}{2} \times 483.6$ kJ

           $H_2O_{(g)} \rightarrow H_{2\,(g)} + \frac{1}{2}O_{2\,(g)}$ $-\Delta H_3 = 241.8$ kJ

TIP

Keep careful track of minus signs when doing Hess's law calculations. Remember to check your answers to see if they make sense.

TIP

If you increase or decrease the amount of reactants in a chemical equation, you must increase or decrease the ΔH of the reaction by a corresponding amount.

TIP

You can think of the $\rightarrow$ in chemical equations as being similar to the $=$ in mathematical equations. If you add two chemical equations together, something that appears on both sides of the $\rightarrow$ cancels out.

4 **Solve** Problems involving Hess's law are solved using simple algebraic techniques. To calculate the heat of reaction for the overall water-gas reaction, add together equations 1, 2, and 3, as shown below:

$$C_{(s)} + \cancel{O_{2(g)}} \rightarrow \cancel{CO_{2(g)}} \qquad\qquad \Delta H_1 = -393.5 \text{ kJ}$$

$$\cancel{CO_{2(g)}} \rightarrow CO_{(g)} + \tfrac{1}{2}\cancel{O_{2(g)}} \qquad -\Delta H_2 = 283.0 \text{ kJ}$$

$$\underline{H_2O_{(g)} \rightarrow H_{2(g)} + \tfrac{1}{2}\cancel{O_{2(g)}} \qquad -\Delta H_3 = 241.8 \text{ kJ}}$$

$$C_{(s)} + H_2O_{(g)} \rightarrow H_{2(g)} + CO_{(g)} \qquad \Delta H_{rxn} = 131.3 \text{ kJ}$$

So, the heat of reaction for the water-gas reaction is 131.3 kJ.

EXAMPLE 3

Calculate ΔH_{rxn} from ΔH_f^0

The following equation represents the overall reaction for photosynthesis in plants, which can occur under standard conditions:

$$6CO_{2 \ (g)} + 6H_2O_{(l)} \rightarrow C_6H_{12}O_{6 \ (s)} + 6O_{2 \ (g)} \qquad \Delta H_{rxn}^0 = ?$$

Use the heats of formation given below to calculate ΔH for the overall reaction:

$C_6H_{12}O_{6 \ (s)}$	$\Delta H_f^0 = -1{,}250 \text{ kJ/mol}$
$CO_{2 \ (g)}$	$\Delta H_f^0 = -393.5 \text{ kJ/mol}$
$H_2O_{(l)}$	$\Delta H_f^0 = -285.8 \text{ kJ/mol}$

Solution

1 **Recall Relevant Information** The standard heat of formation, ΔH_f^0, for a substance is the enthalpy of reaction for the formation of the substance under standard conditions (25°C and 1 atm). By definition, ΔH_f^0 for native elements in their standard states is 0 kJ/mol. From Hess's law, the enthalpy of an overall reaction is equal to the sum of the enthalpies of its component reactions. Use this information to write an equation that is a variation on Hess's law for reactions that occur under standard conditions, as shown below:

$$\Delta H_{rxn}^0 = \sum \Delta H_{f,products}^0 - \sum \Delta H_{f,reactants}^0$$

So, to solve this problem, use the standard heats of formation given to calculate the overall heat of reaction.

2 **Set Up the Equation** When using the equation above, remember to multiply each reactant's or product's heat of formation by its stoichiometric coefficient in the balanced equation. Calculate the heat of reaction using the equation below:

$$\Delta H_{rxn}^0 = (\Delta H_{f,C_6H_{12}O_6}^0 + 6 \cdot \Delta H_{f,O_2}^0) - (6 \cdot \Delta H_{f,CO_2}^0 + 6 \cdot \Delta H_{f,H_2O}^0)$$

3 **Solve** Substituting the given values and solving yields the following (remember that $\Delta H_{f,O_2}^0 = 0$ by definition):

$$\Delta H_{rxn}^0 = (-1{,}250 \text{ kJ} + 6 \cdot (0 \text{ kJ})) - (6 \cdot (-393.5 \text{ kJ}) + 6 \cdot (-285.8 \text{ kJ}))$$

$$= -1{,}250 \text{ kJ} - (-2{,}360 \text{ kJ} - 1{,}710 \text{ kJ})$$

$$= -1{,}250 \text{ kJ} - (-4{,}070 \text{ kJ})$$

$$= 2{,}820 \text{ kJ}$$

TIP

The chemical reaction in Example 3 is the reaction that occurs during photosynthesis. The reaction is very endothermic, which indicates that the glucose ($C_6H_{12}O_6$) produced during the reaction stores a great deal of energy.

Problem Set

1. Use the information below to calculate ΔH_1:

    equation 1: $2S_{(s)} + 3O_{2\,(g)} \rightarrow 2SO_{3\,(g)}$

    $\Delta H_1 = ?$

    equation 2: $2S_{(s)} + 2O_{2\,(g)} \rightarrow 2SO_{2\,(g)}$

    $\Delta H_2 = -594$ kJ

    equation 3: $2SO_{2\,(g)} + O_{2\,(g)} \rightarrow 2SO_{3\,(g)}$

    $\Delta H_3 = -198$ kJ

2. State Hess's law in your own words.

3. Use the information below to calculate ΔH_1:

    equation 1: $C_{(s)} + O_{2\,(g)} \rightarrow CO_{2\,(g)}$

    $\Delta H_1 = ?$

    equation 2: $2C_{(s)} + O_{2\,(g)} \rightarrow 2CO_{(g)}$

    $\Delta H_2 = -220$ kJ

    equation 3: $2CO_{(g)} + O_{2\,(g)} \rightarrow 2CO_{2\,(g)}$

    $\Delta H_3 = -566$ kJ

4. Use the information below to calculate ΔH_2:

    equation 1: $CH_{4\,(g)} + 2O_{2\,(g)} \rightarrow CO_{2\,(g)} + 2H_2O_{(g)}$

    $\Delta H_1 = -890$ kJ

    equation 2: $CH_{4\,(g)} + O_{2\,(g)} \rightarrow CH_2O_{(g)} + H_2O_{(g)}$

    $\Delta H_2 = ?$

    equation 3: $CH_2O_{(g)} + O_{2\,(g)} \rightarrow CO_{2\,(g)} + H_2O_{(g)}$

    $\Delta H_3 = 518$ kJ

5. Use the information below to calculate ΔH_3:

    equation 1: $2H_2O_{(l)} \rightarrow 2H_{2\,(g)} + O_{2\,(g)}$

    $\Delta H_1 = 571.6$ kJ

    equation 2: $N_{2\,(g)} + 3H_{2\,(g)} \rightarrow 2NH_{3\,(g)}$

    $\Delta H_2 = -138$ kJ

    equation 3: $2NO_{2\,(g)} + 7H_{2\,(g)} \rightarrow 2NH_{3\,(g)} + 4H_2O_{(l)}$

    $\Delta H_3 = ?$

    equation 4: $2NO_{2\,(g)} \rightarrow N_{2\,(g)} + 2O_{2\,(g)}$

    $\Delta H_4 = 99.0$ kJ

6. Why is it important to include the phases of substances in Hess's law equations?

7. **Challenge** Use the information below to calculate ΔH_1:

    equation 1: $N_2O_{3\,(s)} \rightarrow NO_{(g)} + NO_{2\,(g)}$

    $\Delta H_1 = ?$

    equation 2: $2N_{2\,(g)} + 3O_{2\,(g)} \rightarrow 2N_2O_{3\,(s)}$

    $\Delta H_2 = 167.4$ kJ

    equation 3: $N_{2\,(g)} + O_{2\,(g)} \rightarrow 2NO_{(g)}$

    $\Delta H_3 = 180.4$ kJ

    equation 4: $N_{2\,(g)} + 2O_{2\,(g)} \rightarrow 2NO_{2\,(g)}$

    $\Delta H_4 = 66.4$ kJ

8. **Challenge** Based on the information below, determine whether ΔH_3 is positive or negative, **without** calculating ΔH_3. Explain your answer.

    equation 1: $6Fe_{(s)} + 4O_{2\,(g)} \rightarrow 2Fe_3O_{4\,(s)}$

    $\Delta H_1 = -3{,}351$ kJ

    equation 2: $3Fe_2O_{3\,(s)} \rightarrow 2Fe_3O_{4\,(s)} + \frac{1}{2}O_{2\,(g)}$

    $\Delta H_2 = 348.3$ kJ

    equation 3: $3Fe_2O_{3\,(s)} \rightarrow 6Fe_{(s)} + \frac{9}{2}O_2$

    $\Delta H_3 = ?$

9. **Challenge** Use the information below to calculate ΔH^0_{rxn}:

    $2H_2O_{2\,(l)} \rightarrow 2H_2O_{(l)} + O_{2\,(g)}$　　　$\Delta H^0_{rxn} = ?$

    $\Delta H^0_{f,H_2O_{(l)}} = -285.5$ kJ/mol

    $\Delta H^0_{f,H_2O_{2(l)}} = -187.8$ kJ/mol

Reaction Rates and Energy of Activation

Different chemical reactions happen at different rates, and those rates depend on many factors.

Chemists often need to know how quickly a reaction will proceed. They define the rate of a chemical reaction in two ways: the rate of *increase* in concentration of products over time, or the rate of *decrease* in concentration of reactants over time. The rate of a chemical reaction is affected by the frequency and velocity with which reactants collide to form the activated complex. The activated complex is the intermediate species between the reactants and the products. Anything that affects the collisions between the reactant particles, such as temperature, concentration, surface area, or the presence of a catalyst, will affect the rate of the chemical reaction. The difference between the energy of the reactants and the energy of the activated complex is the activation energy of the reaction.

OBJECTIVES

- Use collision theory and energy vs. time plots to explain reaction rates and activation energy.
- Know how reaction rates are expressed.

EXAMPLE 1

Interpret a Reaction Diagram

The diagram below shows energy vs. reaction progress for a chemical reaction. Is the reaction endothermic or exothermic? What do A and B represent?

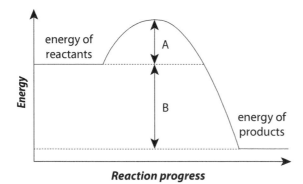

Solution

1 **Examine the Diagram**   The *y*-axis of the diagram represents energy, and the *x*-axis represents how far the reaction has progressed. The energy of the reactants is higher than the energy of the products. The energy of the reaction increases by amount A before decreasing to the energy level of the products.

2 **Solve**   The energy of the reactants is greater than the energy of the products, so the reaction is exothermic. A represents the energy "hump" or barrier that the reactants must surpass to react. Therefore, A must represent the activation energy for the reaction. B represents the difference in energy between the reactants and the products, so it represents ΔH for the reaction.

REMEMBER

REACTION RATE

- The rate of a reaction is defined as the change in concentration of products or reactants over time.

- According to collision theory, a chemical reaction occurs only when reactant particles (atoms, ions, or molecules) collide in the correct orientation and with sufficient energy to overcome the activation energy, or energy barrier, of the reaction.

- Reactions with high activation energies are generally less likely to occur than those with lower activation energies.

- In general, anything that increases the number or velocity of collisions between reactant particles increases the rate of a chemical reaction.

EXAMPLE 2

Relate Collision Theory to Reaction Rates

A small spark can cause coal dust in the air to react explosively, presenting a hazard in places where coal is mined or processed. A lump of coal, on the other hand, burns slowly and safely. In each case the reaction is the same: $C + O_2 \rightarrow CO_2$. Explain in terms of collision theory why the rates of reaction are so different for different forms of coal.

Increasing surface area increases the rate of a reaction, but it does not change the activation energy or the enthalpy change for the reaction.

Solution

1 **Recall** Reaction rate increases when the frequency of collisions between the reactants increases. The frequency of collisions increases as surface area increases.

2 **Solve** When an object like a lump of coal is pulverized into dust, its surface area increases. Oxygen will come in contact with carbon more often if the surface area of the carbon (coal) is increased. Therefore, the coal dust will react more readily than the lump of coal, because the increased surface area of the coal dust will enable more collisions between the carbon and oxygen atoms.

Problem Set

1. The diagram below is a graph of energy vs. reaction progress for a chemical reaction. Is the reaction endothermic or exothermic? Explain your answer.

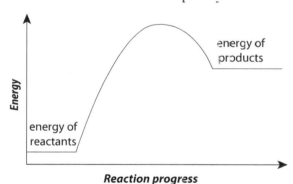

2. How is overall reaction rate related to the change in concentration of reactants? How is rate related to the change in concentration of products?

3. Explain in terms of collision theory why adding heat can increase the rate of a reaction.

4. The graph in the next column shows changes in concentration during the course of a chemical reaction. Use the definition of reaction rate to explain which curve represents the reactants and which curve represents the products.

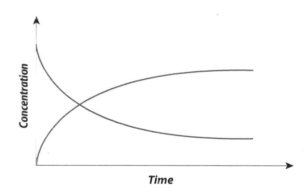

5. **Challenge** When a solution of silver nitrate ($AgNO_3$) is added to a solution of NaCl, a reaction takes place and AgCl precipitates. Explain why the rate of reaction is higher when the concentrations of the solutions are 1.0 M than when the concentrations are 0.1 M.

6. **Challenge** Rusting is a spontaneous reaction, but it occurs very slowly. Based on this information, what can you conclude about the activation energy of the rusting reaction?

Problem Set 83

Factors Affecting Reaction Rates

Many factors, including temperature, concentration, pressure, surface area, and the presence of a catalyst, can change the rate at which a chemical reaction takes place.

Chemical reactions don't all happen at the same rate. Some reactions, such as the explosion that occurs when fire hits a stick of dynamite, are almost instantaneous. Others, such as iron oxidizing to rust, are slower. The conditions under which a chemical reaction occurs can affect its rate. Factors such as temperature, concentration, pressure, surface area, and the presence of a catalyst can all change the rate of a chemical reaction. Higher temperatures can speed up the rate of a reaction by making atoms and molecules move faster, which increases the chances that reactants will bump into each other. Having a greater concentration of reactants also increases the chances that the reactants will come together. Increasing pressure on gases can also make reactions faster, because it forces the gas atoms or molecules closer together, making them more likely to react. For reactions involving solids, a greater surface area increases reaction rates because it exposes more atoms or molecules that are able to react. Finally, the presence of a catalyst—a substance that increases reaction rate without being consumed in the reaction—can provide a faster pathway for reactions to take place.

EXAMPLE 1

Identify How Surface Area Affects Reaction Rate

Some antacid tablets used to treat heartburn contain baking soda ($NaHCO_3$) and citric acid ($C_6H_8O_7$). When dropped into a glass of water, these tablets undergo a chemical reaction and slowly release carbon dioxide (CO_2). A student drops a whole antacid tablet into one container of water and a crushed antacid tablet into another container of water. Which tablet will probably react more quickly, and why?

Solution

1. **Recall Relevant Information** The temperature, concentration, and pressure are the same in both cases, and there is no catalyst in either case. The only thing that changes is the surface area of the tablet. Crushing the tablet increases its surface area.

2. **Solve** In general, increased surface area corresponds to increased reaction rate. Therefore, the crushed tablet will probably react more quickly than the whole tablet.

OBJECTIVE

- Describe the factors that can change the rate of a chemical reaction.

REMEMBER

CHANGING REACTION RATES

- In general, anything that increases the likelihood that reactant particles will collide will increase the rate of a chemical reaction.

- Increasing the temperature increases the rate of most chemical reactions.

- Increasing the concentration of one or more of the reactants increases the rate of most chemical reactions.

- Increasing the surface area of a solid reactant generally increases the rate of a chemical reaction.

- Increasing the pressure on a reaction in which one or more of the reactants are gases generally increases the rate of a chemical reaction.

- A catalyst increases the rate of a chemical reaction by lowering the reaction's activation energy. A catalyst is a substance that participates in the reaction but is not produced or consumed during the reaction—that is, it is neither a reactant nor a product.

EXAMPLE 2

Interpret a Graph of Reaction Rate

The graph below shows the percentage of a reaction that has occurred vs. time for different reaction temperatures. Describe the effects of temperature on the rate of this reaction.

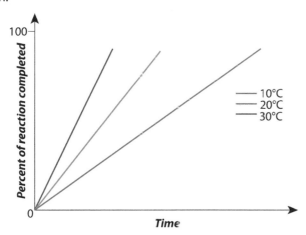

As the temperature increases, the atoms and molecules in a substance move more quickly. This increased motion makes them more likely to collide with one another, and therefore generally increases the rate of the chemical reaction.

Solution

1 Examine the Graph   The different lines on the graph represent different temperatures. The slope of each line is equal to the rate of the reaction at that temperature. The steeper the slope is, the faster the reaction is. The 30°C line has the steepest slope, and the 10°C line has the shallowest slope. Therefore, the reaction proceeds most quickly at 30°C and most slowly at 10°C.

2 Solve   Higher temperatures correspond to higher reaction rates, so increasing the temperature increases the reaction rate, and decreasing the temperature decreases the reaction rate.

Problem Set

1. A cookie recipe says to mix the ingredients (hint: reactants) and bake the cookies for 10 min at 350°F, but a student misreads the recipe and bakes the cookies for 10 min at 305°F. How will the student's mistake most likely affect the cookies? Explain your answer.

2. Describe one way to increase the rate of the following reaction, other than increasing the temperature or adding a catalyst:

   $$AgNO_{3\ (aq)} + NaCl_{(aq)} \rightarrow AgCl_{(s)} + NaNO_{3\ (aq)}$$

   Explain your answer.

3. Describe two ways to decrease the rate of the following reaction, other than decreasing the temperature:

   $$C_{(s)} + O_{2\ (g)} \rightarrow CO_{2\ (g)}$$

   Explain your answer.

4. Adding a small amount of powdered platinum greatly increases the rate of the following reaction:

   $$2H_{2\ (g)} + O_{2\ (g)} \rightarrow 2H_2O_{(l)}$$

   Identify the role of the platinum in the reaction.

5. **Challenge**   For flour to burn, it must react with oxygen. A pile of flour will not burn very easily, but flour dust suspended in the air can explode if there is a spark. Explain this observation.

6. **Challenge**   For wood to burn, it must react with oxygen. A scientist places identical pieces of wood in each of two containers. One container is filled with normal air at 1 atm. The other is filled with pure oxygen at 1 atm. Which piece of wood will burn more quickly when a spark is added? Explain your answer.

Collision Theory

Collision theory can explain the effects of certain factors on reaction rates.

Collision theory is an explanation of why factors such as temperature, concentration, and pressure can affect reaction rates. This theory states that for molecules to undergo a chemical reaction, they must collide with one another. However, not just any collision will cause a reaction. Molecules must collide in the right orientation and with enough energy to break existing bonds and form new ones. Collision theory suggests that only a fraction of the collisions taking place have those qualities. Consequently, anything that increases that fraction can speed up the rate of a reaction, which is why raising temperature can increase reaction rate. Adding heat increases the motions of molecules, improving the chances that they will bump into one another and meet with enough force to cause a reaction. Higher pressure and higher concentration work in a similar way. Both put molecules in closer proximity to one another, increasing the chances that they will collide in the right way.

OBJECTIVES

- Define collision theory.
- Describe how collision theory explains the effects of factors such as temperature, pressure, and concentration on reaction rates.

EXAMPLE 1

Explain Reaction Rate with Collision Theory

As shown in the equation below, hydrogen chloride (HCl) and ethylene (C_2H_4) can react to produce chloroethane (C_2H_5Cl), a compound that once was a common gasoline additive:

$$HCl_{(g)} + C_2H_4{}_{(g)} \rightarrow C_2H_5Cl_{(g)}$$

Increases in heat, pressure, or both can increase the rate of this reaction. Explain this observation in terms of collision theory.

Solution

❶ Recall Relevant Information   Collision theory states that factors that make molecules more likely to collide in the right orientation and with sufficient energy to cause a chemical reaction can speed the reaction rate. Heat causes molecules to move faster, making them more likely to collide. Pressure brings molecules closer together, increasing the chances that they will meet.

❷ Solve   Higher heat and pressure increase the chances that molecules of hydrogen chloride and ethylene will collide in the right orientation and with enough energy to form chloroethane.

REMEMBER

COLLISION AND REACTION RATES

- Collision theory states that molecules need to collide in the correct orientation and with enough energy before a chemical reaction can take place.

- Factors that make molecules move faster or bring them closer together, such as increased heat, pressure, and concentration, increase collision rates and therefore increase reaction rates.

- The more molecules collide, the more likely they are to bump into each other under the right conditions to react.

Identify How Altering Collision Frequency Affects Reaction Rate

Aqueous hydrochloric acid (HCl) and solid sodium hydroxide (NaOH) can react to form water (H_2O) and table salt (NaCl). Solutions of hydrochloric acid can be of various concentrations. Use collision theory to predict how the rate of reaction will be affected if the HCl solution is diluted, thereby reducing its concentration.

TIP

Diluting a solution increases the average distance between atoms or molecules, making it less likely that they will collide and react.

Solution

1 **Recall Relevant Information** According to collision theory, only a fraction of collisions have the qualities needed to cause molecules to react with one another. Anything that decreases collision frequency will also decrease the number of collisions that have the right orientation and sufficient energy to cause a reaction to occur, and will therefore also decrease reaction rate. The lower the concentration of the H^+ (or H_3O^+) from the HCl in an aqueous solution is, the fewer collisions there will be between the H^+ ions and the NaOH particles.

2 **Solve** As the concentration of the HCl solution decreases, the reaction rate will also decrease.

Problem Set

1. Hydrofluoric acid (HF) can form through the following reaction:

   $$H_{2\,(g)} + F_{2\,(g)} \rightarrow 2HF_{(g)}$$

   A scientist mixes H_2 gas and F_2 gas in an enclosed container and then increases the pressure in the container. Use collision theory to explain why the increased pressure increases the rate of the chemical reaction.

2. Vinegar is a solution of acetic acid (CH_3COOH) in water. When baking soda and vinegar mix, the acetic acid reacts with the baking soda to form carbon dioxide, water, and a salt. A student mixes some vinegar with water before combining the solution with baking soda. Use collision theory to explain why the reaction will proceed more slowly than it would if the student had not diluted the vinegar with water.

3. Magnesium metal will react with aqueous hydrochloric acid to produce hydrogen gas and an aqueous solution of magnesium chloride. Use collision theory to explain why hot acid solution will produce a faster reaction than cold acid solution.

4. Sliced apples and bananas turn brown when the compounds in their flesh react with oxygen in the air. Use collision theory to explain why wrapping apples or bananas in plastic immediately after they have been cut can keep them from turning brown.

5. **Challenge** Chemical "glow sticks" are partly filled with a liquid consisting of a fluorescent dye and a hydrogen peroxide solution. Each stick also contains a small capsule filled with an organic compound. When the stick is bent, the capsule breaks, and the compound inside the capsule mixes with the hydrogen peroxide. The two compounds react and release energy, which causes the fluorescent dye to glow. Once a glow stick is activated, it will glow for only a few hours. Putting it into a freezer allows it to glow longer. Explain this observation in terms of collision theory.

6. **Challenge** Explain, in terms of collision theory, why increasing the pressure on the following reaction will probably have very little effect on the reaction rate:

   $$2Al_{(s)} + Fe_2O_{3\,(s)} \rightarrow 2Fe_{(s)} + Al_2O_{3\,(s)}$$

Equilibrium

The equilibrium constant for a reaction describes the balance of reactants and products in a reaction system.

Many chemical reactions, such as the dissociation of a small amount of HCl in water, are irreversible. In other words, the reaction proceeds only from left to right, and all the reactants are converted to products. Chemical equations for irreversible reactions like these include only a single arrow that points from reactants to products. However, many chemical reactions are not irreversible. In these reactions, at the same time that reactants are being converted to products, some of the products are themselves reacting together and turning back into reactants. This type of reaction is a *reversible reaction*. Chemical equations for reversible reactions are indicated by a double arrow. The reaction that proceeds from left to right is called the forward reaction. The reaction that proceeds from right to left is called the reverse reaction. A reaction is said to be at *equilibrium* when the rates of forward and reverse reactions are equal. At equilibrium, the amounts of reactants and products stop changing with time. The equilibrium constant for a reaction represents the ratio of products to reactants at equilibrium.

EXAMPLE 1

Write the Equilibrium Expression for a Reaction

Methanol (CH_3OH) is a simple alcohol that can be used as a fuel or as a reactant in the production of some important industrial chemicals. Methanol can form from carbon monoxide (CO) and hydrogen (H_2) in a reversible reaction, as shown below:

$$CO_{(g)} + 2H_{2\,(g)} \rightleftharpoons CH_3OH_{(g)}$$

Write the equilibrium expression for this reaction.

Solution

1 **Strategize** The equilibrium expression for a reaction is equal to the ratio of products to reactants. Each species in the reaction is raised to a power equal to its stoichiometric coefficient in the balanced chemical equation. The expression includes the concentrations of products and reactants, not just their chemical formulas. For this reaction, the equilibrium expression will include the following terms: [CO], $[H_2]^2$, and $[CH_3OH]$. The square brackets indicate concentration in moles per liter.

2 **Solve** Methanol is the product, and CO and H_2 are the reactants. Therefore, the correct equilibrium expression for this reaction is the one shown below:

$$\frac{[CH_3OH]}{[CO][H_2]^2}$$

EXAMPLE 2

Calculate the Equilibrium Constant for a Reaction

A scientist combines carbon dioxide and hydrogen in a reaction at 210°C to produce methanol according to the equation in Example 1. At equilibrium, the concentrations of methanol, carbon monoxide, and hydrogen for the reaction are as follows:

$[CH_3OH] = 0.0494$ mol/L

$[CO] = 0.151$ mol/L

$[H_2] = 0.151$ mol/L

What is the equilibrium constant, K, for this reaction at 210°C?

Solution

1 Collect and Strategize   The equilibrium expression for the reaction is given below:

$$\frac{[CH_3OH]}{[CO][H_2]^2}$$

To calculate the equilibrium constant for this reaction, substitute the equilibrium concentrations given in the problem into the equilibrium expression.

2 Solve   Substituting the given values and solving yields the following:

$$K = \frac{[CH_3OH]}{[CO][H_2]^2} = \frac{0.0494}{(0.151)(0.151)^2} = \frac{0.0494}{3.44 \times 10^{-3}} = 14.4$$

EXAMPLE 3

Interpret an Equilibrium Constant for a Reaction

Does the reaction for the formation of methanol in Examples 1 and 2 favor the products or the reactants?

Solution

1 Recall Relevant Information   Remember that the equilibrium constant, K, for the reaction is the ratio of products to reactants at equilibrium. The product of the reaction (methanol) is in the numerator, and the reactants (CO and H_2) are in the denominator.

2 Solve   The equilibrium constant for the reaction is greater than 1. Therefore, at equilibrium, the products are favored over the reactants.

TIP

If the equilibrium constant for a reaction is greater than 1, the products of the reaction as written are favored. If the equilibrium constant is less than 1, the reactants of the reaction as written are favored.

EXAMPLE 4

Write an Equilibrium Expression for a Reverse Reaction and Calculate its K'

A scientist places some methanol in a closed container. The methanol begins to decompose into carbon monoxide and hydrogen gas according to the equation below:

$$CH_3OH_{(g)} \rightleftharpoons CO_{(g)} + 2H_{2\ (g)}$$

Write the equilibrium expression for this reaction, and calculate the equilibrium constant, K', for the reaction at 210°C. (This reaction is the reverse of the reaction in Example 1. Chemists often use K' to represent the equilibrium constant for a reverse reaction.)

Solution

1 **Recall Relevant Information** For any reaction, the equilibrium expression is the ratio of products to reactants, with each species raised to a power equal to its stoichiometric coefficient in the balanced equation. In the reaction given, the products are CO and H_2, and the reactant is methanol. Therefore, this reaction is the reverse of the reaction in Example 1. The equilibrium constant K for the reaction in Example 1 at 210°C is 14.4.

2 **Solve** The equilibrium expression is the ratio of products to reactants for the reaction as written, as shown below:

$$\frac{[CO][H_2]^2}{[CH_3OH]}$$

Notice that this is the reciprocal of the equilibrium expression for the reaction in Example 1. Therefore, the equilibrium constant K' for this reaction must be the reciprocal of the equilibrium constant K calculated in Example 2, as shown below:

$$K' = \frac{1}{K} = \frac{1}{14.4} = 0.0694$$

EXAMPLE 5

Write an Equilibrium Expression for a Reaction Involving a Solid

Only a tiny amount of silver chloride (AgCl) can dissolve in water. The equation below shows what happens when silver chloride dissolves in water:

$$AgCl_{(s)} \rightleftharpoons Ag^+_{(aq)} + Cl^-_{(aq)}$$

Write an equation for the equilibrium constant, K, for this dissolution reaction.

Solution

1 **Recall Relevant Information** The equilibrium expression for a reaction is the ratio of products to reactants in the reaction. In this reaction, solid AgCl is the reactant, and Ag^+ ions and Cl^- ions are the products. The equilibrium expression includes the concentrations of the reactants and products. The concentration of a solid is a constant, unlike the concentrations of aqueous ions.

TIP

Equilibrium constants calculated using concentrations are sometimes given the symbol K_c to differentiate them from other types of equilibrium constants, such as K_a for acids, K_b for bases, or K_{sp} for the dissolution of solids.

2 Collect First, write the equilibrium expression in the usual way, as shown below:

$$K = \frac{[Ag^+][Cl^-]}{[AgCl]}$$

3 Solve K is a constant, and so is [AgCl]. Therefore, their product must be a constant, and they can be combined to eliminate [AgCl] from the expression, as shown below:

$$K \times [AgCl] = [Ag^+][Cl^-]$$

$$K = [Ag^+][Cl^-]$$

It is conventional in chemistry to eliminate the concentrations of all solid species from equilibrium expressions in this way. The equilibrium constant for the dissolution of a salt is called the solubility product constant, or K_{sp}. Therefore, the K_{sp} for silver chloride is given by the equation $K_{sp} = [Ag^+][Cl^-]$.

Problem Set

1. The equilibrium constant for the following reaction at 2,000 K is 0.154:

$$2CH_{4\,(g)} \rightleftharpoons C_2H_{2\,(g)} + 3H_{2\,(g)}$$

Are the products or reactants favored in this reaction at 2,000 K? Explain your answer.

2. Write the equilibrium expression for the equation below:

$$N_{2\,(g)} + 3H_{2\,(g)} \rightleftharpoons 2NH_{3\,(g)}$$

3. The reaction between hydrogen and iodine at 700 K is described by the equation below:

$$H_{2\,(g)} + I_{2\,(g)} \rightleftharpoons 2HI_{(g)}$$

For this reaction, $K = \frac{[HI]^2}{[H_2][I_2]}$. At equilibrium, the concentration of H_2 is 0.035 mol/L, the concentration of I_2 is 0.045 mol/L, and the concentration of HI is 0.29 mol/L. Calculate the equilibrium constant for this reaction at 700 K. Are the products or reactants favored at equilibrium?

4. Explain why a chemical equilibrium is called a *dynamic* equilibrium.

5. H_2 and Br_2 are heated to give HBr according to the equation below:

$$H_{2\,(g)} + Br_{2\,(g)} \rightleftharpoons 2HBr_{(g)}$$

At equilibrium, at a specific temperature, the concentration of H_2 is 0.123 mol/L, the concentration of Br_2 is 0.121 mol/L, and the concentration of HBr is 0.712 mol/L. Calculate the equilibrium constant for this reaction at that specific temperature.

6. At 298 K, the equilibrium constant for the reaction $2SO_{2\,(g)} + O_{2\,(g)} \rightleftharpoons 2SO_{3\,(g)}$ is 7.2×10^{23}. Are the products or the reactants favored?

7. **Challenge** The solubility product constant, K_{sp}, for silver chloride (AgCl) is 1.8×10^{-10} at 25°C. Use a scientific calculator to calculate the concentrations of Ag^+ ions and Cl^- ions in a saturated AgCl solution. (Hint: Use the balanced chemical equation for the dissolution of AgCl to find a relationship between $[Ag^+]$ and $[Cl^-]$.)

8. **Challenge** Nitrogen dioxide (NO_2) can form from N_2O_4 according to the following reaction:

$$N_2O_{4\,(g)} \rightleftharpoons 2NO_{2\,(g)}$$

At equilibrium at a certain temperature, the concentration of N_2O_4 is 0.029 mol/L, and the concentration of NO_2 is 0.112 mol/L. Is the reactant or product favored at equilibrium?

9. **Challenge** Ethanol (C_2H_5OH) is manufactured by reacting ethane (C_2H_4) with steam according to the equation $C_2H_{4\,(g)} + H_2O_{(g)} \rightleftharpoons C_2H_5OH_{(g)}$. The equilibrium constant for this reaction at a specific temperature is 448.6. In a particular reaction system, the equilibrium concentrations of C_2H_4 and C_2H_5OH are 0.019 mol/L and 0.179 mol/L, respectively. What is the equilibrium concentration of $H_2O_{(g)}$?

Le Châtelier's Principle

You can predict whether a reversible chemical reaction will shift to make more reactants or more products by understanding how changes in temperature, pressure, and concentration affect a system.

When a reversible chemical reaction reaches equilibrium, there are no more changes in the amounts of reactants or products. From the outside, the system appears to be at rest. However, equilibrium continues only as long as pressure, heat, and concentrations stay steady. If these conditions change, you can use Le Châtelier's principle to predict the effects. This rule states that if pressure, heat, or concentration changes while a system is at equilibrium, the system adjusts to try to minimize that change. For example, if you add heat to an exothermic reaction (one that releases heat), then the reaction will shift in a way that favors making more reactants and less products to offset that temperature change. If you increase pressure on a system, the reaction will shift to whichever side of the equation has the fewest moles of gas so the pressure will be reduced. If you increase concentration of a product, the reaction equation will shift to favor the side making more reactants. Of course, the reverse of all these situations is also true.

OBJECTIVES

- Explain Le Châtelier's principle.
- Predict the effects of changes in temperature, pressure, and concentration on chemical equilibrium.

EXAMPLE 1

Predict the Effect of Adding Heat to a Reaction

Sulfur dioxide (SO_2), a gas produced by volcanoes and in industrial processes, can combine with oxygen gas (O_2) to make sulfur trioxide (SO_3), a gas that can form acid rain when it mixes with water in the atmosphere. The reaction that forms sulfur trioxide is exothermic and reversible, as shown below:

$$2SO_{2\,(g)} + O_{2\,(g)} \rightleftharpoons 2SO_{3\,(g)} + heat$$

If you add heat to this system, which way will the reaction shift?

Solution

1 **Recall Relevant Concepts**   Le Châtelier's principle states that a system in equilibrium reacts to environmental changes in such a way as to maintain equilibrium. In this reaction, heat can be considered a product. According to Le Châtelier's principle, if the concentration of products increases, the system will shift toward the reactant side of the equation.

2 **Solve**   Because heat is present as a by-product on the right side of the equation, the reaction will shift to the left to favor the reactants. The concentrations of SO_2 and O_2 in the system will increase, and the concentration of SO_3 will decrease.

REMEMBER

LE CHÂTELIER'S PRINCIPLE

- Le Châtelier's principle states that if temperature, pressure, or concentration changes while a system is at equilibrium, the system tends to adjust in such a way as to maintain equilibrium.

- If a reactant is added, the system will shift toward the products. If a product is added, the system will shift toward the reactants. This applies to heat as well. Heat is considered a product of an exothermic reaction, and it is considered a reactant in an endothermic reaction.

- If pressure increases, the equilibrium will shift to the side of the equation that has fewer moles of gas. If the pressure decreases, the equilibrium will shift to the side of the equation that has more moles of gas.

EXAMPLE 2

Predict the Effect of Removing Heat from a Reaction

Hydrogen gas (H_2) can combine with chlorine gas (Cl_2) to make hydrogen chloride gas (HCl). When you dissolve this gas in water, it makes hydrochloric acid, a chemical that helps dissolve food in your stomach and also has a wide range of industrial uses. The equation for the formation of HCl is shown below:

$$H_{2\,(g)} + Cl_{2\,(g)} \rightleftharpoons 2HCl_{(g)} + heat$$

If you cool this system, which way will the reaction shift?

Solution

1 **Recall Relevant Information**   Again, heat can be considered a product of this reaction. According to Le Châtelier's principle, removing a product from a reaction at equilibrium will tend to shift the reaction toward the products side of the equation.

2 **Solve**   Cooling a system involves removing heat. Therefore, the reaction will shift toward the products (the right side of the equation). The concentrations of H_2 and Cl_2 in the system will decrease and the concentration of HCl will increase.

EXAMPLE 3

Predict the Effect of Increasing Pressure on a Reaction

Nitrogen gas (N_2) can react with hydrogen gas (H_2) to produce ammonia (NH_3). This reaction is at the core of the Haber process, the main process for producing ammonia on an industrial scale. Fritz Haber, a German chemist for whom the process is named, took advantage of Le Châtelier's principle to maximize the production of ammonia. The Haber process equation is shown below:

$$N_{2\,(g)} + 3H_{2\,(g)} \rightleftharpoons 2NH_{3\,(g)}$$

In the Haber process, nitrogen and hydrogen are allowed to react under very high pressure. Explain why high pressures would increase the amount of ammonia produced by this reaction.

Solution

1 **Recall Relevant Information**   As pressure increases, gases become less stable in the system. Therefore, an increase in pressure will tend to favor the side of a chemical equation that contains fewer moles of gas. In this reaction, there are four moles of gas on the reactants side (1 mol N_2 and 3 mol H_2) and two moles of gas on the products side (2 mol NH_3).

2 **Solve**   Because increasing pressure causes the reaction to proceed toward the side with fewer moles of gas, the high pressure of the Haber process will cause the equilibrium of the ammonia reaction to shift toward the product side of the equation—that is, toward ammonia.

TIP

Remember that the coefficients in a chemical reaction indicate the number of molecules of each species that are involved in the reaction. The coefficients also indicate the ratio of the number of moles of each species that are involved in the reaction. Therefore, to determine the number of moles of gas on each side of the reaction, add up the coefficients in front of all the gaseous species. (Remember that a species with no written coefficient actually has a coefficient of 1.)

EXAMPLE 4

Predict the Effect of Decreasing Pressure on a Reaction

Solid nickel (Ni) can combine with carbon monoxide gas (CO) to make nickel carbonyl ($Ni(CO)_4$). This compound is extremely toxic. It is used in nickel plating and nickel ore refining. Here is the equation for making nickel carbonyl:

$$Ni_{(s)} + 4CO_{(g)} \rightleftharpoons Ni(CO)_{4\,(l)}$$

If you decrease pressure in this system, which way will the reaction shift?

Solution

1 **Recall Relevant Information**   As pressure decreases, gases become more stable in the system. Therefore, a decrease in pressure will tend to favor the side of a chemical equation that contains the greatest number of moles of gas. In this reaction, there are four moles of gas on the reactants side and zero moles of gas on the products side.

2 **Solve**   Because the reactant side of the equation contains more moles of gas than the products side, a decrease in pressure will cause the equilibrium in this reaction to shift toward the reactants.

EXAMPLE 5

Predict the Effect of Increasing Concentration on a Reaction

Hydrogen gas (H_2) can combine with iodine gas (I_2) to make hydrogen iodide (HI). This compound is a colorless and odorless gas that can be dissolved in water to make a strong acid. Here is the equation for making hydrogen iodide:

$$H_{2\,(g)} + I_{2\,(g)} \rightleftharpoons 2HI_{(g)}$$

If HI is added to this system, which way will the reaction shift?

Solution

1 **Recall Relevant Information**   According to Le Châtelier's principle, if you increase the concentration of products in a system at equilibrium, the equilibrium will shift toward the reactant side of the equation.

2 **Solve**   Adding HI to the system will shift the reaction toward the reactants. The concentrations of H_2 and I_2 in the system will increase, and the concentration of HI in the system will decrease.

TIP

In the context of Le Châtelier's principle, *concentration* can mean either a typical solution concentration or the concentration of a reactant or product *in the system*—that is, the relative number of moles of the reactant or product in the system as a whole.

EXAMPLE 6

Predict the Effect of Decreasing Concentration on a Reaction

Solid cobalt (Co) can combine with chlorine gas (Cl_2) to form cobalt chloride ($CoCl_2$). This compound is a blue solid that turns rose-colored when it becomes hydrated (absorbs water). Papers or other materials that are coated with cobalt chloride can be used to detect humidity, or moisture, in the air because of this color change. Here is the equation for making $CoCl_2$:

$$Co_{(s)} + Cl_{2\ (g)} \rightleftharpoons CoCl_{2\ (s)}$$

If some Cl_2 is removed from this system, which way will the reaction shift?

Solution

❶ Recall Relevant Information According to Le Châtelier's principle, decreasing the concentration of reactants in a system at equilibrium causes the equilibrium to shift toward the reactant side of the equation.

❷ Solve Removing Cl_2 from the system will cause the equilibrium to shift to the left, toward the reactants. The concentrations of Co and Cl_2 in the system will increase, and the concentration of $CoCl_2$ will decrease.

Problem Set

1. Predict the effect of removing O_2 from the following system:

   $$2SO_{2\ (g)} + O_{2\ (g)} \rightleftharpoons 2SO_{3\ (g)}$$

2. Predict the effect of removing heat on the system shown below:

   $$2H_{2\ (g)} + O_{2\ (g)} \rightleftharpoons 2H_2O_{(l)} + heat$$

3. Predict the effect of increasing pressure on this system:

   $$N_2O_{4\ (g)} \rightleftharpoons 2NO_{2\ (g)}$$

4. As you have learned, the Haber process occurs under high pressure. It also occurs under relatively low temperatures. Use the equation for the Haber process below to explain why reducing temperature increases the production of ammonia:

   $$N_{2\ (g)} + 3H_{2\ (g)} \rightleftharpoons 2NH_{3\ (g)} + heat$$

5. Give three ways to increase the production of CO_2 in the reaction below:

   $$CO_{2\ (g)} + H_{2\ (g)} + heat \rightleftharpoons CO_{(g)} + H_2O_{(g)}$$

6. Describe three ways to increase the production of CO in the reaction below:

   $$CO_{2\ (g)} + C_{(s)} \rightleftharpoons 2CO_{(g)}$$

7. **Challenge** Predict the effect of increasing pressure on the system shown below:

   $$H_{2\ (g)} + I_{2\ (g)} \rightleftharpoons 2HI_{(g)}$$

8. **Challenge** A chemist has two solutions of CH_3COOH, one with a concentration of 0.1 M and the other with a concentration of 0.01 M. Which solution should she mix with 0.1 M NaOH solution to favor the production of $NaCH_3COO$ in the reaction below?

   $$CH_3COOH_{(aq)} + NaOH_{(aq)} \rightleftharpoons NaCH_3COO_{(aq)} + H_2O_{(l)}$$

   Explain your answer.

9. **Challenge** Predict the effect of decreasing pressure and adding NaOH on the system shown below:

   $$NaOH_{(aq)} + HCl_{(aq)} \rightleftharpoons NaCl_{(aq)} + H_2O_{(l)}$$

Spontaneous Reactions

You can determine whether a reaction will be spontaneous by determining whether it releases free energy into its surroundings or takes in free energy from its surroundings.

In everyday life, many physical changes happen spontaneously, or on their own without any outside intervention. For example, if you leave a cup of hot coffee at room temperature, it will eventually get cooler—there's no need to chill it. Many chemical reactions are also spontaneous. A *spontaneous* chemical reaction is one that does not have to absorb energy from its surroundings to proceed. The reason why some reactions are spontaneous and others aren't has to do with a concept called *free energy*, which is a result of the interaction of the heat of the reaction and the entropy of the reactants and products. A reaction will occur spontaneously only if it releases free energy. A reaction that absorbs free energy is *nonspontaneous*. Scientists use the symbol G to represent free energy. The free energy change of a reaction, ΔG, gives you information about whether the reaction is spontaneous. Reactions with negative ΔG values are spontaneous. Reactions with positive ΔG values are nonspontaneous.

OBJECTIVES

- Define free energy.
- Describe how free energy can be used to predict whether a reaction happens spontaneously.

EXAMPLE 1

Determine Whether a Reaction is Spontaneous

When allowed to proceed to equilibrium, the following system consists almost entirely of CO_2 and H_2O:

$$C_6H_{12}O_6 + 6O_2 \rightarrow 6CO_2 + 6H_2O$$

Is the reaction spontaneous or nonspontaneous as written?

Solution

1 **Recall Relevant Information**   A spontaneous reaction is one that naturally—at the temperature and pressure conditions stated—proceeds as written. In other words, a spontaneous reaction is one that will naturally result in a substantial increase in the amount of products present; its equilibrium lies mainly to the right. A nonspontaneous reaction is one that does not naturally proceed as written. At equilibrium, a nonspontaneous reaction system will consist mainly of reactants rather than products.

2 **Solve**   In the reaction as written, CO_2 and H_2O are products. According to the problem statement, the equilibrium of the reaction as written lies to the right, with the products. Therefore, the reaction is spontaneous as written.

REMEMBER

FREE ENERGY AND SPONTANEOUS REACTIONS

- The free energy, or ΔG, of a reaction indicates whether the reaction is spontaneous. Reactions with negative ΔG are spontaneous, and those with positive ΔG are nonspontaneous.

- ΔG is related to ΔH, but they are not the same thing.

- The ΔG of a reaction is a more reliable measure of spontaneity than is ΔH. A reaction may have a negative ΔH but still be nonspontaneous, but any reaction with a negative ΔG is spontaneous.

- The ΔG of a reaction indicates whether the reaction is spontaneous, but it does not indicate how quickly the reaction occurs. Many spontaneous reactions occur very slowly.

EXAMPLE 2

Predict the Sign of ΔG for a Reaction

Water can form according to the following reaction:

$$2H_{2\,(g)} + O_{2\,(g)} \rightarrow 2H_2O_{(l)}$$

It is possible to convert water back into hydrogen and oxygen gases by running a current of electricity through the water, a process called *electrolysis*. Is the ΔG value for the electrolysis reaction positive or negative?

Solution

1 **Recall Relevant Information** A reaction has a positive ΔG value if it can proceed only by absorbing energy from its surroundings. It has a negative ΔG value if it releases energy into its surroundings. Electricity is a form of energy.

2 **Solve** To turn water back into hydrogen and oxygen, you need to run an electric current through it. The electricity is a form of energy. Therefore, the electrolysis reaction absorbs energy from its surroundings, and it has a positive ΔG value.

TIP

Remember that, if you reverse the direction of a reaction, you must reverse the sign on ΔH for the reaction. The same is true of ΔG: If a given reaction has a negative ΔG value, its reverse reaction has a positive ΔG value, and vice versa.

Problem Set

1. Nitric oxide (NO) and chlorine gas can react to form the poisonous gas nitrosyl chloride (NOCl) according to the following reaction:

$$2NO_{(g)} + Cl_{2\,(g)} \rightarrow 2NOCl_{(g)} \quad \Delta G = -40.9 \text{ kJ}$$

Is this reaction spontaneous or nonspontaneous as written? Explain your answer.

2. Nitric oxide can form by the reaction of nitrogen gas and oxygen gas, as shown in the equation below:

$$N_{2\,(g)} + O_{2\,(g)} \rightarrow 2NO_{(g)}$$

When allowed to come to equilibrium at room temperature and 1 atmosphere pressure, the system above consists mainly of nitrogen gas and oxygen gas. Is the reaction above spontaneous or nonspontaneous as written under these conditions? Explain your answer.

3. When an electric current is passed through molten sodium chloride (NaCl), chlorine gas (Cl_2) bubbles off of one electrode, and solid sodium (Na) forms at the other. Based on this information, predict the sign of ΔG for the following reaction:

$$2NaCl_{(l)} \rightarrow 2Na_{(s)} + Cl_{2\,(g)}$$

Explain your answer.

4. In a classroom laboratory, a student mixes vinegar (CH_3COOH) with baking soda ($NaHCO_3$). The mixture bubbles and becomes slightly warm. Predict the sign of ΔG for this reaction. Explain your answer.

5. **Challenge** Carbonyl sulfide (COS) is a colorless, toxic gas with a strong odor. Two reactions that lead to the formation of COS are shown below:

reaction 1: $SO_{2\,(g)} + 3CO_{(g)} \rightarrow COS_{(g)} + 2CO_{2\,(g)}$

$\Delta G_1 = -246.4 \text{ kJ}$

reaction 2: $CO_{(g)} + H_2S_{(g)} \rightarrow COS_{(g)} + H_{2\,(g)}$

$\Delta G_2 = 1.4 \text{ kJ}$

Compare the spontaneity of these two reactions.

6. **Challenge** When 1 mol magnesium hydroxide ($Mg(OH)_2$) is mixed with 2 mol hydrochloric acid (HCl), 1 mol magnesium chloride ($MgCl_2$) and 2 mol water (H_2O) form spontaneously. Predict the sign of ΔG for the following reaction:

$$\frac{1}{2}MgCl_2 + H_2O \rightarrow \frac{1}{2}Mg(OH)_2 + HCl$$

Study the problem and equation carefully and explain your answer.

Entropy and Free Energy

Understanding entropy and enthalpy allows you to determine whether or not a chemical reaction is spontaneous.

Entropy, which is represented by the symbol S, is a measure of the randomness or disorder in a system. Reactions that result in an increase in disorder have positive ΔS values. Those that result in a decrease in disorder have negative ΔS values. Reactions with positive ΔS values tend to be more favored than those with negative ΔS values. In general, the following processes result in an increase in entropy:

- The formation of a mixture from two or more separate components
- The formation of a liquid from a solid
- The formation of a gas from a liquid or a solid
- An increase in the number of different substances in a system
- An increase in the number of particles (atoms, ions, or molecules) in a system

Neither ΔH nor ΔS can be used to absolutely predict the spontaneity of a reaction, because in some reactions the ΔS value is favorable but the ΔH value is unfavorable. Instead, chemists use free energy (G) to predict the spontaneity of a reaction. Remember that spontaneous reactions have negative ΔG (free energy change) values. Free energy is a combination of enthalpy and entropy. The equation for ΔG is $\Delta G = \Delta H - T\Delta S$, where T is temperature.

OBJECTIVES

- Define *entropy*.
- Describe the relationship between entropy, enthalpy, and free energy.
- Use the equation for free energy to determine the spontaneity of a chemical reaction.

REMEMBER

ENTROPY AND FREE ENERGY

- Entropy is a measure of the amount of disorder or randomness in a system.
- A positive ΔS value indicates that entropy has increased during a reaction. A negative ΔS value indicates that entropy has decreased during a reaction.
- The equation $\Delta G = \Delta H - T\Delta S$ gives the relationship between free energy (ΔG), enthalpy (ΔH), temperature (T), and entropy (ΔS). Temperature must be in kelvins for this equation to apply.
- You cannot use ΔS or ΔH to predict the spontaneity of a reaction. Only the ΔG value of a reaction can be used to predict the spontaneity of the reaction.

EXAMPLE 1

Predict the Sign of ΔS for a Reaction

Will the ΔS value of the reaction that is represented by the equation below be positive or negative?

$$C_6H_{12}O_{6\,(s)} \rightarrow 2C_2H_5OH_{(l)} + 2CO_{2\,(g)}$$

Solution

1. **Recall Relevant Information** Entropy is a measure of the randomness, or disorder, of a system. A reaction with a positive ΔS value results in an increase in entropy.

2. **Solve** The equation shows that, during the reaction, one mole of a solid changes into two moles of a liquid and two moles of a gas. This reaction therefore involves an increase in the number of particles in the system. It also results in production of a liquid and a gas from a solid. Both of these processes increase entropy, so the equation has a positive ΔS value.

EXAMPLE 2

Calculate ΔG from ΔH and ΔS

Determine whether the reaction represented by the following equation is spontaneous at 298 K.

$$N_{2\,(g)} + 3H_{2\,(g)} \rightarrow 2NH_{3\,(g)} \qquad \Delta H = -92.0 \text{ kJ}; \Delta S = -0.199 \text{ kJ/K}$$

Solution

1 **Collect and Strategize** Both ΔS and ΔH are negative. Therefore, it is necessary to calculate ΔG for the reaction to determine its spontaneity. The equation for calculating ΔG is $\Delta G = \Delta H - T\Delta S$. The T, ΔS, and ΔH values are given above.

2 **Solve** Substitute the given values and solve for ΔG, as shown below:

$$\Delta G = \Delta H - T\Delta S = -92.0 \text{ kJ} - (298 \text{ K})(-0.199 \text{ kJ/K})$$

$$\Delta G = -92.0 \text{ kJ} - (-59.3 \text{ kJ}) = -32.7 \text{ kJ}$$

The ΔG value is negative, so this reaction is spontaneous as written at 298 K.

TIP

Remember to use absolute temperature (that is, temperature in kelvins, not in degrees Celsius) in the free energy equation, and make sure to keep careful track of negatives.

Problem Set

1. Describe the difference between entropy, enthalpy, and free energy.

2. Explain why it is more appropriate and accurate to use ΔG values than ΔS or ΔH values to predict the spontaneity of a reaction.

3. Are the reactions represented by the equations below spontaneous or nonspontaneous? Explain your answer.

   $$N_{2\,(g)} + O_{2\,(g)} \rightarrow 2NO_{(g)} \qquad \Delta G = 173 \text{ kJ}$$
   $$2HI_{(g)} \rightarrow H_{2\,(g)} + I_{2\,(g)} \qquad \Delta G = -2.6 \text{ kJ}$$

4. Explain why the equation below has a positive ΔS value:

   $$N_2O_{4\,(g)} \rightarrow 2NO_{2\,(g)}$$

5. Consider the equation below:

   $$CH_{4\,(g)} + 2O_{2\,(g)} \rightarrow CO_{2\,(g)} + 2H_2O_{(l)}$$

   At 298 K, $\Delta S = -0.242$ kJ/K, and $\Delta H = -891$ kJ. Is the reaction spontaneous or nonspontaneous at 298 K? Explain your answer.

6. Predict the sign of the ΔS value for the equation below. Explain your answer.

   $$C_2H_{2\,(g)} + 2I_{2\,(g)} \rightarrow C_2H_2I_{6\,(g)}$$

7. **Challenge** Predict the sign of the ΔS value for the equation below. Explain your answer.

   $$4Fe_{(s)} + 3O_{2\,(g)} \rightarrow 2Fe_2O_{3\,(s)}$$

8. **Challenge** The descriptions below give information about the ΔH and ΔS values for four different reactions. Use this information to state whether each of the reactions is spontaneous or nonspontaneous. If it is not possible to determine the spontaneity from the information given, explain why.

   reaction 1: positive ΔH, positive ΔS

   reaction 2: positive ΔH, negative ΔS

   reaction 3: negative ΔH, positive ΔS

   reaction 4: negative ΔH, negative ΔS

9. **Challenge** Use the equation for ΔG to explain why a reaction with a positive ΔH value and a positive ΔS value may be spontaneous at high temperatures, but not at low temperatures.

Electrochemical Processes

The transfer of electrons in an oxidation-reduction reaction can be used to generate electricity, and applying an electrical voltage can transform electrical energy into chemical energy by driving an oxidation-reduction reaction in the opposite direction.

Electrochemical cells are of two types: those that transform chemical energy into electrical energy and those that transform electrical energy into chemical energy. Cells consist of two electrodes (usually two metals) suspended in a salt solution (the electrolyte) and connected by a conducting wire. The two salt solutions are joined by a salt bridge. When one metal is oxidized, electrons flow from it through the wire to the other electrode, where metal ions in solution gain electrons and are reduced. The circuit is completed by ions migrating through the salt bridge from one electrode to the other. If the overall oxidation-reduction reaction proceeds spontaneously, it generates electrical energy and the cell is called a *voltaic cell* (also known as a *galvanic cell*). If the reaction is forced in the other direction by applying a voltage, chemical energy is produced and the cell is called an *electrolytic cell*.

OBJECTIVES

- Describe an electro-chemical cell.

- Describe how electro-chemical cells can convert chemical energy into electrical energy or electrical energy into chemical energy.

EXAMPLE 1

Describe an Electrochemical Cell

The diagram below shows an electrochemical cell connected to a lightbulb. The glowing bulb indicates that the cell is generating electricity.

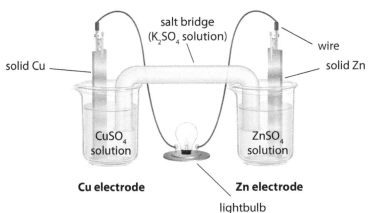

At the zinc (Zn) electrode, zinc metal is being converted to zinc ions (Zn^{2+}) by losing electrons. At the copper (Cu) electrode, copper ions (Cu^{2+}) are being converted into copper metal by gaining electrons. Write the chemical equation for the half-reaction occurring at each electrode. Does the diagram represent a voltaic cell or an electrolytic cell? Explain what would have to happen to convert this cell to the other type of electrochemical cell.

REMEMBER

ELECTROCHEMICAL PROCESSES

- In a voltaic cell, chemical energy in the form of atoms, ions, or molecules is converted into electrical energy in the form of moving electrons.

- Electrons spontaneously flow from one electrode to the other in a voltaic cell. That is, no energy must be added to the cell to cause electrons to flow.

- In an electrolytic cell, electrical energy in the form of moving electrons is converted into chemical energy in the form of atoms, ions, or molecules.

- The flow of electrons in an electrolytic cell is nonspontaneous. Energy in the form of electricity must be added to an electrolytic cell to cause electrons to flow.

Solution

1 Recall Relevant Information   In a voltaic cell, chemical energy is converted into electrical energy. In an electrolytic cell, electrical energy is converted into chemical energy. A half-reaction shows only the chemical species that is oxidized or reduced during a redox reaction. Oxidation occurs when a species loses electrons. Reduction occurs when a species gains electrons.

2 Solve   At the zinc electrode, zinc is oxidized. Each zinc atom loses two electrons to form a Zn^{2+} ion, so the oxidation half-reaction is $Zn \rightarrow Zn^{2+} + 2e^-$. At the copper electrode, copper ions are reduced. Each Cu^{2+} ion gains two electrons to form a copper atom, so the reduction half-reaction is $Cu^{2+} + 2e^- \rightarrow Cu$. The glowing bulb indicates that the cell is producing electricity. Therefore, it must be converting chemical energy into electrical energy, and it is a voltaic cell. This cell could be converted to an electrolytic cell by replacing the lightbulb with a source of voltage, such as a battery. The voltage source would force the electrons to flow from the copper electrode to the zinc electrode—that is, the electrons would flow in the opposite direction to that in which they flow in the voltaic cell. The zinc would be reduced, and the copper would be oxidized.

> **TIP**
>
> You can think of an electrolytic cell as the opposite of a voltaic cell. If electrons flow in one direction in a voltaic cell, they will flow in the opposite direction if the voltaic cell is converted to an electrolytic cell.

Problem Set

1. Describe the difference between a voltaic cell and an electrolytic cell.

2. Define *electrochemical cell* in your own words.

3. When a person starts a car, chemical reactions in the car battery generate electricity, which is used to start the car's engine. When the engine is running, some of the energy from the engine is used to produce electricity. Some of the electricity is used to regenerate the chemicals in the car battery. Explain how this shows that a car battery can operate as both an electrolytic cell and as a voltaic cell.

4. In a particular voltaic cell, silver ions (Ag^+) gain electrons to form silver metal (Ag), and zinc metal (Zn) loses electrons to form zinc ions (Zn^{2+}). Write the oxidation and reduction half-reactions for this voltaic cell.

5. **Challenge**   The following equation describes the overall reaction in a galvanic cell:

   $$Cd + 2Fe^{3+} \rightarrow Cd^{2+} + 2Fe^{2+}$$

   What are the two half-reactions taking place at the electrodes? (Hint: Identify which species is oxidized and which is reduced.)

6. **Challenge**   A particular electrochemical cell can be used to produce electricity to ring a bell. Is this cell acting as a voltaic cell or as an electrolytic cell? What is the sign on the ΔG value for the cell? Explain your answer. (Hint: Remember that a spontaneous reaction has a negative ΔG value.)

Voltaic Cells

A voltaic cell converts chemical energy to electrical energy when an oxidation reaction takes place in one half-cell and a reduction reaction takes place in the other half-cell.

A voltaic cell (also called a *galvanic cell*) consists of two half-cells, each of which contains an electrolyte solution and a suspended electrode. An oxidation half-reaction takes place at one half-cell, and a reduction half-reaction takes place at the other half-cell. The half-cell at which the oxidation reaction takes place is called the *anode*. The half-cell at which the reduction reaction takes place is called the *cathode*. The electrolyte solutions are connected by a salt bridge, and the electrical circuit is completed by a conductive wire connecting the electrodes.

EXAMPLE 1

Describe a Voltaic Cell

A copper-zinc voltaic cell is shown below.

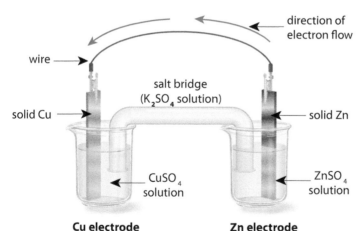

Cu electrode   **Zn electrode**

The flow of electrons is shown in the diagram. Identify the anode and the cathode in the cell, and write the overall reaction that occurs in the cell.

Solution

1 **Study the Diagram**   One of the electrodes consists of solid copper suspended in a solution of copper sulfate ($CuSO_4$). The other electrode consists of solid zinc suspended in a solution of zinc sulfate ($ZnSO_4$). Electrons flow from the zinc electrode to the copper electrode.

② **Analyze**   The oxidation state of copper is 0 in the solid copper and $+2$ in the $CuSO_4$ solution. The oxidation state of zinc is 0 in the solid zinc and $+2$ in the $ZnSO_4$ solution. If electrons are flowing from the Zn electrode to the Cu electrode, the solid Zn must be losing electrons to form Zn^{2+} ions. In addition, the Cu^{2+} ions must be gaining electrons to form solid Cu. Therefore, zinc is being oxidized, and Cu^{2+} is being reduced.

③ **Solve**   Oxidation occurs at the anode, and reduction occurs at the cathode. Therefore, the zinc electrode must be the anode, and the copper electrode must be the cathode. The reactions taking place in the two half-cells are shown below:

anode: $\qquad$ $Zn \rightarrow Zn^{2+} + 2e^-$

cathode: $Cu^{2+} + 2e^- \rightarrow Cu$

Each of these reactions involves two electrons, so you can add the half-reactions together as written to obtain the overall reaction for the cell, as shown below:

$$Zn \rightarrow Zn^{2+} + \cancel{2e^-}$$
$$\underline{Cu^{2+} + \cancel{2e^-} \rightarrow Cu}$$
$$Cu^{2+} + Zn \rightarrow Cu + Zn^{2+}$$

> **TIP**
>
> You can use an acronym to remember which half-reaction occurs at which half-cell. For example, consider the acronym *an ox, red cat*. This acronym can help you remember that the *anode* is where *oxidation* takes place, and that *reduction* takes place at the *cathode*.

Problem Set

1. Which of these reactions could take place at the anode of a voltaic cell?
   A. $Ag^+ + e^- \rightarrow Ag$
   B. $Fe^{3+} + e^- \rightarrow Fe^{2+}$
   C. $H_2 \rightarrow 2H^+ + 2e^-$
   D. $I_2 + 2e^- \rightarrow 2I^-$

2. The following half-reactions occur in a voltaic cell:

   $\qquad$ $Al \rightarrow Al^{3+} + 3e^-$

   $Sn^{2+} + 2e^- \rightarrow Sn$

   Which reaction occurs at the cathode, and which occurs at the anode? Explain your answer.

3. Which is more likely to be produced at the anode of a voltaic cell, Cd^{2+} or Cl^-? Explain your answer.

4. Follow the electrons. The half-reaction shown below takes place in a voltaic cell:

   $MnO_4^- + 8H^+ + 5e^- \rightarrow Mn^{2+} + 4H_2O$

   At which electrode does this reaction take place? Explain your answer.

5. **Challenge**   The cathode of a particular voltaic cell consists of solid silver suspended in a solution of silver nitrate ($AgNO_3$). If the oxidation state of silver in $AgNO_3$ is $+1$, what is the half-reaction that occurs at the cathode in this voltaic cell?

6. **Challenge**   In a particular voltaic cell, the anode is made of solid magnesium suspended in a solution of magnesium sulfate, $MgSO_4$. The cathode is made of solid lead suspended in a solution of lead sulfate, $PbSO_4$. Draw a sketch of this voltaic cell. Use an arrow to show the direction electrons are moving, identify the half-reaction that occurs at each electrode, and write the overall reaction that occurs in the cell. (Hint: Magnesium has an oxidation state of $+2$ in $MgSO_4$, and lead has an oxidation state of $+2$ in $PbSO_4$.)

Dry Cells

Electrochemistry has many applications in industry as well as in the home. The dry cell is an important application of electrochemistry.

Most of the batteries people use in everyday devices, such as cameras and flashlights, are dry cells. Dry cells are voltaic cells. They are called *dry-cell batteries* because, unlike other kinds of voltaic cells, they do not contain liquid electrolyte solutions. Instead, in a dry cell, the electrolyte is a paste or gel. More generally, a dry cell is a voltaic cell that does not contain free liquid. Dry cells are generally smaller, safer, and more portable than voltaic cells that contain liquids.

OBJECTIVE

- Describe the chemistry of various kinds of dry-cell batteries.

EXAMPLE 1

Describe a Simple Dry Cell

One kind of simple dry cell is known as a *voltaic pile*. A voltaic pile consists of sheets of metal layered with an absorbent material that has been soaked in a salt or acid solution, as shown here.

If you connect a wire to each end of the voltaic pile, an electric current will flow through the wire. Identify the role of the salt- or acid-soaked absorbent material in a voltaic pile, and explain why the metals must be different for current to flow.

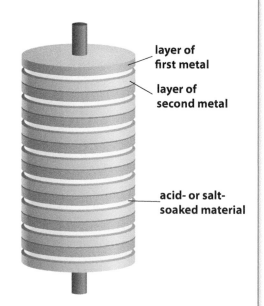

layer of
first metal

layer of
second metal

acid- or salt-
soaked material

Solution

1 **Recall Relevant Information**   In a voltaic cell, electrons move from one electrode to the other. A wire carries the electrons, and an electrolyte allows other ions to move to keep the charges balanced. Different metals have different reduction potentials— that is, some metals are more easily reduced than others.

2 **Solve**   The salt- or acid-soaked material acts as the electrolyte in the voltaic pile. The two metals must be different so that electrons can move between them. If the two metals were the same, electrons would not move, because there would be no potential difference between the layers.

REMEMBER

DRY CELLS

- A dry cell is a voltaic cell—that is, it operates on the same principles as a voltaic cell: oxidation and reduction. As in all voltaic cells, oxidation occurs at the anode, and reduction occurs at the cathode.

- In a dry cell, the electrolyte is a paste or gel. This is different from a wet voltaic cell, in which the electrolyte is a liquid.

- There are different kinds of dry cells. Some can be recharged when an electric current runs through them, but others cannot.

EXAMPLE 2

Describe How a Dry Cell Works

The diagram shows a kind of dry cell called an *alkaline battery*.

The graphite rod conducts electrons into the MnO_2/KOH paste. Zn^{2+} ions are produced at the anode, and Mn_2O_3 is produced at the cathode. In MnO_2, manganese has an oxidation state of $+4$. In Mn_2O_3, it has an oxidation state of $+3$. Which substance is the anode in this battery, and which is the cathode?

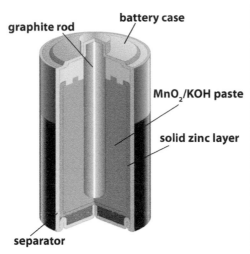

graphite rod

battery case

MnO_2/KOH paste

solid zinc layer

separator

Solution

① **Recall Relevant Information** Oxidation occurs at the anode, and reduction occurs at the cathode. During oxidation, a species loses electrons. During reduction, a species gains electrons. Manganese gains electrons, so it is reduced. The zinc loses electrons, so it is oxidized.

② **Solve** The zinc is oxidized, so it must be the anode. The MnO_2 is reduced, so it must be the cathode.

Problem Set

1. Which of these statements describes a dry cell, but **not** a wet voltaic cell?
   A. The electrolyte is a paste.
   B. Oxidation occurs at the anode.
   C. Electrons flow through a wire.
   D. Reduction occurs at the cathode.

2. Give two reasons why dry cells are used in portable electronic devices, but wet voltaic cells are not.

3. Follow the electrons. Silver-zinc "button" batteries are common in calculators, watches, and hearing aids. One of the half-reactions that occurs in a button battery is shown below:

   $$Ag_2O + H_2O + 2e^- \rightarrow 2Ag + 2OH^-$$

   Does this reaction occur at the anode or the cathode? Explain your answer.

4. The following overall reaction occurs in a nickel-cadmium dry-cell battery:

   $$Cd + 2NiO(OH) + 2H_2O \rightarrow 2Ni(OH)_2 + Cd(OH)_2$$

   Identify which metal (Cd or Zn) is oxidized at the anode, and which is reduced at the cathode.

5. **Challenge** Some kinds of dry cells can be recharged if an electric current runs through them. During recharging, the reactions that occur at the anode and the cathode when the battery produces electricity are reversed. The following reactions occur in a nickel-cadmium rechargeable battery when it is being recharged:

   $$2Ni(OH)_2 + 2OH^- \rightarrow 2NiO(OH) + 2H_2O + 2e^-$$

   $$Cd(OH)_2 + 2e^- \rightarrow Cd + 2OH^-$$

   What half-reactions occur at the anode and cathode when the battery is *producing* electric current?

6. **Challenge** The following half-reactions occur in a silver-zinc button battery:

   $$Ag_2O + H_2O + 2e^- \rightarrow 2Ag + 2OH^-$$

   $$Zn + 2OH^- \rightarrow ZnO + H_2O + 2e^-$$

   Write the chemical equation for the overall reaction that occurs in a button battery.

Electrolytic Cells

An electrolytic cell converts electrical energy to chemical energy by using an applied voltage to drive an oxidation-reduction reaction in a direction in which it does not occur spontaneously.

When an electrolytic cell is operating, a voltage drives an oxidation-reduction reaction in the direction opposite to the spontaneous direction. Therefore, an electrolytic cell converts electrical energy into chemical energy. A rechargeable battery, such as a car battery, acts as an electrolytic cell when it is being recharged and as a voltaic cell when it is discharging. Electrolytic cells are also used in industry. For example, during electroplating, a voltage is used to force the deposition (plating) of a metal onto one of the electrodes in an electrolytic cell. Electrolytic cells can also be used to drive decomposition reactions to produce useful chemicals.

EXAMPLE 1

Describe an Electrolytic Cell

The diagram below shows an electrolytic cell that is used in the industrial production of sodium (Na) and chlorine (Cl_2) from molten sodium chloride (NaCl).

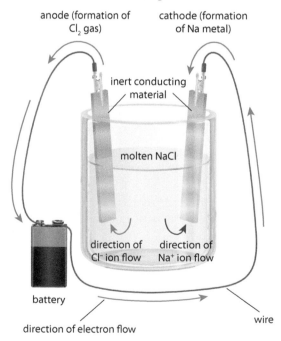

anode (formation of Cl_2 gas)

cathode (formation of Na metal)

inert conducting material

molten NaCl

direction of Cl^- ion flow

direction of Na^+ ion flow

battery

wire

direction of electron flow

The flow of electrons is shown. Identify the half-reactions that occur at the anode and cathode, and write the overall reaction that occurs in the cell.

REMEMBER

ELECTROLYTIC CELLS
- In any electrochemical cell, oxidation occurs at the anode and reduction occurs at the cathode. This is true of both electrolytic cells and voltaic cells. Therefore, electrons always flow from the anode to the cathode.
- The chemical reaction that occurs in an electrolytic cell is nonspontaneous. This is different from a voltaic cell. In a voltaic cell, the chemical reaction is spontaneous.
- The nonspontaneity of the chemical reaction in an electrolytic cell is the reason energy (in the form of a voltage) must be applied to the cell to cause the reaction to proceed.

Solution

1 **Study the Diagram** The diagram shows Na^+ ions flowing to the cathode and Cl^- ions flowing to the anode. Solid sodium (Na) forms at the cathode, and gaseous chlorine (Cl_2) forms at the anode. Electrons flow from the anode to the cathode.

2 **Analyze** The oxidation states of sodium and chlorine in their pure elemental states are 0. In sodium chloride, sodium (Na^+) has an oxidation state of $+1$, and chlorine (Cl^-) has an oxidation state of -1. Therefore, sodium ions gain electrons and are reduced, and chloride ions lose electrons and are oxidized.

3 **Solve** Oxidation occurs at the anode, and reduction occurs at the cathode. Therefore, the half-reactions occurring in the cell are the ones shown below:

anode: $2Cl^- \rightarrow Cl_2 + 2e^-$

cathode: $Na^+ + e^- \rightarrow Na$

To balance the number of electrons in the reactions, multiply the cathode reaction by 2. Then, add together the two half-reactions to yield the overall reaction, as shown below:

$$2Cl^- \rightarrow Cl_2 + \cancel{2e^-}$$
$$\underline{2Na^+ + \cancel{2e^-} \rightarrow 2Na}$$
$$2Na^+ + 2Cl^- \rightarrow Cl_2 + 2Na$$

TIP

Remember that oxidation is the loss of electrons and reduction is the gain of electrons.

Problem Set

1. Describe how the battery in a cellular phone can act as both an electrolytic cell and a voltaic cell.

2. Describe the difference between a voltaic cell and an electrolytic cell.

3. An electrolytic cell used to gold-plate objects is shown here.

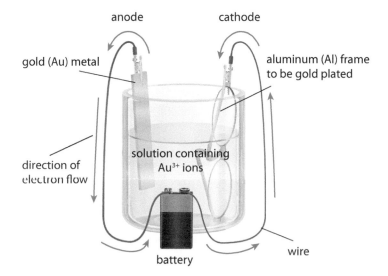

anode   cathode

gold (Au) metal

aluminum (Al) frame to be gold plated

direction of electron flow

solution containing Au^{3+} ions

battery

wire

Explain how the glasses frame acquires a coating of gold when a voltage is applied. The electrolyte solution contains Au^{3+} ions.

4. The following redox reaction occurs in a voltaic cell:

$$Cu^{2+} + Zn \rightarrow Zn^{2+} + Cu$$

What reaction would occur if a voltage were applied to the cell, converting it into an electrolytic cell?

5. **Challenge** The following overall reaction occurs in an electrolytic cell:

$$2Al_2O_3 + 3C \rightarrow 4Al + 3CO_2$$

Identify the chemical species that are oxidized and reduced in the cell. If electrons were allowed to flow spontaneously, which species would be oxidized, and which would be reduced?

6. **Challenge** During the electrolysis of water, electricity is used to decompose water. O_2 gas and H^+ ions are produced at the anode, and H_2 gas and OH^- ions are produced at the cathode. Write the half-reactions and the overall reaction for this electrolytic cell. (Hint: An H^+ ion and an OH^- ion are equivalent to one water molecule.)

Hydrocarbons and Other Organic Chemicals

Carbon atoms can form up to four bonds. This allows them to form a wide variety of chemicals, many of which are the basic compounds that make up living things.

Almost every compound in your body, and in the bodies of other living things, is based on the element carbon. Most carbon-containing compounds are *organic compounds.* The most common kind of organic compound is the hydrocarbon. A *hydrocarbon* is an organic compound that consists of only carbon and hydrogen atoms. However, not all organic compounds are hydrocarbons. Some organic compounds contain oxygen, nitrogen, sulfur, or other elements in addition to carbon and hydrogen. Organic compounds are classified into different groups depending on how the atoms in them are arranged. For example, a hydrocarbon in which all the carbon-carbon bonds are single bonds is called an *alkane*. A hydrocarbon that contains one or more carbon-carbon double bonds is called an *alkene*. A hydrocarbon that contains one or more carbon-carbon triple bonds is called an *alkyne*. Organic compounds that are not hydrocarbons are also named and grouped according to the arrangement of their atoms. For example, an *alcohol* is a hydrocarbon in which one of the hydrogen atoms has been replaced by a hydroxyl group ($-OH$).

OBJECTIVES

- Draw structural formulas for organic compounds.
- Identify different types of organic compounds.

REMEMBER

ORGANIC COMPOUNDS

- A condensed formula shows the atoms in a molecule, but it does not show the structure of the molecule.

- Many condensed formulas show the relative positions of the carbon atoms in a molecule. This information can help you write a structural formula for the molecule.

- A structural formula, which is similar to a Lewis dot structure, shows the relative positions of all the atoms in the molecule, as well as the bonds between them. It does not show the molecule's actual three-dimensional shape.

- Most organic compounds are classified according to their functional groups. A functional group is a group of atoms arranged in a specific way that give an organic compound a specific set of chemical properties. For example, the functional group in an alcohol is the hydroxyl group ($-OH$), and the functional group in a ketone is a carbonyl group (a double-bonded oxygen atom).

EXAMPLE 1

Describe the Formation of Organic Compounds

Carbon compounds are essential to the existence of living organisms. Which unique chemical properties of carbon make possible the great variety of organic compounds needed by living organisms?

Solution

❶ **Recall Relevant Information** Carbon is a nonmetal. Carbon forms covalent bonds with itself and with other nonmetals. Carbon, hydrogen, oxygen, and nitrogen are all nonmetals. Carbon can form four covalent bonds, and it can form single, double, and triple bonds.

❷ **Reason** Covalent bonds between nonmetal atoms vary in strength, and can be broken and changed during chemical reactions. The ability to form four bonds allows the formation of branching chains of atoms.

❸ **Solve** Carbon compounds exist in greater variety than compounds of other elements because of the greater variety of bonding possibilities. Because each carbon atom can form four bonds, carbon compounds can have multiple branches and structures. The relatively low strength of some covalent bonds allows biological processes to rearrange the atoms of carbon compounds to form new organic molecules.

EXAMPLE 2

Draw a Structural Formula for a Hydrocarbon

The condensed formula of the hydrocarbon methyl butane is $CH_3CH(CH_3)CH_2CH_3$. It consists of a chain of four carbons with a single carbon atom bonded to the second carbon atom in the chain. Each of the carbon-carbon and carbon-hydrogen bonds is a single bond. Draw the structural formula for methyl butane.

Solution

1 **Collect and Strategize**   Each carbon atom will form four bonds. The problem states that the longest chain of carbon atoms in methyl butane is four atoms long. Start by drawing the longest carbon chain. Then, add the rest of the molecule.

2 **Solve**   First, draw the carbon atoms. The molecule has a four-carbon backbone with one carbon branching off from the second carbon in the chain. All of the bonds are single bonds, as shown below:

$$
\begin{array}{c}
\text{C} \\
| \\
\text{C}-\text{C}-\text{C}-\text{C}
\end{array}
$$

Each of the carbons must form four bonds. The only other element in the compound is hydrogen, so fill in the missing bonds with hydrogen atoms to form the complete structural formula, as shown below:

$$
\begin{array}{c}
\text{H} \\
| \\
\text{H}-\text{C}-\text{H} \\
\text{H} \quad | \quad \text{H} \quad \text{H} \\
| \quad | \quad | \quad | \\
\text{H}-\text{C}-\text{C}-\text{C}-\text{C}-\text{H} \\
| \quad | \quad | \quad | \\
\text{H} \quad \text{H} \quad \text{H} \quad \text{H}
\end{array}
$$

Note that the carbon-carbon bond between the second carbon in the chain and the single-carbon branch is not actually longer than the other carbon-carbon bonds. It is simply drawn longer to allow space for all of the hydrogen atoms.

TIP

In organic compounds, each hydrogen atom forms one bond, each oxygen atom forms two bonds, each nitrogen atom forms three bonds, and each carbon atom forms four bonds (counting double bonds as two bonds and triple bonds as three).

EXAMPLE 3

Draw a Structural Formula for a Hydrocarbon with Multiple Bonds

The condensed formula for the hydrocarbon 2-hexene is $CH_3CHCH(CH_2)_2CH_3$. It consists of a chain of six carbon atoms with a double bond between the second and third carbon atoms. The other bonds in the molecule are single bonds. Draw the structural formula for 2-hexene.

Solution

1 **Collect and Strategize**   Each carbon atom will form four bonds. The problem states that the longest chain of carbon atoms in 2-hexene is six atoms long. Start by drawing the carbon chain. Then, add the hydrogen atoms.

2   **Solve**   First, draw the carbon chain. There is a double bond between the second and third carbons. All the other carbons are joined by single bonds, as shown below:

$$C-C=C-C-C-C$$

Now, add the hydrogen atoms. Each carbon atom will form four bonds. Add as many hydrogen atoms to each carbon as are necessary to give each carbon four bonds, as shown below:

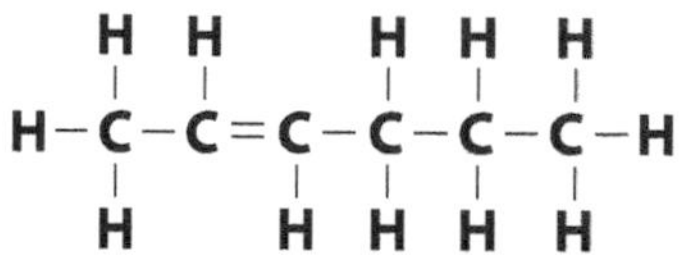

EXAMPLE 4

Draw a Structural Formula for a Cyclic Hydrocarbon

Benzene is a cyclic hydrocarbon. It consists of a ring of six carbon atoms. Double bonds join the first and second, third and fourth, and fifth and sixth carbon atoms. Draw the structural formula for benzene.

Solution

1   **Collect and Strategize**   Each carbon atom will form four bonds. The structure consists of a ring of six carbon atoms. First, draw the ring. Then, add hydrogen atoms to give each carbon atom the correct number of bonds.

2   **Solve**   The ring is shown below:

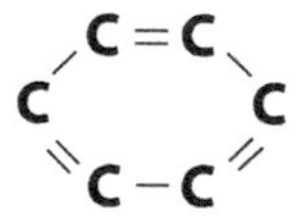

Now, add the hydrogen atoms. Each carbon atom will form four bonds. Add as many hydrogen atoms to each carbon as are necessary to give each carbon four bonds, as shown below:

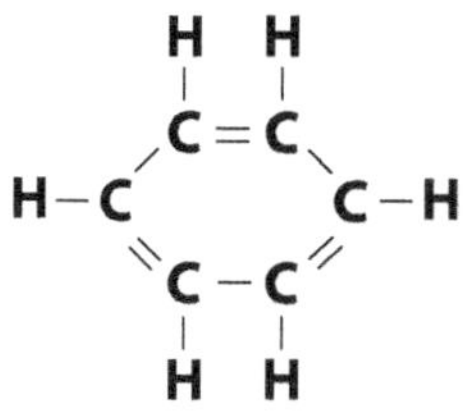

TIP

Cyclic hydrocarbons are hydrocarbons with a ring structure. The prefix *cyclo–* in a compound's name indicates that the compound is a cyclic hydrocarbon.

EXAMPLE 5

Use Structures to Identify Organic Compounds

One of the structural formulas below shows a carboxylic acid, one shows an aldehyde, and one shows a ketone. Identify which structural formula shows which kind of organic compound.

$$
\begin{array}{cccc}
& H & O & H & H \\
& | & || & | & | \\
H - & C & - C & - C & - C - H \\
& | & & | & | \\
& H & & H & H
\end{array}
$$

Compound A

$$
H - C - C - C - C - C - OH
$$

Compound B

$$
H - C - C - C - H
$$

Compound C

Solution

1 **Collect and Strategize**   Different classes of organic compounds have different structural formulas. The table below shows the structural formulas of some of the most common types of organic compounds. In the structural formulas below, *R* stands for a chain of carbon atoms.

Type of Compound	General Formula	Type of Compound	General Formula
Aldehyde	O ‖ R—C—H	Carboxylic acid	O ‖ R—C—OH
Ketone	O ‖ R—C—R	Ester	O ‖ R—C—O—R
Alcohol	R—OH	Ether	R—O—R
Amine	R—NH$_2$	Amide	O H ‖ | R—C—N—R

2 **Analyze**   Compound A consists of a chain of carbon atoms with an oxygen atom double-bonded to one of the central carbon atoms. Compound B consists of a chain of carbon atoms with an oxygen atom double-bonded to one of the end carbon atoms. Compound B also has a hydroxyl group bonded to the end carbon atom. Compound C consists of a chain of carbon atoms with an oxygen atom double-bonded to one of the end carbon atoms, but with no hydroxyl group. The table shows that the types of organic compounds that contain double-bonded oxygen atoms are aldehydes, ketones, carboxylic acids, esters, and amides.

3 **Solve**   The table shows that a ketone consists of a chain of carbon atoms with an oxygen atom double-bonded to one of the central carbon atoms. Therefore, compound A must be a ketone. (It is the compound 2-butanone.) According to the table, a carboxylic acid is a chain of carbon atoms with a double-bonded oxygen atom and a hydroxyl group bonded to the end carbon. Therefore, compound B must be a carboxylic acid. (It is the compound pentanoic acid.) The table shows that an aldehyde consists of a chain of carbon atoms with a double-bonded oxygen atom and a hydrogen atom bonded to the end carbon. Therefore, compound C must be an aldehyde. (It is the compound propanal.)

TIP

Use functional groups to help you identify different types of organic compounds. Look for oxygen and nitrogen atoms, and study their relationships with the carbon atoms. Each functional group consists of a specific arrangement of atoms.

TIP

Be careful not to confuse carboxylic acids, aldehydes, and ketones. Pay attention to the relative positions of the oxygen and carbon atoms.

EXAMPLE 6

Draw Structures of Organic Compounds

The structural formula for pentane is shown here.

Pentane can form one of three different alcohols when it gains a hydroxyl group. Write the structural formulas for these three alcohols.

$$
\begin{array}{ccccc}
H & H & H & H & H \\
| & | & | & | & | \\
H-C-C-C-C-C-H \\
| & | & | & | & | \\
H & H & H & H & H
\end{array}
$$

TIP

When you are trying to figure out different structural formulas, it can help to imagine the molecule in three dimensions. Try rotating the three-dimensional structure in different directions to see if it is different from other versions of the molecule.

Solution

1 Recall Relevant Information An alcohol consists of a chain of carbon atoms with a hydroxyl group (—OH) substituted for one of the hydrogen atoms. Organic compounds exist in three dimensions. Therefore, it is necessary to consider symmetry and reflection when determining whether two molecules have the same structure. Two organic molecules with the same physical structure are molecules of the same compound. Only molecules with different physical structures are considered to be different compounds.

2 Reason Begin by studying the structural formula for pentane. There are 12 hydrogen atoms in pentane, any of which could be replaced by a hydroxyl group to form an alcohol. However, the problem states that there are only three possible structural formulas for alcohols formed from pentane. That is because many of the structural formulas are equivalent. For example, the two alcohols shown below are actually the same compound, because if the first one is flipped it becomes the second one.

$$
\begin{array}{ccccc}
H & H & H & H & OH \\
| & | & | & | & | \\
H-C-C-C-C-C-H \\
| & | & | & | & | \\
H & H & H & H & H
\end{array}
\qquad
\begin{array}{ccccc}
H & H & H & H & H \\
| & | & | & | & | \\
H-C-C-C-C-C-H \\
| & | & | & | & | \\
H & H & H & H & OH
\end{array}
$$

If you examine the structure with possible symmetries in mind, it is clear that there are only three positions for a hydroxyl group that produce unique structural formulas: the first, second, and third carbon atoms in the chain.

3 Solve The three possible alcohols that can form from pentane are shown below:

$$
\begin{array}{ccccc}
H & H & H & H & OH \\
| & | & | & | & | \\
H-C-C-C-C-C-H \\
| & | & | & | & | \\
H & H & H & H & H
\end{array}
\qquad
\begin{array}{ccccc}
H & H & H & OH & H \\
| & | & | & | & | \\
H-C-C-C-C-C-H \\
| & | & | & | & | \\
H & H & H & H & H
\end{array}
$$

$$
\begin{array}{ccccc}
H & H & OH & H & H \\
| & | & | & | & | \\
H-C-C-C-C-C-H \\
| & | & | & | & | \\
H & H & H & H & H
\end{array}
$$

The names of these compounds indicate the carbon atom to which the hydroxyl group is attached. The top left compound is 1-pentanol (or just pentanol), the top right compound is 2-pentanol, and the bottom compound is 3-pentanol.

Problem Set

1. Draw the structural formula of 3-heptene, a seven-carbon chain with a double bond between the third and fourth carbon atoms.

2. The structural formula of an organic compound is shown below:

$$
\begin{array}{c}
\quad\ \ H\ \quad\quad O\ \ H \\
\quad\ \ | \quad\quad\quad || \ \ | \\
A: \ \ H-C-O-C-C-H \\
\quad\ \ | \quad\quad\quad\quad\ \ | \\
\quad\ \ H \quad\quad\quad\quad H
\end{array}
$$

   What type of organic compound is this? Explain how you know. (Hint: Use the table in Example 5.)

3. How do chemists classify organic compounds?

4. The hydrocarbon 2-butyne consists of a chain of four carbon atoms. The second and third atoms are joined by a triple bond. All other bonds in the molecule are single bonds. Draw the structural formula for 2-butyne.

5. Draw the structural formulas of a carboxylic acid, an alcohol, and an amine. Assume that each contains two carbon atoms. (Hint: Use the table in Example 5.)

6. Which of the structural formulas below shows an ether?

   A.
$$
\begin{array}{c}
\quad\ \ H\ \quad\quad O\ \ H \\
\quad\ \ | \quad\quad\quad || \ \ | \\
H-C-O-C-C-H \\
\quad\ \ | \quad\quad\quad\quad\ \ | \\
\quad\ \ H \quad\quad\quad\quad H
\end{array}
$$

   B.
$$
\begin{array}{c}
\quad\ \ H\ \quad\quad H\ \ H \\
\quad\ \ | \quad\quad\quad | \ \ \ | \\
H-C-O-C-C-H \\
\quad\ \ | \quad\quad\quad | \ \ \ | \\
\quad\ \ H \quad\quad\quad H\ \ H
\end{array}
$$

7. **Challenge** Draw the two possible structural formulas for a four-carbon chain that contains one double bond.

8. **Challenge** Write the structural formula for the compound with the condensed formula $CH_3COCH_2CH_3$. What type of compound is this? (Hint: All of the atoms in the molecule are shown. The condensed formula shows the relative positions of the carbon atoms. Remember that carbon forms four bonds.)

9. **Challenge** The structural formula below is incomplete. It shows all of the carbon-hydrogen bonds, but none of the carbon-carbon bonds.

$$
\begin{array}{c}
\quad\quad\quad\quad H\ \ H \\
\quad\quad\quad\quad | \ \ \ | \\
H-C\quad C\quad C\quad C\quad C-H \\
\quad\quad\quad\quad | \ \ \ \quad\ | \\
\quad\quad\quad\quad H \quad\quad H
\end{array}
$$

   Complete the structural formula by filling in the missing bonds.

Polymers

Polymer molecules consist of long chains of repeating units.

A *polymer* is a substance that forms when many small, similar molecules bond together to form a chain or network. Some polymers occur naturally, and others are synthesized. Natural polymers include polysaccharides, such as the cellulose in plant cell walls; polypeptides (proteins); and polynucleotides (the nucleic acids DNA and RNA). Synthetic polymers include plastics, such as polyethylene, and certain fibers, such as polyesters. The smaller units that make up a polymer are called *monomers*. Polymers form when many monomers bond together to form a long chain or network. This process is called *polymerization*.

OBJECTIVES
- Describe a polymer.
- Describe how polymers form.

EXAMPLE 1

Describe How a Polymer Forms

The structural formula of ethylene (ethene) is shown below:

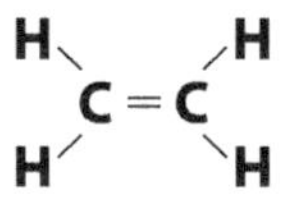

Ethylene monomers can react to form polyethylene, a polymer. During the reaction, each carbon atom in the monomer forms a single bond with a carbon atom on another monomer. As part of this reaction process, the double bond between the two carbon atoms in the monomer is converted into a single bond. Draw the structural formula for polyethylene.

Solution

1 **Collect and Strategize** The polymer will consist of many repeating units. The backbone of the polymer will be a string of carbon atoms. All the carbon atoms will be joined by single bonds.

2 **Solve** The diagram below shows the structural formula of polyethylene. Notice that the ends of the molecule are incomplete. By convention, the ends of a polymer are not shown in the structural formula. Only a small portion of the polymer is shown.

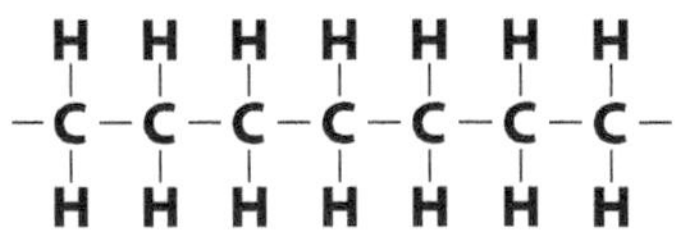

REMEMBER

POLYMERS

- A polymer is a molecule that forms when many smaller, similar molecules combine in a chain or network.

- The small units that make up a polymer are called *monomers*.

- The monomers that make up a polymer do not all have to be identical. They simply have to have similar structures. For example, proteins are polymers made up of amino acids. The amino acids are the monomers. All the proteins in living things are made up of combinations of only about 20 amino acids.

EXAMPLE 2

Identify a Polymer

Which of the structural formulas below shows a polymer?

structural formula A:

$$H-\underset{\underset{H}{|}}{\overset{\overset{H}{|}}{C}}-\underset{\underset{H}{|}}{\overset{\overset{H}{|}}{C}}-\underset{\underset{H}{|}}{\overset{\overset{H}{|}}{C}}-\underset{\underset{H}{|}}{\overset{\overset{H}{|}}{C}}-\underset{\underset{H}{|}}{\overset{\overset{H}{|}}{C}}-O-\underset{}{\overset{\overset{O}{\|}}{C}}-\underset{\underset{H}{|}}{\overset{\overset{H}{|}}{C}}-\underset{\underset{H}{|}}{\overset{\overset{H}{|}}{C}}-\underset{\underset{H}{|}}{\overset{\overset{H}{|}}{C}}-H$$

structural formula B:

$$-\underset{\underset{H}{|}}{\overset{\overset{H}{|}}{C}}-\underset{\underset{H}{|}}{\overset{\overset{Cl}{|}}{C}}-\underset{\underset{H}{|}}{\overset{\overset{H}{|}}{C}}-\underset{\underset{H}{|}}{\overset{\overset{Cl}{|}}{C}}-\underset{\underset{H}{|}}{\overset{\overset{H}{|}}{C}}-\underset{\underset{H}{|}}{\overset{\overset{Cl}{|}}{C}}-\underset{\underset{H}{|}}{\overset{\overset{H}{|}}{C}}-$$

Solution

1 **Collect and Strategize** A polymer consists of a long chain of repeating units. Therefore, to answer this question, examine the two structural formulas. Identify which structural formula shows a molecule made of repeating units.

2 **Solve** Structural formula B is made up of the unit below repeated many times:

$$\underset{\underset{H}{|}}{\overset{\overset{H}{|}}{C}}-\underset{\underset{H}{|}}{\overset{\overset{Cl}{|}}{C}}$$

Therefore, structural formula B represents a polymer. It is the structural formula of polyvinyl chloride (PVC), a polymer used in water pipes, trash cans, and other products.

TIP

Most polymers consist of hundreds of monomers linked together. Some polymers contain more than 1,000 monomers. Therefore, a polymer's structural formula generally does not show the entire polymer.

Problem Set

1. Describe the relationship between a monomer and a polymer.

2. Identify two polymers made by living things.

3. Describe how a polymer forms, in general terms.

4. Materials made from some synthetic polymers last for decades, and others decay to short-chain molecules more quickly. Decay can be caused by heat, light, and the hydrolysis (breaking) of bonds in the polymer chain. Give one example of a use for a polymer in which quick decay would be an advantage, and one example of a use in which quick decay would be a disadvantage.

5. **Challenge** The polymer polydichloroethylene (Saran™) is synthesized from the monomer 1,1-dichloroethene, which has the structural formula shown in the next column.

$$\underset{\underset{H}{|}}{\overset{\overset{H}{|}}{C}}=\underset{\underset{Cl}{|}}{\overset{\overset{Cl}{|}}{C}}$$

What is the structural formula of this polymer?

6. **Challenge** The structural formula of the synthetic polymer polypropylene is shown below:

$$-\underset{\underset{CH_3}{|}}{\overset{\overset{H}{|}}{C}}-\underset{\underset{H}{|}}{\overset{\overset{H}{|}}{C}}-\underset{\underset{CH_3}{|}}{\overset{\overset{H}{|}}{C}}-\underset{\underset{H}{|}}{\overset{\overset{H}{|}}{C}}-\underset{\underset{CH_3}{|}}{\overset{\overset{H}{|}}{C}}-\underset{\underset{H}{|}}{\overset{\overset{H}{|}}{C}}-\underset{\underset{CH_3}{|}}{\overset{\overset{H}{|}}{C}}-$$

What is the monomer from which this polymer is synthesized? (Hint: Polypropylene forms in a similar way to polyethylene.)

Carbohydrates and Fats

Living things use carbohydrates and lipids for energy, support, and storage.

Both carbohydrates and lipids are made mostly of carbon, hydrogen, and oxygen, and they both store energy in the form of carbon-carbon and carbon-hydrogen bonds. However, these two classes of compounds have very different structures. Carbohydrates consist of one or more rings of carbon, oxygen, and hydrogen. A single one of these rings is called a *monosaccharide*. Two of them joined together form a compound called a *disaccharide*. When large numbers of monosaccharides bond together, they form a polymer called a *polysaccharide*. In contrast, a lipid consists of fatty acids bonded together in different ways. These fatty acids are chains of carbon atoms with hydrogen atoms attached. Chemists divide lipids into three main groups: oils, fats, and waxes. In oils and fats, three fatty acid chains are bonded to a molecule of glycerol. Oils are liquid at room temperature, and fats are solid at room temperature. In waxes, two fatty acid chains are linked together. Like fats, waxes tend to be solid at room temperature. By mass, lipids hold more than twice as much energy as carbohydrates.

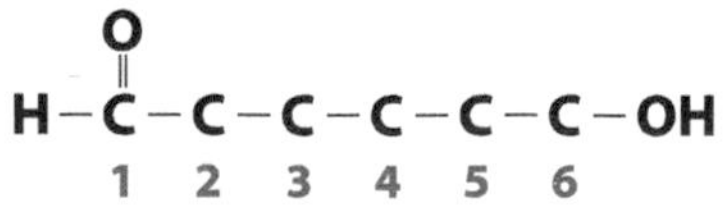

OBJECTIVES

- Draw structural formulas for simple carbohydrates and lipids.
- Describe the formation of polysaccharides and lipids.

REMEMBER

CARBOHYDRATES

- The simplest carbohydrates are monosaccharides. The most common monosaccharides are glucose and fructose.
- Monosaccharides can bond together to form polysaccharides, which are polymers.
- When glucose molecules bond together to form a long chain, they form either starch or cellulose, depending on which carbon atoms in each glucose molecule are involved in the bonding.
- Glycogen, another polysaccharide, forms when glucose molecules bond together to form a large, branching chain.
- Glucose is the main energy source for most living things. Glycogen and starch store energy for later use. Cellulose gives support to plant cells. A related polysaccharide, chitin, is the main component in many insect exoskeletons.

EXAMPLE 1

Draw the Structure of Glucose

Glucose is the most common monosaccharide. When it is dissolved in water, its molecules can change from rings to straight chains. The structural formula for a straight-chain glucose molecule is shown below:

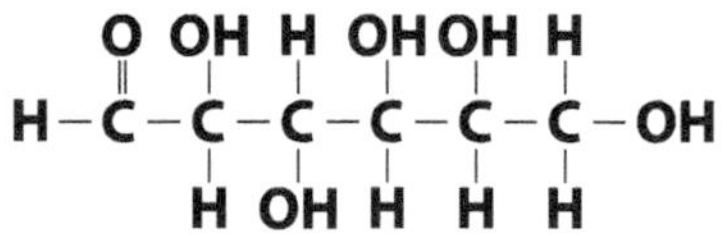

$$
\begin{array}{ccccccc}
 & O & OH & H & OH & OH & H \\
 & \| & | & | & | & | & | \\
H- & C- & C- & C- & C- & C- & C-OH \\
 & | & | & | & | & | \\
 & H & OH & H & H & H
\end{array}
$$

When this molecule forms a ring, the double-bonded oxygen atom in the aldehyde group becomes single-bonded to the second carbon atom from the other end of the chain. Draw the ring structure of glucose.

Solution

1 **Collect and Strategize**   First, draw the main ring. Then, add the side chains. To keep track of the carbon atoms, number them as shown in the diagram below. For clarity, most of the hydrogen atoms and hydroxyl groups have been omitted from the diagram.

$$
\begin{array}{cccccc}
 & O & & & & \\
 & \| & & & & \\
H- & C- & C- & C- & C- & C-OH \\
 & 1 & 2 & 3 & 4 & 5 & 6
\end{array}
$$

2 Solve To form the ring, the double-bonded oxygen atom attached to carbon 1 will form two single bonds, one to carbon 1 and one to carbon 5. This will lead to the basic ring structure shown below:

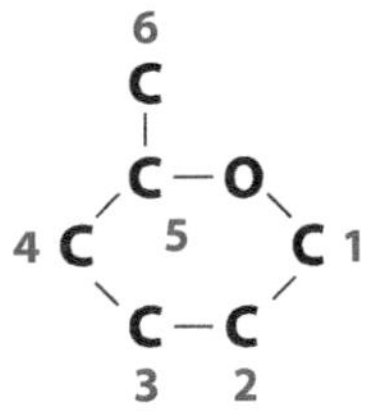

Now, compare this structure with the straight-chain structure. Add the correct side chains to the ring structure to produce the complete glucose structure shown below:

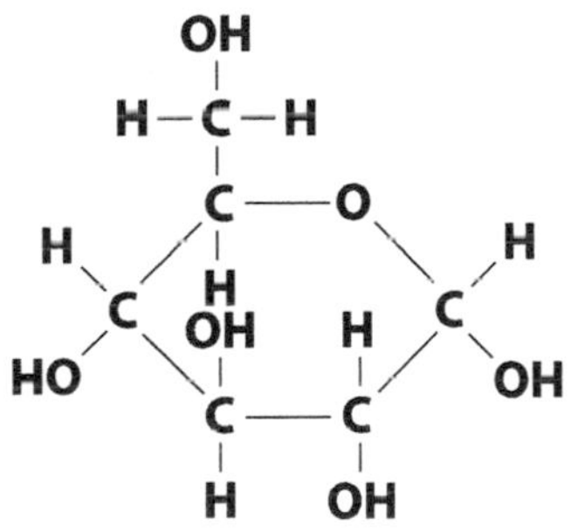

TIP

Numbering the carbon atoms in an organic molecule can help you keep track of where the carbon atoms end up after a reaction.

EXAMPLE 2

Describe Polysaccharides

The diagram below shows the structural formula of starch, a polysaccharide. For simplicity, the hydrogen atoms and some of the oxygen atoms are not shown.

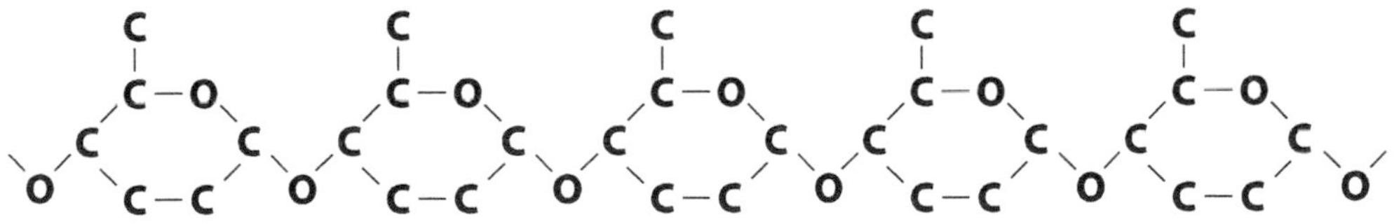

Describe how glucose molecules join to form starch.

Solution

1 Recall Relevant Information Polysaccharides are polymers that form when many monosaccharides bond together. Glucose is a monosaccharide.

2 Identify Monomers In the diagram on the next page, the repeating subunit in a starch molecule is circled in red.

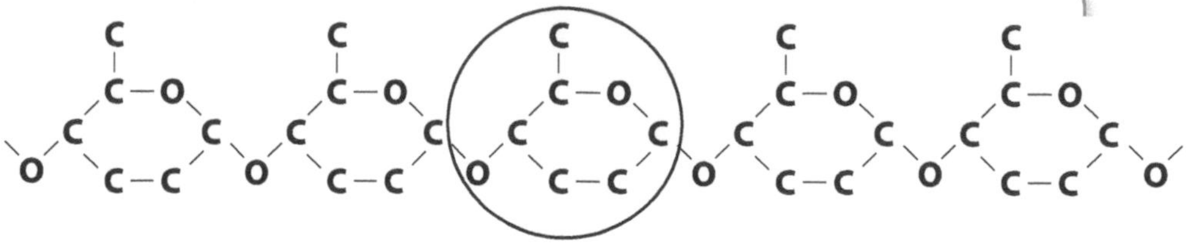

Compare this subunit to the ring structure of glucose.

3 **Solve**   The subunit in a starch molecule is a glucose ring that is missing a hydrogen atom on one side and a hydroxyl group on the other. Therefore, to form a molecule of starch, many glucose molecules must join together as shown below:

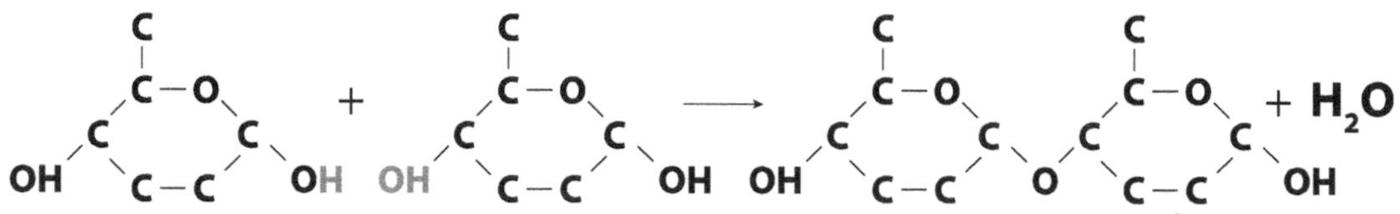

$$+ \text{H}_2\text{O}$$

EXAMPLE 3

Draw the Structure of a Lipid

Fats and oils consist of a molecule of glycerol bonded to three fatty acids. The structural formula of a glycerol molecule and the general structural formula of a fatty acid are shown below. (Remember that *R* stands for a chain of carbon atoms.)

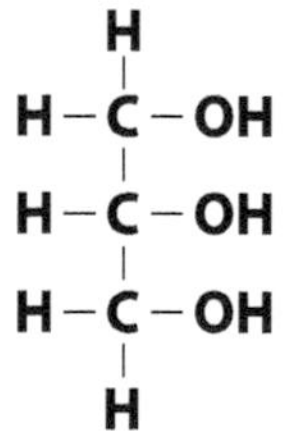

$$
\begin{array}{c}
\text{H} \\
\text{H}-\text{C}-\text{OH} \\
\text{H}-\text{C}-\text{OH} \\
\text{H}-\text{C}-\text{OH} \\
\text{H}
\end{array}
$$

glycerol

$$
\begin{array}{c}
\text{O} \\
\parallel \\
\text{OH}-\text{C}-\text{R}
\end{array}
$$

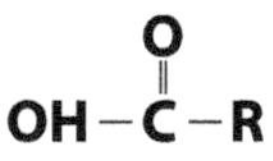

fatty acid

When a fat or oil forms, the hydrogen atom in each of the hydroxyl groups in glycerol reacts with a hydroxyl group at the end of a fatty acid. The hydrogen and hydroxyl combine to form a molecule of water. In addition, a single bond forms between the oxygen atom of the glycerol molecule and the end carbon atom of the fatty acid. Draw a diagram showing the general structure of a fat or oil.

Solution

1 **Collect and Strategize**   Each of the hydroxyl groups in the glycerol molecule will react with a fatty acid. Therefore, three fatty acids are required to react with one molecule of glycerol. The diagram on the next page shows how the molecules will react. The hydrogen atoms and hydroxyl groups that combine to form water are circled in red.

LIPIDS

- All lipids consist of fatty acid chains bonded to alcohols.

- A fatty acid is a carboxylic acid. Many fatty acids have long carbon chains.

- Fats and oils form when fatty acids bond to a molecule of glycerol. Glycerol is a three-carbon chain with three hydroxyl groups.

- A wax forms when a long-chain alcohol bonds with a long-chain fatty acid.

- Fats and waxes are solid at room temperature. Oils are liquid at room temperature.

$$
\begin{array}{cc}
\text{H} & \\
\text{H}-\text{C}-\text{OH} & \quad \text{HO}-\overset{\overset{\text{O}}{\|}}{\text{C}}-\text{R} \\
\text{H}-\text{C}-\text{OH} & \quad \text{HO}-\overset{\overset{\text{O}}{\|}}{\text{C}}-\text{R} \\
\text{H}-\text{C}-\text{OH} & \quad \text{HO}-\overset{\overset{\text{O}}{\|}}{\text{C}}-\text{R} \\
\text{H} &
\end{array}
$$

2 Solve As each water molecule forms, a single bond forms between a carbon atom and an oxygen atom. Therefore, the general structure of a fat or oil is the one shown below:

$$
\begin{array}{c}
\text{H} \quad\quad \text{O} \\
\text{H}-\text{C}-\text{O}-\overset{\overset{\text{O}}{\|}}{\text{C}}-\text{R} \\
\text{H}-\text{C}-\text{O}-\overset{\overset{\text{O}}{\|}}{\text{C}}-\text{R} \\
\text{H}-\text{C}-\text{O}-\overset{\overset{\text{O}}{\|}}{\text{C}}-\text{R} \\
\text{H}
\end{array}
$$

Because fats and oils contain three fatty acids bonded to a glycerol molecule, they are also called *triglycerides*.

TIP

The reaction between glycerol and fatty acids to form a lipid and water is called a *dehydration reaction* or *condensation reaction*, because water is one of the products.

Problem Set

1. Cellulose, a carbohydrate that gives structure to plants, is a compound formed by linking many glucose molecules together with strong chemical bonds. Is cellulose a monosaccharide, a disaccharide, or a polysaccharide? Explain your answer.

2. Draw the structural formula of a fat that has four carbons in each fatty acid chain. Assume that all of the carbon-carbon bonds in the fatty acid chains are single bonds.

3. Sucrose is a disaccharide. It forms when two monosaccharides bond together. If the chemical formula for each monosaccharide is $C_6H_{12}O_6$, what is the chemical formula for sucrose? (Hint: One water molecule forms during the reaction.)

4. A triglyceride in which the carbon atoms in the fatty acid chains are all joined by single bonds is called a *saturated fat*. If the fatty acid chains contain double bonds between some of the carbon atoms, the triglyceride is called an *unsaturated fat*. Draw the structural formula of an unsaturated fat with five carbon atoms in each of its fatty acid chains. (Hint: There are many different possible structures. You may draw any one of them.)

5. **Challenge** A wax is formed by the reaction of an alcohol and a fatty acid. The general forms of an alcohol and a fatty acid are shown below.

$$
\text{R}-\text{OH} \quad\quad \text{OH}-\overset{\overset{\text{O}}{\|}}{\text{C}}-\text{R}
$$
$$
\text{alcohol} \quad\quad \text{fatty acid}
$$

Draw the general form of a wax. (Hint: The reaction that forms a wax is the same kind of reaction that forms a triglyceride. A water molecule is one of the products of the reaction.)

6. **Challenge** Fructose is a monosaccharide. Like glucose, it can exist in both straight-chain and cyclic forms. The structural formula below shows the straight-chain form of fructose:

$$
\begin{array}{c}
\text{OH} \quad \text{O} \quad \text{H} \quad \text{OH}\,\text{OH} \quad \text{H} \\
\text{H}-\text{C}-\overset{\overset{\text{O}}{\|}}{\text{C}}-\text{C}-\text{C}-\text{C}-\text{C}-\text{OH} \\
\text{H} \quad\quad \text{OH} \quad \text{H} \quad \text{H} \quad \text{H}
\end{array}
$$

Draw the cyclic form of fructose. (Hint: The cyclic form consists of a five-member ring. It forms through the same type of reaction that forms glucose.)

Proteins and Nucleic Acids

Proteins perform many different functions for living things, including support, movement, and catalysis of reactions. Nucleic acids store genetic information.

Proteins are among the most versatile of all organic molecules. Some proteins act as catalysts in the chemical reactions that occur in cells. Some proteins provide support and strength for organisms. Still other proteins help organisms move. Despite their many different roles, all proteins have a similar basic structure. Proteins, which are also called *polypeptides,* are polymers. They are made up of subunits called *amino acids.* All the proteins in living things are combinations of about 20 different amino acids, which can be combined in millions of different ways to form proteins. These chains of amino acids then fold upon themselves to form the large, three-dimensional molecules called *proteins.* The directions for assembling the chains of amino acids in their proper order are stored in another type of organic polymer, nucleic acids. Nucleic acids (DNA and RNA) are composed of repeating units called *nucleotides,* which contain a phosphate group, a sugar, and a nitrogen-containing molecule called a *base.*

OBJECTIVES

- Describe the structure of proteins.
- Identify a peptide bond.
- Describe the structure of a nucleic acid.

EXAMPLE 1

Identify an Amino Acid

Which of the following diagrams shows the structural formula of an amino acid?

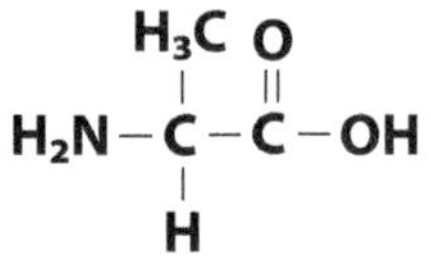

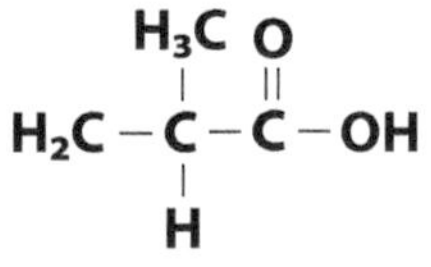

REMEMBER

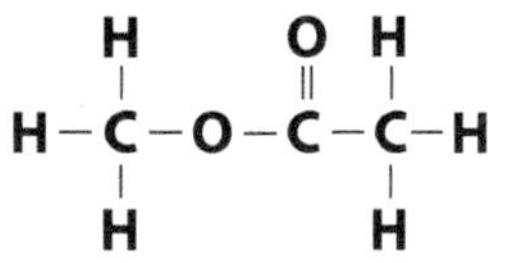

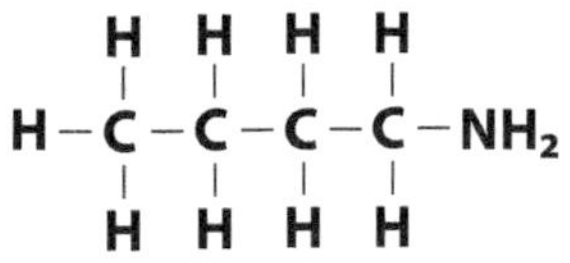

PROTEINS AND NUCLEIC ACIDS

- An amino acid contains both an amino group and a carboxylic acid.

- Proteins are long chains of amino acids joined together by peptide bonds.

- Nucleic acids are chains of nucleotides. Each nucleotide is composed of a sugar, a phosphate group, and a nitrogen-containing base.

- There are four main nitrogen-containing bases in DNA, the nucleic acid that stores the genetic information of organisms. The bases can bond with one another only in specific ways.

Solution

1 **Collect and Strategize** An amino acid contains an amino group ($—NH_2$) and a carboxylic acid. To solve this problem, examine each answer choice to see whether it contains both an amino group and a carboxylic acid.

2 **Solve** A carboxylic acid contains a double-bonded oxygen atom. Choices A and B do not contain double-bonded oxygen atoms, so they cannot be amino acids. An amino group contains a nitrogen atom. Choice D does not contain a nitrogen atom. Choice C contains both an amino group and a carboxylic acid, as shown below:

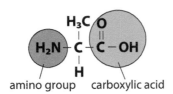

Therefore, C is the correct answer.

EXAMPLE 2

Describe the Formation of a Peptide Bond

The amino acids in proteins are joined by a bond known as a peptide bond. *Peptide bonds* form when one of the hydrogen atoms in the amino group of one amino acid reacts with the hydroxyl group on another amino acid. At the same time, the nitrogen atom of the amino group and the carbon atom of the acid group bond together to form a peptide bond. The hydrogen atom and hydroxyl group combine to form a molecule of water. Draw the general structural formula for a dipeptide (two amino acids joined by a peptide bond).

Solution

1 **Draw the Reactants** The diagram below shows how two amino acids can react to form a peptide bond. The hydrogen atom and hydroxyl group that combine to form water are circled in red.

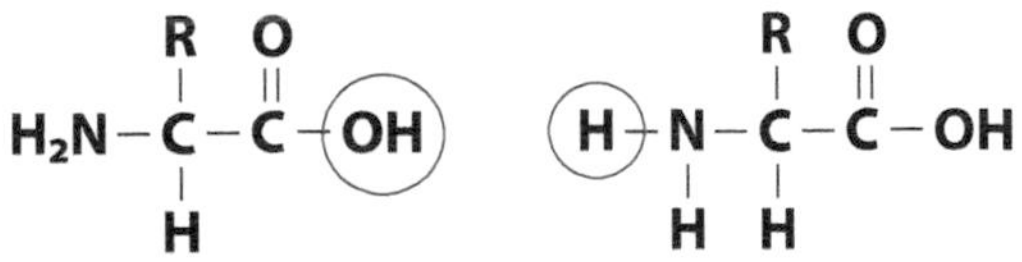

2 **Solve** The two amino acids will react to form the dipeptide shown below. The peptide bond is circled in green.

TIP

Remember that the letter *R* is used to represent a side chain in an organic compound. In most cases, the *R* stands for a carbon chain. However, it can also represent other structures, such as rings.

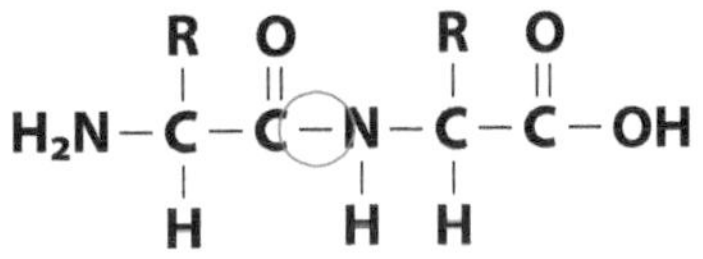

EXAMPLE 3

TIP

This diagram shows the structural formulas of the four nitrogen-containing bases in DNA.

Describe the Parts of a Nucleic Acid Molecule

The diagram below shows part of a molecule of DNA, a nucleic acid. Each nucleic acid molecule is a polymer made of subunits called *nucleotides*. Each nucleotide is made up of three parts: a phosphate group, a cyclic monosaccharide, and a nitrogen-containing base.

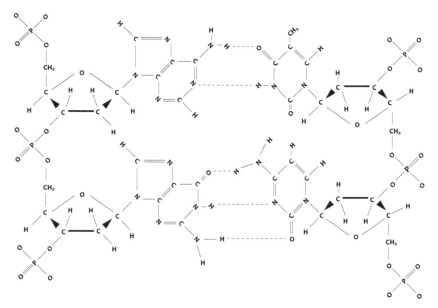

Identify the nucleotides in the diagram, and identify the phosphate groups, monosaccharides, and nitrogen-containing bases that make them up.

Solution

1 **Recall Relevant Information**   A phosphate group consists of a phosphorus atom and four oxygen atoms. A cyclic monosaccharide is a ring that contains an oxygen atom.

2 **Solve**   Examine the structure of the nucleotide above. The phosphate group consists of a phosphorus atom and four oxygen atoms. The monosaccharide is a ring that contains an oxygen atom. The nitrogen-containing base is the remaining part of the molecule. The diagram on the next page shows these three components shaded in different colors. The red shading shows the phosphate groups. The blue shading shows the monosaccharides. The green shading shows the nitrogen-containing bases.

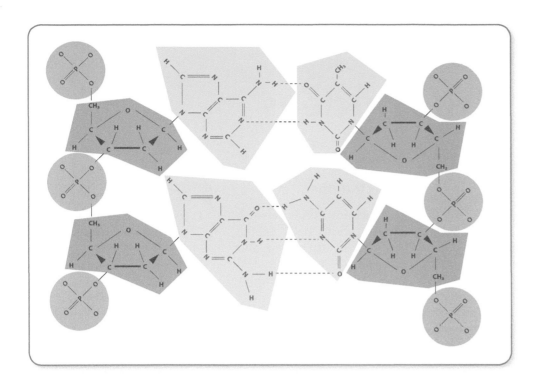

Problem Set

1. Which of the following structural formulas shows an amino acid?

   A.

   $$H_2N-\underset{\underset{H}{|}}{C}-\underset{\overset{\parallel}{O}}{C}-OH$$

   B.

   $$H-\underset{\underset{H}{|}}{\overset{\overset{H}{|}}{C}}-O-\underset{\overset{\parallel}{O}}{C}-OH$$

   C.

   $$H_2N-\underset{\underset{H}{|}}{\overset{\overset{H}{|}}{C}}-\underset{\underset{H}{|}}{\overset{\overset{H}{|}}{C}}-H$$

   D.

2. Nucleic acids are sometimes called *polynucleotides*. Explain why this is an accurate name for nucleic acids.

3. Describe the relationship between amino acids and proteins.

4. Draw the general structural formula of a nucleotide. Use a hexagon to represent the nitrogen-containing base.

5. **Challenge** Identify one similarity and one difference between the structure of proteins and the structure of nucleic acids.

6. **Challenge** Aspartame is an artificial sweetener that is made of two amino acids. The structural formula

   $$HO-\overset{\overset{\parallel}{O}}{C}-\underset{\underset{H}{|}}{\overset{\overset{H}{|}}{C}}-\underset{\underset{H}{|}}{\overset{\overset{NH_2}{|}}{C}}-\overset{\overset{\parallel}{O}}{C}-\underset{}{N}-\underset{\underset{C}{|}}{\overset{\overset{H}{|}}{C}}-\overset{\overset{\parallel}{O}}{C}-O-\underset{\underset{H}{|}}{\overset{\overset{H}{|}}{C}}-H$$

   of aspartame is shown below:

   Circle the peptide bond in aspartame.

Forces Within the Nucleus

Very strong forces hold the particles in the nucleus together.

Chemical reactions involve the breaking and forming of chemical bonds between atoms. These reactions occur mainly because of interactions between the electrons of the atoms. Therefore, electrostatic forces—that is, attractions and repulsions between charged particles—are the main forces involved in chemical reactions. In contrast, nuclear reactions involve changes in the nuclei of atoms. The main force controlling nuclear reactions is called the *strong nuclear force*. The strong nuclear force holds the protons and neutrons in an atom together. Strong nuclear forces are much stronger than electrostatic forces. However, they do not affect chemical reactions because they act only over very short distances. The strong nuclear force also plays another important role in the structure of atoms. Protons and neutrons are themselves made up of smaller particles called *quarks*. The strong nuclear force holds quarks together to form protons and neutrons.

OBJECTIVES

- Describe the differences between chemical and nuclear reactions.
- Identify the force that holds protons and neutrons together in a nucleus.
- Identify the particles that make up protons and neutrons.

EXAMPLE 1

Describe Nuclear Forces

Explain why the strong nuclear force must be stronger than the electrostatic force in order to hold atomic nuclei together.

Solution

1 Recall Relevant Information The electrostatic force is responsible for the attractions and repulsions between charged particles. Particles with like charges repel one another, and particles with opposite charges attract one another. Protons are positively charged. The strong nuclear force holds protons and neutrons together in a nucleus.

2 Solve Electrostatic forces between protons cause them to repel one another, because they are all positively charged. The strong nuclear force must be strong enough to overcome those repulsions and force the protons to stay together in the nucleus.

REMEMBER

NUCLEAR FORCES

- Electrostatic forces between protons in the nucleus cause them to repel one another.
- Strong nuclear forces hold the protons in a nucleus together.
- The strong nuclear force is much stronger than the electrostatic force, but the strong nuclear force acts over much smaller distances.
- The strong nuclear force also holds together the quarks that make up protons and neutrons.

EXAMPLE 2

Describe the Structure of the Nucleus

Use the terms *quarks, protons, neutrons, nucleus,* and *strong nuclear force* to fill in the concept map below.

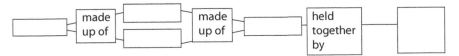

Solution

1 **Recall Relevant Information**   First, recall the definitions of the terms. An atom's nucleus is the dense, central part of the atom. Protons and neutrons are the two subatomic particles that are found in the nucleus. Quarks are the tiny particles that make up protons and neutrons. The strong nuclear force is the force that holds atomic nuclei together, and that holds quarks together in protons and neutrons.

2 **Solve**   The completed concept map is shown below.

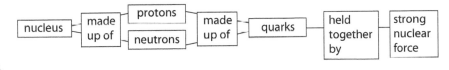

Problem Set

1. Which of the following statements is true?
   A. Electrostatic forces hold the nucleus together.
   B. Strong nuclear forces hold quarks together.
   C. Strong nuclear forces are involved in chemical reactions.
   D. Electrostatic forces cause electrons to attract one another.

2. What is the difference between chemical reactions and nuclear reactions?

3. Arrange the following particles in order of size, from smallest to largest: atom, neutron, nucleus, quark.

4. In one kind of nuclear reaction, two nuclei fuse, or join together, to form a larger nucleus. This kind of reaction happens only at very high pressures. Explain why such high pressures are necessary to cause these reactions to occur. (Hint: Remember that the strong nuclear force acts over a much smaller distance than the electrostatic force.)

5. **Challenge**   In one kind of nuclear reaction, a nucleus splits into smaller nuclei. When this occurs, the two parts move away from each other just slightly at first, and then fly away from each other at very high speed. Explain this high-energy event in terms of the strength and range of both the strong nuclear force and the electrostatic force.

6. **Challenge**   Scientists have determined that there are six main kinds of quarks. Two of these quarks are called *up quarks* and *down quarks*. Quarks have electric charges. An up quark has a charge of $+\frac{2}{3}$, and a down quark has a charge of $-\frac{1}{3}$. A proton is made up of two up quarks and one down quark. A neutron is made up of two down quarks and one up quark. Calculate the charge on a proton and a neutron. (Hint: The charges on the quarks add algebraically.)

Radioactivity and Half-Life

During radioactive decay, an atomic nucleus gives off particles, electromagnetic radiation, or both. As a result of radioactive decay, an element may change into a different element.

Most elements have some isotopes that are unstable. The nuclei of these radioactive isotopes can break down to form new elements. The breakdown of radioactive isotopes is called *radioactive decay*. The nuclei of a radioactive isotope decay at a specific, constant rate. The amount of time required for one-half of a sample of a radioactive isotope to decay is called the isotope's *half-life*. There are three main types of radioactive decay: alpha emission, beta emission, and gamma emission. During alpha emission, a nucleus gives off an alpha particle. An *alpha particle* is a helium nucleus. During beta emission, a nucleus gives off a beta particle. A *beta particle* is an electron. During gamma emission, a nucleus gives off a photon of high-frequency electromagnetic radiation (a *gamma ray*). Alpha emission and beta emission both change the makeup of a nucleus. That is, they change the number of protons and neutrons in the nucleus. Gamma emission has no effect on the number of protons and neutrons in the nucleus. It often accompanies other radioactive processes and is the energy given off as the nucleus reorganizes itself after an alpha or beta emission. The table below gives some of the properties of these different forms of radioactive decay.

Type of Radiation	Symbol	Mass	Charge
Alpha particles	α or $_2^4\text{He}$	4 amu	$+2$
Beta particles	β or $_{-1}^0\text{e}$	5.4×10^{-4} amu	-1
Gamma rays	γ	0	0

EXAMPLE 1

Compare Radioactive Decay Processes

Which of these nuclear reactions gives off the most penetrating radiation?

A. $_6^{14}\text{C} \rightarrow {}_7^{14}\text{N} + {}_{-1}^0\text{e}$

B. $_{92}^{238}\text{U} \rightarrow {}_{90}^{234}\text{Th} + {}_2^4\text{He}$

C. $_{88}^{226}\text{Ra} \rightarrow {}_{86}^{222}\text{Rn} + {}_2^4\text{He}$

D. $_{90}^{230}\text{Th} \rightarrow {}_{88}^{226}\text{Ra} + {}_2^4\text{He} + \gamma$

OBJECTIVES

- Describe the three most common types of radioactive decay.
- Define *half-life*.
- Perform half-life calculations.

REMEMBER

RADIOACTIVITY

- The three main types of radioactive decay are alpha emission, beta emission, and gamma emission.

- Alpha radiation and beta radiation are made up of particles. Gamma radiation is made up of electromagnetic rays.

- The half-life of a radioactive isotope is the amount of time required for one-half of the radioactive nuclei present to decay.

- The half-life of a given isotope is constant. It cannot be changed by chemical reactions, time, or any other known process.

Solution

1 **Recall Relevant Information** To answer this question, consider the penetrating power of each kind of radiation. Alpha particles (alpha radiation) can be blocked by a sheet of paper. Beta particles (beta radiation) can pass through a sheet of paper, but can be blocked by a piece of aluminum foil or a few centimeters of wood. Gamma rays (gamma radiation) can pass through most substances. They can be blocked only by thick sheets of lead or concrete.

2 **Examine the Equations** Equation A describes a beta emission process. Equations B and C describe alpha emission processes. Equation D also describes an alpha emission, but in this case the alpha emission is accompanied by a gamma emission.

3 **Solve** Gamma radiation is the most penetrating of the three main kinds of radiation. Equation D is the only equation describing a gamma emission process, so D is the correct answer.

TIP

A nuclear decay equation shows changes to atomic nuclei. A nucleus of an element is represented by that element's chemical symbol, along with its atomic number and atomic mass number. For example, the symbol $^{4}_{2}\text{He}$ represents a helium-4 nucleus with an atomic number of 2 and an atomic mass number of 4.

EXAMPLE 2

Describe Half-Life

Carbon-14 ($^{14}_{6}\text{C}$) is a radioactive isotope of carbon. It decays by beta emission to nitrogen-14 ($^{14}_{7}\text{N}$). The graph below shows the number of carbon-14 nuclei present in a sample as a function of time. What is the half-life of carbon-14?

TIP

It is difficult to determine an isotope's exact half-life from a graph. However, a graph can help you approximate the half-life of an isotope.

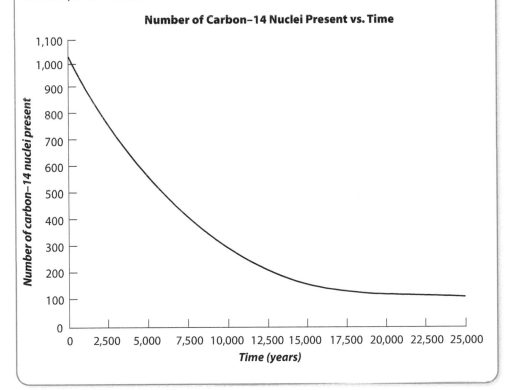

Number of Carbon–14 Nuclei Present vs. Time

Solution

1 **Collect and Strategize**   The half-life of a radioactive isotope is the amount of time required for one-half of the nuclei present in a sample to decay. Therefore, to answer this question, use the graph to identify how long it takes for one-half of the carbon-14 nuclei in the sample to decay.

2 **Study the Graph**   First, find a starting point on the curve. The half-life for a given isotope is constant, so it doesn't matter which point on the curve you start with. Therefore, choose a point that will be easy to work with, such as the point that has 400 as its y-coordinate. The x-coordinate of this point is about 7,500. So, after 7,500 years, the sample will contain 400 carbon-14 nuclei. It will take one half-life for the number of nuclei to decrease by one-half, from 400 to 200. So, the next step is to find the x-coordinate of the point on the curve that has a y-coordinate of 200. Examining the graph shows that this point has an x-coordinate of about 13,000. In other words, after about 13,000 years, the sample will contain approximately 200 nuclei.

3 **Solve**   The graph shows that approximately $13,000 - 7,500 = 5,500$ years are required for the number of carbon-14 nuclei in a sample to decrease by one-half. Therefore, the half-life of carbon-14 is approximately 5,500 years. (The actual half-life of carbon-14 is 5,730 years.)

EXAMPLE 3

Perform Half-Life Calculations

Organisms that live on land, such as plants, have a relatively constant level of carbon-14 in their bodies when they are alive. The carbon-14 level remains constant because organisms take in carbon-14 from the air. Any carbon-14 that decays is replaced by new carbon-14 from the air. After an organism dies, the amount of carbon-14 in its body begins to decrease, because it is no longer taking in carbon-14. What fraction of the original carbon-14 present in a piece of tree branch will still be present 22,920 years after the tree dies? The half-life of carbon-14 is 5,730 years.

Solution

1 **Collect and Strategize**   The amount of carbon-14 in the branch will decrease by one-half every 5,730 years. To solve this problem, calculate the number of half-lives that have passed. Then, use the equation below to calculate the fraction of carbon-14 remaining:

$$\text{fraction remaining} = \frac{1}{2^n}$$

In this equation, n is the number of half-lives that have passed.

TIP

Remember that you can convert a fraction to a percentage by dividing the numerator by the denominator and then multiplying by 100.

2 Calculate the Number of Half-Lives One half-life is equal to 5,730 years. Use this conversion factor to calculate the number of half-lives that have passed, as shown below:

$$22{,}920 \, y \times \frac{1 \text{ half-life}}{5{,}730 \, y} = 4 \text{ half-lives}$$

3 Solve Substitute the number of half-lives into the equation given in Step 1, as shown below:

$$\text{fraction remaining} = \frac{1}{2^4} = \frac{1}{16}$$

So, one-sixteenth (6.25 percent) of the original carbon-14 will remain in the branch after 22,920 years.

Problem Set

1. The penetrating power of different kinds of radiation depends on the amount of energy the radiation has. The more energy a given form of radiation has, the greater its penetrating power. Arrange the three most common forms of radiation in order from highest energy to lowest energy. Explain your answer.

2. A sample of radium-226 contains 1.0×10^8 atoms of radium-226. How many atoms of radium-226 will remain in the sample after three half-lives?

3. A particular radioactive isotope has a half-life of 5.0 s. What fraction of the original amount of isotope will remain in a sample after 20.0 s?

4. Thorium-234 has a half-life of 24.1 days. What percentage of the original thorium-234 in a sample will remain after 144.6 days?

5. A scientist allows alpha, beta, and gamma radiation to pass between two electrically charged plates. The beam of alpha radiation curves toward the negatively charged plate. The beam of beta radiation curves toward the positively charged plate. The beam of gamma radiation does not curve. Explain these observations. (Hint: Think about the charges of alpha particles, beta particles, and gamma rays.)

6. A common rule of thumb is that a radioactive substance is safe to handle after 10 half-lives. Approximately what percentage of a radioactive element will remain in a sample after 10 half-lives?

7. **Challenge** The half-life of cesium-137 is 30.2 years. How long will it take for a sample of cesium-137 to decay to one-eighth of its original quantity?

8. **Challenge** Radon-222 has a half-life of 3.8 days. A scientist determined that a sample of a substance contained 1.0×10^6 atoms of radon-222 at a certain time. How many atoms of radon-222 did the sample contain 11.4 days before the scientist took the measurement?

9. **Challenge** Radiation can damage cells and cause disease. However, not all forms of radiation are equally harmful or harmful in the same form. For example, most substances that emit alpha particles can be safely handled with bare hands. However, if these substances are ingested or inhaled, they can cause significant damage. In contrast, most substances that emit gamma rays are harmful to touch as well as to ingest or inhale. Explain why an alpha emitter may be harmful only if it is taken internally, but a gamma emitter is harmful both internally and externally. (Hint: Think about the penetrating power of each type of radiation.)

Transmutation of Elements

You can use a transmutation equation to predict the product(s) of a transmutation reaction.

Nuclear transmutation is the transformation of an atom of one element into an atom of another element. This can occur naturally or artificially. Both natural and artificial transmutations involve changing the number of protons in the atomic nucleus. Natural transmutation occurs when radioactive elements spontaneously decay and transform into other elements. Transmutation of elements can also be achieved artificially by bombarding elements with high-speed particles.

OBJECTIVES

- Define *transmutation*.
- Identify isotopes that are the products of transmutation reactions.

EXAMPLE 1

Complete a Transmutation Equation

Complete each of the following transmutation equations. Assume that each equation has only one unknown product.

equation 1: $^{212}_{84}\text{Po} \rightarrow ^{4}_{2}\text{He} + ?$

equation 2: $^{87}_{37}\text{Rb} \rightarrow ^{0}_{-1}\text{e} + ?$

Solution

1 **Recall Relevant Information** Transmutation equations describe nuclear reactions. The superscript and subscript on the chemical symbol of an isotope give its atomic number and atomic mass number, respectively. In a balanced transmutation equation, the sum of the atomic numbers (subscripts) of the reactants must be equal to the sum of the atomic numbers of the products, and the sum of the atomic mass numbers (superscripts) of the reactants must be equal to the sum of the atomic mass numbers of the products. The atomic number of an atom determines its identity.

2 **Strategize** Use algebra to calculate the atomic number and atomic mass number of the unknown product in each reaction. The table below gives the atomic numbers and atomic mass numbers of the substances involved.

	Atomic Numbers		Atomic Mass Numbers	
	Reactant	Products	Reactant	Products
Equation 1	84	2 + ?	212	4 + ?
Equation 2	37	−1 + ?	87	0 + ?

REMEMBER

TRANSMUTATION

- Transmutation occurs when an atom of one element changes into an atom of another element.
- Alpha emission and beta emission can accompany transmutation.
- Scientists can cause the transmutation of some elements by firing high-energy particles, such as alpha particles or neutrons, at other elements. Many of the transuranium elements are produced in this way.

3 **Write Equations** Set up and solve equations to determine the atomic number and atomic mass number of each unknown product. For equation 1, the calculations are as follows:

atomic number: $84 = 2 + x$
$$x = 84 - 2 = 82$$

atomic mass number: $212 = 4 + x$
$$x = 212 - 4 = 208$$

For equation 2, the calculations are as follows:

atomic number: $37 = -1 + x$
$$x = 37 + 1 = 38$$

atomic mass number: $87 = 0 + x$
$$x = 87$$

4 **Solve** Use the periodic table at the back of the book to identify each product. The table shows that the element with atomic number 82 is lead (Pb), and the element with atomic number 38 is strontium (Sr). The unknown product of equation 1 is therefore $^{208}_{82}\text{Pb}$, and the unknown product of equation 2 is $^{87}_{38}\text{Sr}$. The completed equations are the ones shown below:

equation 1: $^{212}_{84}\text{Po} \rightarrow {}^{4}_{2}\text{He} + {}^{208}_{82}\text{Pb}$

equation 2: $^{87}_{37}\text{Rb} \rightarrow {}^{0}_{-1}\text{e} + {}^{87}_{38}\text{Sr}$

TIP

A beta particle (electron) technically has no atomic number or atomic mass number, because it contains no protons or neutrons. However, for the purposes of writing and balancing nuclear equations, the electron is assumed to have an atomic number of –1 and an atomic mass number of 0. These numbers are used in calculations, but they do not actually describe the properties of an electron.

Problem Set

1. Complete the transmutation equation shown below. Assume that there is only one unknown product.

   $^{235}_{92}\text{U} \rightarrow {}^{4}_{2}\text{He} + ?$

2. Define *transmutation* in your own words.

3. Complete the transmutation equation below. Assume that there is only one unknown product.

   $^{239}_{93}\text{Np} \rightarrow {}^{239}_{94}\text{Pu} + ?$

4. Complete the transmutation equation shown below. Assume that there is only one unknown reactant.

   $? \rightarrow {}^{66}_{30}\text{Zn} + {}^{0}_{-1}\text{e}$

5. **Challenge** Transmutation reactions can be artificially produced by bombarding isotopes with high-speed particles. The incomplete equation below shows one example of this kind of reaction:

   $^{14}_{7}\text{N} + {}^{4}_{2}\text{He} \rightarrow ?$

   Complete the transmutation equation to identify the product of the reaction. Assume that there is only one unknown product.

6. **Challenge** What type of decay process produces astatine-208 from francium-212? (Hint: Write a transmutation equation for the process. Refer to the periodic table at the back of the book.)

Nuclear Fission and Fusion

Nuclear reactions release much more energy than chemical reactions do.

Nuclear reactions are very different from chemical reactions. In chemical reactions, elements combine to form new compounds, but the elements in those compounds retain their original identities. In nuclear reactions, atomic nuclei interact to produce new elements. The nuclear reactions that are most common are *fission*, in which heavy nuclei break up into lighter nuclei, and *fusion*, in which light nuclei combine to form heavier nuclei. Both fission and fusion can release many times the amount of energy released by even the most exothermic of chemical reactions. The enormous amounts of energy released during nuclear reactions are the result of matter being converted into energy. Energy and matter are related by the equation $E = mc^2$, where E is energy (in joules), m is mass (in kilograms), and c is the speed of light (in meters per second). Because the speed of light is a very large number (2.997925×10^8 m/s), even the tiny amount of mass that is lost in a typical nuclear reaction produces a huge amount of energy.

OBJECTIVES

- **Contrast the energy released during chemical reactions with the energy released during nuclear reactions.**
- **Use the equation $E = mc^2$ to relate mass and energy.**

EXAMPLE 1

Identify Nuclear Fission and Fusion

An atom of californium-248 (^{248}Cf) can undergo radioactive decay to form an atom of curium-244 (^{244}Cm) and an alpha particle. Is this an example of nuclear fission or nuclear fusion?

Solution

1 **Recall Relevant Information**   In a nuclear fusion reaction, light nuclei combine to form a heavier nucleus. In a nuclear fission reaction, a heavy nucleus breaks down into lighter nuclei.

2 **Solve**   When ^{248}Cf decays, it forms two lighter nuclei: ^{244}Cm and an alpha particle. (Remember that an alpha particle is a helium nucleus.) The reaction involves a heavy nucleus breaking down to form lighter nuclei. Therefore, it is a fission reaction.

REMEMBER

NUCLEAR REACTIONS

- Nuclear reactions result in the formation of new elements. In contrast, chemical reactions do not produce new elements.

- Mass is lost during nuclear reactions. The lost mass is converted into energy.

- The equation $E = mc^2$ describes the relationship between mass and energy.

EXAMPLE 2

Calculate the Energy Released During a Nuclear Reaction

One mole of thorium-231 (^{231}Th) can decay to form one mole of radium-227 (^{227}Ra) and one mole of alpha particles. The atomic mass of 1 mol ^{231}Th is 231.0363 g. The atomic mass of 1 mol ^{227}Ra is 227.0292 g. The mass of 1 mol alpha particles is 4.0015 g. How much energy is released during the decay of 1 mol ^{231}Th to ^{227}Ra?

Solution

1 **Collect and Strategize**   The mass lost during a nuclear reaction is converted into the energy released during the reaction. Therefore, to calculate the energy released during the reaction, first calculate the amount of mass lost during the reaction. Then, use the equation $E = mc^2$ to convert mass to energy. To use $E = mc^2$, mass must be in kilograms. The following information is given in the problem:

mass of 1 mol ^{231}Th $= 231.0363$ g
mass of 1 mol ^{227}Ra $= 227.0292$ g
mass of 1 mol alpha particles $= 4.0015$ g

2 **Calculate Lost Mass**   During the reaction, each ^{231}Th atom changes into one ^{227}Ra atom and one alpha particle. The mass lost during the reaction is equal to the initial mass of 1 mol ^{231}Th minus the sum of the masses of 1 mol ^{227}Ra and 1 mol alpha particles. The mass lost is calculated as shown below:

231.0363 g $-$ (227.0292 g $+$ 4.0015 g) $= 5.600 \times 10^{-3}$ g $= 5.600 \times 10^{-6}$ kg

3 **Solve**   Use the equation $E = mc^2$ to calculate energy, as shown below:

$E = (5.600 \times 10^{-6}$ kg$)(2.997925 \times 10^8$ m/s$)^2 = 5.033 \times 10^{11}$ J

As you can see, this is several orders of magnitude more energy than is released during a typical chemical reaction. Most exothermic chemical reactions do not release more than a few kilojoules per mole of reactant. This reaction releases more than one hundred million kilojoules of energy per mole of thorium 231.

TIP

One joule is equal to one kilogram–meter squared per second squared (1 J $= 1$ kg $\cdot$ m^2/s^2). Therefore, to use $E = mc^2$ to calculate energy in joules, mass must be in kilograms and the speed of light must be in meters per second.

Problem Set

1. In stars like our sun, hydrogen nuclei (protons) combine to form helium nuclei. Is this a fusion reaction or a fission reaction? Explain your answer.

2. In most nuclear power plants, uranium-238 (^{238}U) nuclei break down to form thorium-234 (^{234}Th) nuclei and alpha particles. Is this a fusion reaction or a fission reaction? Explain your answer.

3. Samarium-146 (^{146}Sm) can decay to form neodymium-142 (^{142}Nd). Each atom of ^{146}Sm that decays produces one atom of ^{142}Nd and one alpha particle. If the mass of 1 mol ^{146}Sm is 145.9130 g, the mass of 1 mol ^{142}Nd is 141.9077 g, and the mass of 1 mol alpha particles is 4.0015 g, how much mass is lost during the decay of 1 mol ^{146}Sm to ^{142}Nd?

4. Calculate the amount of energy released during the decay described in Question 3. Give your answer in joules. (Hint: Convert mass to kilograms. $c = 2.997925 \times 10^8$ m/s)

5. **Challenge**   Does the law of conservation of mass apply to nuclear reactions? Explain your answer.

6. **Challenge**   What is the conversion factor between joules and kilograms? (Hint: Use the equation $E = mc^2$ to calculate the energy equivalent of 1 kg of mass.)

General Information

Important Physical Constants

Constant	Constant Value
Atomic mass unit	1 amu $= 1.6605 \times 10^{-24}$ g
Avogadro's number	6.02×10^{23}
Gas constant	8.31 L $\cdot$ kPa/mol $\cdot$ K or 0.0821 L $\cdot$ atm/mol $\cdot$ K
Volume of one mole of an ideal gas	22.4 L
Speed of light in a vacuum	2.997925×10^{8} m/s

Electronegativity Values of Some Common Elements

Element	Electronegativity	Element	Electronegativity
Hydrogen (H)	2.1	Gallium (Ga)	1.6
Lithium (Li)	1.0	Germanium (Ge)	1.8
Beryllium (Be)	1.5	Arsenic (As)	2.0
Boron (B)	2.0	Selenium (Se)	2.4
Carbon (C)	2.5	Bromine (Br)	2.8
Nitrogen (N)	3.0	Rubidium (Rb)	0.8
Oxygen (O)	3.5	Strontium (Sr)	1.0
Fluorine (F)	4.0	Indium (In)	1.7
Sodium (Na)	0.9	Tin (Sn)	1.8
Magnesium (Mg)	1.2	Antimony (Sb)	1.9
Aluminum (Al)	1.5	Tellurium (Te)	2.1
Silicon (Si)	1.8	Iodine (I)	2.5
Phosphorus (P)	2.1	Cesium (Cs)	0.7
Sulfur (S)	2.5	Barium (Ba)	0.9
Chlorine (Cl)	3.0	Thallium (Tl)	1.8
Potassium (K)	0.8	Lead (Pb)	1.9
Calcium (Ca)	1.0	Bismuth (Bi)	1.9

Order of Electron Orbital Filling

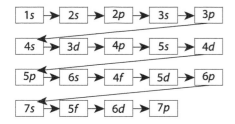

Common Metric Prefixes

Prefix	Symbol	Meaning	Example
nano-	n	10^{-9}	$1 \text{ nm} = 1 \times 10^{-9} \text{ m}$
micro-	μ	10^{-6}	$1 \text{ } \mu\text{m} = 1 \times 10^{-6} \text{ m}$
milli-	m	10^{-3}	$1 \text{ mm} = 1 \times 10^{-3} \text{ m}$
centi-	c	10^{-2}	$1 \text{ cm} = 1 \times 10^{-2} \text{ m}$
deci-	d	10^{-1}	$1 \text{ dm} = 1 \times 10^{-1} \text{ m}$
kilo-	k	10^{3}	$1 \text{ km} = 1 \times 10^{3} \text{ m}$

Symbols for Common Units and Quantities

Unit or Quantity	Symbol	Unit or Quantity	Symbol
kelvin	K	meter	m
Celsius degree	°C	liter	L
atmosphere	atm	second	s
Pascal	Pa	calorie	cal
molality	m	joule	J
molarity	M	gram	g
mole fraction	X	atomic mass unit	amu
free energy	G	mole	mol
entropy	S	acid dissociation constant	K_a
enthalpy	H	equilibrium constant	K_{eq}
pressure	P	base dissociation constant	K_b
gas constant	R	solubility product constant	K_{sp}
volume	V	heat of formation	H_f
temperature	T	half-life	$t_{1/2}$
number of moles	n	standard temperature and pressure	STP

Problem-Set Information

These tables give equations, expressions, and conversion factors you may need to solve problems in each problem set. If there is no table listed for a given problem set, then no equations, expressions, or conversions are necessary to answer the questions in the problem set.

Problem Set 6: Problem Solving in Chemistry	
Equation or Expression	**Explanation of Symbols**
$C = \left(\frac{5}{9}\right)(F - 32)$	$C =$ temperature in degrees Celsius $F =$ temperature in degrees Fahrenheit
$C = K - 273$	$C =$ temperature in degrees Celsius $K =$ temperature in kelvins

Problem Set 8: Metric System: Derived Units	
Equation or Expression	**Explanation of Symbols**
1 cal $=$ 4.186 J	cal $=$ calorie J $=$ joule
$D = \frac{m}{V}$	$D =$ density $m =$ mass $V =$ volume
$V = l \times w \times h$	$V =$ volume of a rectangular prism $l =$ length of the prism $w =$ width of the prism $h =$ height of the prism

Problem Set 13: Atomic Number and Mass Number	
Equation or Expression	**Explanation of Symbols**
$N = A - Z$	$N =$ number of neutrons $A =$ mass number $Z =$ atomic number

Problem Set 14: Ions	
Equation or Expression	**Explanation of Symbols**
$C = P - E$	$C =$ charge of an ion or atom $P =$ number of protons in the ion or atom $E =$ number of electrons in the ion or atom

Problem Set 15: Isotopes and Atomic Mass

Equation or Expression	Explanation of Symbols
$m_X = (A_1)(m_1) + (A_2)(m_2) + \ldots$	m_X = average atomic mass of element X A_1 = abundance of first isotope of element X, as a decimal m_1 = atomic mass of first isotope of element X A_2 = abundance of second isotope of element X, as a decimal m_2 = atomic mass of second isotope of element X (include additional isotopes as needed in a similar way)

Problem Set 29: The Ionic Bond and Salts

Equation or Expression	Explanation of Symbols
$C = P + N$	C = charge on a formula unit of an ionic compound P = sum of positive ion charges in the formula unit N = sum of negative ion charges in the formula unit

Problem Set 46: Mole-Number Relationships

Equation or Expression	Explanation of Symbols
$1 \text{ mol} = 6.02 \times 10^{23}$ particles	mol = mole

Problem Set 48: Mole-Volume Relationships

Equation or Expression	Explanation of Symbols
1 mol gas = 22.4 L	mol = mole L = liter

Problem Set 51: Percent Yield

Equation or Expression	Explanation of Symbols
$\text{percent yield} = \dfrac{\text{actual yield}}{\text{theoretical yield}} \times 100$	actual yield = observed amount of product theoretical yield = amount of product predicted from stoichiometric calculations

Problem Set 53: Boyle's Law

Equation or Expression	Explanation of Symbols
$PV = k$	P = pressure of a gas V = volume of a gas k = a constant (This equation applies only to situations in which neither the temperature nor the number of moles of gas is changing.)
$P_1 V_1 = P_2 V_2$	P_1 = initial pressure of a gas V_1 = initial volume of a gas P_2 = final pressure of the gas V_2 = final volume of the gas (This equation applies only to situations in which neither the temperature nor the number of moles of gas is changing.)

Problem Set 54: Charles's Law

Equation or Expression	Explanation of Symbols
$V = kT$	V = volume of a gas k = a constant T = temperature of a gas (This equation applies only to situations in which neither the pressure nor the number of moles of gas is changing.)
$\dfrac{V_1}{T_1} = \dfrac{V_2}{T_2}$	V_1 = initial volume of a gas T_1 = initial temperature of a gas V_2 = final volume of the gas T_2 = final temperature of the gas (This equation applies only to situations in which neither the pressure nor the number of moles of gas is changing.)

Problem Set 55: Gay-Lussac's Law

Equation or Expression	Explanation of Symbols
$P = kT$	P = pressure of a gas k = a constant T = temperature of a gas (This equation applies only to situations in which neither the volume nor the number of moles of gas is changing.)
$\dfrac{P_1}{T_1} = \dfrac{P_2}{T_2}$	P_1 = initial pressure of a gas T_1 = initial temperature of a gas P_2 = final pressure of the gas T_2 = final temperature of the gas (This equation applies only to situations in which neither the volume nor the number of moles of gas is changing.)

Problem Set 56: The Ideal Gas Law

Equation or Expression	Explanation of Symbols
$PV = nRT$	P = pressure of a gas V = volume of a gas n = number of moles of a gas R = gas constant T = temperature of a gas
$\dfrac{P_1 V_1}{n_1 T_1} = \dfrac{P_2 V_2}{n_2 T_2}$	P_1 = initial pressure of a gas V_1 = initial volume of a gas n_1 = initial number of moles of a gas T_1 = initial temperature of a gas P_2 = final pressure of the gas V_2 = final volume of the gas n_2 = final number of moles of the gas T_2 = final temperature of the gas

Problem Set 58: Dalton's Law of Partial Pressures

Equation or Expression	Explanation of Symbols
$P_{total} = P_1 + P_2 + \ldots$	P_{total} = total pressure of a mixture of gases P_1 = partial pressure of first gas in the mixture P_2 = partial pressure of second gas in the mixture (include additional gases as needed in a similar way)
$PV = nRT$	P = pressure of a gas V = volume of a gas n = number of moles of a gas R = gas constant T = temperature of a gas
$X_A = \dfrac{\text{moles of A}}{\text{total moles}}$	X_A = mole fraction of substance A
$P_A = X_A P_{total}$	P_A = partial pressure of gas A X_A = mole fraction of gas A P_{total} = total pressure of gas mixture

Problem Set 59: Graham's Law of Effusion

Equation or Expression	Explanation of Symbols
$\dfrac{r_A}{r_B} = \dfrac{\sqrt{M_B}}{\sqrt{M_A}}$	r_A = effusion or diffusion rate of gas A r_B = effusion or diffusion rate of gas B M_A = molar mass of gas A M_B = molar mass of gas B

Problem Set 65: Molarity and Mole Fraction

Equation or Expression	Explanation of Symbols
$M = \dfrac{\text{mol solute}}{\text{L solution}}$	M = molarity of solution mol = mole L = liter
$X_A = \dfrac{\text{moles of A}}{\text{total moles}}$	X_A = mole fraction of substance A

Problem Set 66: Molality and Mass Percent

Equation or Expression	Explanation of Symbols
$m = \dfrac{\text{mol solute}}{\text{kg solvent}}$	m = molality of solution mol = mole kg = kilogram
mass percent A $= \dfrac{\text{mass of A}}{\text{total mass}} \times 100$	total mass = total mass of solution or mixture

Problem Set 67: Colligative Properties

Equation or Expression	Explanation of Symbols
$\Delta T_f = K_f m$	ΔT_f = change in freezing point of solvent K_f = freezing-point depression constant for solvent m = molality of solution
$\Delta T_b = K_b m$	ΔT_b = change in boiling point of solvent K_b = boiling-point elevation constant for solvent m = molality of solution
$\Delta P_{sol} = P^\circ_A X_B$	ΔP_{sol} = change in vapor pressure of solvent P°_A = vapor pressure of pure solvent X_B = mole fraction of solute in solution

Problem Set 72: Measuring Acids and Bases

Equation or Expression	Explanation of Symbols
$pH = -\log[H_3O^+]$	pH = pH of solution $[H_3O^+]$ = concentration of H_3O^+ ions in solution

Problem Set 74: Strength of Acids and Bases

Equation or Expression	Explanation of Symbols
$pK_a = -\log(K_a)$	pK_a = pK_a of an acid K_a = dissociation constant for the acid
$pK_b = -\log(K_b)$	pK_b = pK_b of a base K_b = dissociation constant for the base

Problem Set 77: Specific Heat

Equation or Expression	Explanation of Symbols
$q = mC_p\Delta T$	q = amount of heat gained or lost m = mass of substance C_p = specific heat of substance ΔT = temperature change of substance

Problem Set 81: Hess's Law

Equation or Expression	Explanation of Symbols
$\Delta H^0_{rxn} = \sum \Delta H^0_{f, products} - \sum \Delta H^0_{f, reactants}$	ΔH^0_{rxn} = enthalpy change of a reaction $\sum \Delta H^0_{f, products}$ = sum of enthalpies of formation of products $\sum \Delta H^0_{f, reactants}$ = sum of enthalpies of formation of reactants

Problem Set 88: Entropy and Free Energy

Equation or Expression	Explanation of Symbols
$\Delta G = \Delta H - T\Delta S$	ΔG = free energy change for a process ΔH = enthalpy change for a process T = temperature ΔS = entropy change for a process

Problem Set 98: Radioactivity and Half-Life

Equation or Expression	Explanation of Symbols
fraction remaining $= \dfrac{1}{2^n}$	fraction remaining = fraction of original mass of isotope still left in sample n = number of half-lives that have passed

Problem Set 100: Nuclear Fission and Fusion

Equation or Expression	Explanation of Symbols
$E = mc^2$	E = energy in joules m = mass in kilograms c = speed of light in meters per second

Answer Key

Note that all numerical answers have been rounded to the correct number of significant figures.

Chemistry and Society

Pages 2–3

1. Blood is a substance in living things, so a biochemist may study its compounds. Some compounds in blood contain carbon, so an organic chemist may study them. Other compounds in blood do not contain carbon, so an inorganic chemist may study them. An analytical chemist may also study blood compounds to characterize their physical and chemical qualities. **3.** Designing new types of makeup might require an understanding of organic chemistry, inorganic chemistry, and biochemistry. **5.** Analytical chemists can analyze the nutritional contents of our food and add compounds to make food more nutritious. Organic chemists and inorganic chemists have invented new foods and food products, such as artificial sweeteners, that do not exist in nature. Biochemists have studied how what we eat affects our health, and have suggested new ways to improve our diets.

Matter and Energy

Pages 4–5

1. solid **3.** The student should examine the volume of the substance. If the volume of the substance changes depending on the size of the container it is in, it is a gas. If it does not, it is a liquid. Liquids do not take the volumes of their containers, but gases do. **5.** A solid has a fixed shape and volume. This is because the particles in a solid have fixed positions. They cannot move around very much. A liquid has a fixed volume, but takes the shape of its container. This is because the particles in a liquid can easily move past one another, but they cannot move too far from one another. A gas can take the size and shape of its container. This is because the gas particles are so far apart that they do not interact with one another very much.

Pure Substances

Pages 6–7

1. NH_3 **3.** Water is made up of more than one kind of atom, so it is a compound, not an element. **5.** Al_2O_3

Mixtures

Pages 8–9

1. D **3.** Chemical changes produce new substances.

Physical changes do not. Also, chemical changes, such as combustion, are generally not reversible, but physical changes, such as boiling, almost always are. Therefore, it is almost always more appropriate to use physical properties as the basis of the separation. **5.** Household ammonia is a common mixture of a gas (ammonia) in a liquid (water).

Properties of Substances

Pages 10–11

1. A **3.** Sample answer: Mass and volume depend on the amount of material present. Density and temperature do not depend on the amount of material present. **5.** Sample answer: Each of the substances listed has a different density, so identifying the sample's density would allow identification of the substance. Steel is attracted to magnets, but the other substances are not, so magnetic susceptibility could help the scientist either identify the substance as steel or eliminate steel as a possibility.

Problem Solving in Chemistry

Pages 12–13

1. the yard **3.** 8.791 g **5.** −273°C; −459.4°F
7. 5.0×10^{-6} g/mL **9.** 2.832×10^4 mL

Metric System: Base Units

Pages 14–15

1. kg, K, and cd **3.** 0.452 m; 1.956×10^{-4} kg
5. 2.997925×10^{10} cm/s **7.** 11.5 kPa **9.** 8.56×10^{-5} J

Metric System: Derived Units

Pages 16–17

1. Density is measured in grams per cubic centimeter. This is a derived unit because it consists of a combination of several base units. **3.** When a substance expands, its volume increases, but its mass remains the same. Density is equal to mass divided by volume. Therefore, if volume increases but mass remains the same, density must decrease.

5. 1.36×10^6 J **7.** 67.8 J **9.** $1\dfrac{m^2 \cdot kg}{A \cdot s^3}$

Graphing

Pages 18–19

1. For data that range from 0.45 cm to 18.42 cm, the best range for the axis is probably 0 cm to 20 cm, with intervals of 2 cm or 5 cm. **3.** A sample graph is shown on the next page.

Temperature vs. Heat Added

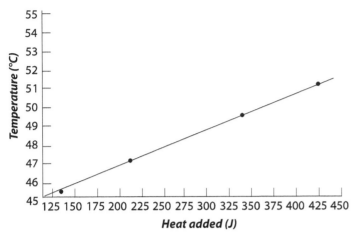

5. A sample graph is shown below.

Reaction Rate vs. Temperature

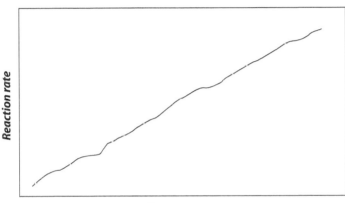

Scientific Methods in Chemistry

Pages 20–21

1. D   **3.** Controlled experiments can only be used to investigate situations that can be controlled and carried out in the laboratory. It is impossible to recreate the conditions of continent formation in a laboratory for the following reasons:

- The continents formed over millions of years, so the time scale is not appropriate for a laboratory experiment.
- To re-create continent formation in a controlled experiment, a scientist would have to create several earth-sized planets in the laboratory, which is obviously impossible.
- So many factors affect continent formation that it would be impossible to control for all of them.

5. The student will need to make sure that the size and type of cloth tested with each laundry soap is the same. She should also make sure the grease stain on each piece of cloth was made by the same type of grease under the same conditions. She will also need to make sure that she uses the same amount of water and laundry soap on the grease stains, and that she washes all the pieces for the same

amount of time. She should include one group of cloth pieces that get washed in water alone, with no laundry soap. She should record the size, shape, and color of each grease stain before and after each piece of cloth is washed.

Early Theories of the Atom

Pages 22–23

1. Robert Millikan's oil drop experiments were used to calculate the charge and then the mass of the electron. Knowing the charge and mass of the electron allowed scientists to determine the amount of positive charge in an atom, and to begin to understand the structure of atoms.   **3.** The statement means that atoms of the same elements always combine in the same way to form particles of a given compound. For example, two atoms of oxygen and one atom of carbon combine in the same way to form each particle of carbon dioxide (CO_2).   **5.** Democritus's ideas about atoms were not based on observation or experimentation, and they were not supported by scientific investigations. Therefore, they cannot be considered a scientific theory.

The Nuclear Atom

Pages 24–25

1.

Particle	Relative Mass	Charge	Location
Proton	1	+1	In the nucleus
Neutron	1	0	In the nucleus
Electron	0	-1	Outside the nucleus

3. The nucleus contains positively charged protons and neutral neutrons. Because the neutrons have no charge, they do not contribute to the overall charge of the nucleus. This leaves the nucleus with a positive charge. The electrons outside the nucleus balance the positive charge of the nucleus, leaving the whole atom with no net charge.
5. Rutherford probably assumed that Thompson's model of the atom was correct. If Thompson's model were correct, the mass of the atom would be spread out evenly throughout its volume. In that case, Rutherford would have expected that all the alpha particles would travel straight through the foil, with only slight deflections, much as a bullet travels straight through a piece of tissue paper. He also would have expected that particles would be equally likely to be deflected in any direction.

Atomic Mass and Mass Number

Pages 26–27

1. For an atom's atomic number to be greater than its mass number, the atom would have to contain a negative number of neutrons, which is impossible. Therefore, an atom's atomic number can never be larger than its mass number.   **3.** Yes, the prospector found gold.   **5.** Knowing only the mass number of the atom is not enough to determine which element it is an atom of. You would also have to know the atom's atomic number before you could identify the element. **7.** It is an atom of iron (Fe), with atomic number 26 and mass number 56. **9.** Its atomic number is 53, and its mass number is 126. It has 53 protons and 53 electrons.

Ions

Pages 28–29

1. Sample definition: An ion is a particle that has a positive or negative electric charge. A neutral atom becomes a positively charged ion when it loses electrons. A neutral atom becomes a negatively charged ion when it gains electrons. **3.** 56 protons and 54 electrons **5.** He^{2+} **7.** 10 electrons **9.** +1

Isotopes and Atomic Mass

Pages 30–31

1. ^{38}Ar **3.** ^{63}Cu **5.** ^{85}Rb **7.** about 1:1 **9.** 36.96 amu

The Bohr Atom

Pages 32–33

1. C **3.** three **5.** The Bohr model for an atom of oxygen is shown below:

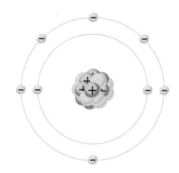

According to this model, oxygen has six valence electrons, so it has six electrons that can participate in chemical reactions.

Electron Orbitals

Pages 34–35

1. s: 2; p: 6; d: 10; f: 14

3.

5. sulfur **7.** $1s^2\ 2s^2\ 2p^6\ 3s^2\ 3p^6$ **9.** A look at some of the configurations will show that all these elements have valence electrons in the d subshell. This is, in fact, the defining characteristic of transition metals—they fall in the area of the periodic table in which d subshells are being filled. The elements span 10 groups because d subshells hold 10 electrons.

The Quantum Atom and Atomic Spectra

Pages 36–37

1. Each element absorbs and emits electromagnetic radiation of specific wavelengths. No two elements absorb or emit exactly the same wavelengths of radiation. The pattern of wavelengths an element gives off is called its emission spectrum. An emission spectrum acts as a "fingerprint" for an element. Therefore, by examining the emission spectra of stars, scientists can determine which elements are present in the stars. **3.** ultraviolet **5.** Hydrogen's single electron normally exists in the 1s subshell. However, it can jump to any of the other subshells that exist in other atoms if it absorbs enough energy. For example, it can jump to a 3d subshell or a 4s subshell. Each of these jumps corresponds to a different absorption line. (The electron can also jump between higher energy levels—for example, from a 3d subshell to a 5s subshell.)

Atomic Number and the Periodic Law

Pages 38–39

1. C **3.** In Mendeleev's time, most elements were identified and characterized based on their reaction with other elements, such as oxygen and hydrogen. The noble gases are very nonreactive. Therefore, it would be a valid assumption that they had not been discovered at the time when Mendeleev developed his periodic table, so he could not include them. **5.** Mendeleev arranged the elements in his periodic table partly according to their properties. In some cases, the element with the next-highest atomic mass did not have the same properties as other elements that would have been in its column if he had arranged the elements strictly by atomic mass. Therefore, he concluded that there must be other elements with the correct properties that had not yet been discovered. He therefore left some spaces in his periodic table blank to represent these as-yet-undiscovered elements.

The Periodic Table

Pages 40–41

1. Sample answer: Carbon has the same number of valence electrons as silicon. Fluorine has the same number of electron shells as oxygen. **3.** tin (Sn) **5.** The marine animals use chemical reactions to form their calcium carbonate shells. Reactivity is a chemical property. If strontium can take the place of some of the calcium in the animals' shells, it must be able to participate in the same reactions as the calcium can. Therefore, strontium must have properties similar to calcium. Look at the periodic table at the back of the book, and note that strontium and calcium are in the same group. Elements in the same group have similar chemical properties, so it makes sense that strontium and calcium would be able to participate in similar chemical reactions.

Electron Arrangement Patterns

Pages 42–43

1. 4; possible answer: germanium   **3.** group 1A, period 7
5. Fe: $1s^2\ 2s^2\ 2p^6\ 3s^2\ 3p^6\ 4s^2\ 3d^6$ Ni: $1s^2\ 2s^2\ 2p^6\ 3s^2\ 3p^6\ 4s^2\ 3d^8$

Trends Within the Periodic Table

Pages 44–47

1. a calcium atom   **3.** barium, tellurium, chlorine
5. N^{3-}, N, N^{3+}, N^{5+}

Metals

Pages 48–49

1. D   **3.** Most metals are solid at room temperature and can easily be pounded into sheets, stretched into wires, or bent into other shapes. These properties make them ideal for use in jewelry.   **5.** potassium

Nonmetals

Pages 50–51

1. A   **3.** Only nonmetals are gases at room temperature, and most nonmetals form negatively charged ions when they react with other elements. Therefore, fluorine and chlorine are nonmetals.   **5.** 4A, 5A, 6A, or 7A

Metalloids

Pages 52–53

1. D   **3.** silicon   **5.** Si or Ge

Inner Transition Metals

Pages 54–55

1. C   **3.** Unlike most elements on the periodic table, the transuranium elements do not exist in nature. They are formed only in laboratories.   **5.** Sm-Nd

Monatomic Ions

Pages 56–57

1. The noble gases all have full valence electron shells. Therefore, they are very stable and tend not to lose, gain, or share electrons.   **3.** To attain a full octet in its valence electron shell, a carbon atom would have to gain four electrons or lose four electrons. Atoms tend not to gain or lose more than three electrons, so carbon atoms tend not to form ions.   **5.** Nitrogen's $2p$ subshell is half full, but oxygen's $2p$ subshell is not. A neutral nitrogen atom is therefore more stable than a neutral oxygen atom.

Polyatomic Ions

Pages 58–59

1. The polyatomic ion is phosphate (PO_4^{3-}) in Na_3PO_4, ammonium (NH_4^+) in NH_4Cl, and hydroxide (OH^-) in KOH.
3. S and O   **5.** LiO^- is not a common polyatomic ion because Li and O have very different electronegativities.

The Ionic Bond and Salts

Pages 60–61

1. B   **3.** Possible answer: A crystal is a solid that is made up of cations and anions that are arranged in a specific pattern in space.   **5.** Fe_2O_3

Properties of Ionic Compounds

Pages 62–63

1. Most ionic compounds are solid at room temperature, have high melting points, and dissolve easily in water to produce solutions that conduct electricity well.   **3.** calcium chloride
5. When a salt melts, its ions dissociate. The dissociated ions can move from place to place and carry electric current.

Naming Ionic Compounds

Pages 64–65

1. lithium chloride   **3.** $CuBr_2$ **5.** iron(II) sulfide

Bonding in Metals

Pages 66–67

1. C   **3.** The delocalized electrons are attracted to all the positively charged atoms. This attraction holds the metal lattice tightly together, giving it strength and resisting the freedom of movement necessary for it to melt.
5. In solid sodium, as in all metals, the valence electrons of the Na atoms are delocalized. This allows them to move past one another easily and allows the Na to conduct electricity well. In solid NaCl, the electrons are not delocalized. All the electrons are strongly associated with either the Na^+ ions or the Cl^- ions. The ions themselves are unable to move easily, because the oppositely charged ions are strongly attracted to one another, and the similarly charged ions strongly repel one another. Therefore, there is no way for charged particles to flow from one place to another in solid NaCl, and it does not conduct electricity well.

The Covalent Bond and Molecules

Pages 68–71

1. sulfur dioxide   **3.** C   **5.** The C–O bonds are double bonds.   **7.** N_2O_4 **9.** carbon tetrabromide

Lewis Dot Structures

Pages 72–73

1. H–S–H   **3.** H–O–H   **5.** O=C=O

7. $[O–H]^-$ **9.** F–S–F structure with F above and below

Molecular Shapes

Pages 74–77

1. Covalent bonds consist of shared electrons. Electrons are all negatively charged. Like charges repel, so the electrons in a bond repel the electrons in another bond or in a lone pair.   **3.** The H–N bonds in ammonia are polar, because they are bonds between two different atoms. The bonds are not evenly arranged around the central nitrogen atom. Therefore, the partial charges on the bonds will not cancel each other out. Ammonia is therefore a polar molecule.
5. A molecule of N_2 is linear.   **7.** nonpolar   **9.** Chloramine will have a similar molecular shape to ammonia.

Van der Waals Forces

Pages 78–79

1. C   **3.** hydrogen bonds   **5.** Fluorine, chlorine, bromine, iodine, and astatine are all in the same group on the periodic table. Of the elements in the group, fluorine and chlorine have the fewest electrons, and iodine and astatine have the most. The more electrons the atoms in a substance have, the stronger the dispersion forces in the substance are. Therefore, iodine and astatine have the strongest dispersion forces, and fluorine and chlorine have the weakest dispersion forces. The stronger the dispersion forces in a substance are, the higher its melting and boiling points are. Iodine and astatine are solids at room temperature because they have the highest melting points of the elements in the group. Their melting points are above room temperature. (At room temperature and pressure, solid iodine sublimes, or changes directly from a solid to a gas.) Similarly, fluorine and chlorine are gases at room temperature because they have the lowest boiling points of the elements in the group. Their boiling points are below room temperature. Bromine is a liquid at room temperature because its melting point is below room temperature, but its boiling point is above room temperature.

The Conservation of Mass

Pages 80–81

1. The reactants are Mg and O_2, and the product is MgO.
3. $C + O_2 \rightarrow CO_2$ **5.** $4Fe + 3O_2 \rightarrow 2Fe_2O_3$

Balancing Chemical Equations

Pages 82–83

1. $2NaOH + Cl_2 \rightarrow NaOCl + NaCl + H_2O$
3. $CH_4 + 2O_2 \rightarrow CO_2 + 2H_2O$
5. $N_2 + 3H_2 \rightarrow 2NH_3$
7. $2NH_4Cl + Ba(OH)_2 \rightarrow 2NH_3 + BaCl_2 + 2H_2O$
9. $PCl_5 + 4H_2O \rightarrow H_3PO_4 + 5HCl$

Combustion Reactions

Pages 84–85

1. C   **3.** $C_6H_{12}O_6 + 6O_2 \rightarrow 6CO_2 + 6H_2O$
5. $C_2H_5OH + 3O_2 \rightarrow 2CO_2 + 3H_2O$
   $C_4H_9OH + 6O_2 \rightarrow 4CO_2 + 5H_2O$

Synthesis Reactions

Pages 86–87

1. $2H_2 + O_2 \rightarrow 2H_2O$ **3.** It has only one reactant.
5. $P_4 + 6Cl_2 \rightarrow 4PCl_3$

Decomposition Reactions

Pages 88–89

1. $2H_2O \rightarrow 2H_2 + O_2$ **3.** $CaCO_3 \rightarrow CaO + CO_2$ **5.** In a decomposition reaction, one substance breaks down into two or more different substances. However, by definition, an element cannot be broken down into simpler substances by a chemical reaction. Therefore, an element can never be the reactant in a decomposition reaction, because it cannot break down into any simpler substances.

Single-Displacement Reactions

Pages 90–91

1. $Mg + H_2SO_4 \rightarrow MgSO_4 + H_2$
3. $Zn + 2HCl \rightarrow ZnCl_2 + H_2$
5. $3Cu + Al_2(SO_4)_3 \rightarrow 3CuSO_4 + 2Al$

Double-Displacement Reactions

Pages 92–93

1. $NaCl_{(aq)} + AgNO_{3\ (aq)} \rightarrow AgCl_{(s)} + NaNO_{3\ (aq)}$
3. $CaCO_3 + H_2SO_4 \rightarrow H_2CO_3 + CaSO_4$
5. $BaCl_2 + K_2CO_3 \rightarrow BaCO_3 + 2KCl$

Oxidation-Reduction Reactions

Pages 94–97

1. The hydrogen atoms lose electrons, so they are oxidized. The fluorine atoms gain electrons, so they are reduced.
3. The reduction half-reaction is $Cl_2 + 2e^- \rightarrow 2Cl^-$. The oxidation half-reaction is $2Br^- \rightarrow Br_2 + 2e^-$. The balanced chemical equation is $Cl_2 + 2HBr \rightarrow 2HCl + Br_2$.
5. The I atoms lose electrons, so they are oxidized. The N atoms gain electrons, so they are reduced.   **7.** The unbalanced chemical equation is $HI + H_2SO_4 \rightarrow H_2S + I_2$. The oxidation number of the hydrogen atoms in H_2SO_4, HI, and H_2S is +1. The oxidation number of oxygen in sulfuric acid is –2. The oxidation number of I in HI is –1. The iodine atoms in I_2 have oxidation numbers of 0. The oxidation number of sulfur in the sulfate ion is +6. The oxidation number of sulfur in H_2S is –2.   **9.** Chromium is reduced. Sulfur is oxidized. The balanced equation involves 12 electrons.

Stoichiometry and Its Uses

Pages 98–99

1. One atom of nitrogen and three atoms of hydrogen are needed to form each molecule of NH_3.   **3.** Each molecule of ethyl alcohol consists of two atoms of carbon, one atom of oxygen, and six atoms of hydrogen.   **5.** 1.25×10^5 formula units of Fe_2O_3

Mole-Number Relationships

Pages 100–101
1. 2.00 mol   **3.** 9.03×10^{23} atoms   **5.** 1.43×10^{-21} mol   **7.** 3.01×10^{24} molecules   **9.** One mole of O_3 and one mole of O_2 contain the same number of molecules. One mole of O_3 contains more atoms than one mole of O_2 or one mole of O.

Mole-Mass Relationships

Pages 102–103
1. 342.29 g/mol   **3.** 60.8 g of sodium hydroxide   **5.** 3,040 g of acetone   **7.** One mole of ^{14}C-curcumin would have a mass 41.83 g greater than one mole of curcumin.   **9.** 0.0455 g of KI

Mole-Volume Relationships

Pages 104–105
1. 0.157 mol   **3.** 0.500 mol   **5.** 52.6 L   **7.** 23.7 L   **9.** 188 L

Moles and Chemical Equations

Pages 106–107
1. 44.8 L   **3.** According to the chemical equation, 2 mol Na produces 1 mol H_2, so 1 mol Na produces 0.5 mol H_2. Therefore, 6.02×10^{23} atoms of sodium will react to produce $0.5 \times (6.02 \times 10^{23}) = 3.01 \times 10^{23}$ molecules of H_2.   **5.** C

Calculating Yields of Reactions

Pages 108–111
1. 3.25 mol CO_2 **3.** 188 g Fe   **5.** 81.3 g O_2 **7.** 7.0 mol NaCl   **9.** 0.0455 g KI

Percent Yield

Pages 112–113
1. 44.0%   **3.** 60.8%   **5.** 77.6%   **7.** 43.5 g MnO_2 **9.** 39.5 g CO_2, 32.2 g H_2O

The Behavior of Gases

Pages 114–115
1. The gas particles that carry the odor of the marker move constantly and randomly. They collide with the other gas particles in the air. These collisions are random, so they tend to cause the odor-carrying gas particles to move in all directions. Eventually, odor-carrying gas particles will spread to all parts of the room, so everyone in the room can smell the marker.   **3.** The nitrogen and oxygen molecules in air are probably evenly distributed.   **5.** Pumping air into a tire increases the number of gas particles inside the tire. The volume of the tire does not increase very much. Therefore, the larger number of air particles increases the frequency with which the particles collide with the walls of the tire. This increased collision frequency increases the force the particles exert on the walls of the tire. The increased force results in increased pressure.

Boyle's Law

Pages 116–117
1. 0.25 L   **3.** 4.0 atm   **5.** 5.0 atm   **7.** one-half
9. A sample graph is shown below:

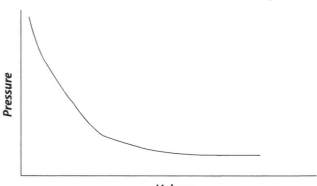

Pressure vs. Volume for a Gas at Constant Temperature

Charles's Law

Pages 118–119
1. According to Charles's law, as temperature decreases at constant pressure, volume decreases. When the balloon is placed in the freezer, the air inside the balloon becomes cooler, but its pressure stays the same. Therefore, according to Charles's law, the air inside the balloon decreases in volume as it decreases in temperature. As the volume of the air inside the balloon decreases, the balloon shrinks.
3. 160 K   **5.** 3.0×10^7 K   **7.** three   **9.** A sample graph is shown below:

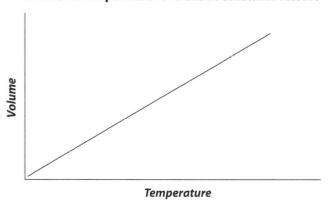

Volume vs. Temperature for a Gas at Constant Pressure

Gay-Lussac's Law

Pages 120–121
1. 2.6 atm   **3.** 1.0 atm   **5.** Air will rush into the jar when it is opened.   **7.** 7.32 atm

9. A sample graph is shown below:

Pressure vs. Temperature for a Gas at Constant Volume

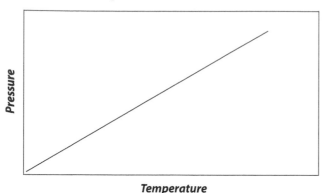

The Ideal Gas Law

Pages 122–125

1. 19 L   **3.** 0.22 mol   **5.** Yes, there is enough SO_2 in the tank to carry out the reaction. The scientist will have 6.9 mol SO_2 left over.   **7.** 17 atm   **9.** The temperature does not change.

Absolute Zero

Pages 126–127

1. –273°C   **3.** 300 K   **5.** substance B

Dalton's Law of Partial Pressures

Pages 128–129

1. The partial pressure of N_2 is 24 atm. The partial pressure of F_2 is 16 atm. The partial pressure of H_2 is 8 atm. The total pressure is 48 atm.   **3.** 3.4 atm   **5.** O_2 **7.** 5.2 atm
9. 7.4 mol

Graham's Law of Effusion

Pages 130–131

1. Diagram A represents effusion. Diagram B represents diffusion.   **3.** CO_2 diffuses 0.85270 times as fast as O_2.
5. 37.9 g/mol

Phase Diagrams

Pages 132–133

1. gas   **3.** at least 15 atm   **5.** It will melt.

Some Properties of Liquids

Pages 134–135

1. The intermolecular forces in a solid hold the particles in the solid in fixed locations. As the solid is heated, the particles in it gain energy. Eventually, the particles have enough energy to overcome the intermolecular forces holding them in place. When this happens, the solid begins to melt. When all of the particles have broken free of their fixed positions, the solid has entirely melted to form a liquid. The intermolecular forces in the liquid are strong enough to hold the liquid particles close together, but not so strong that they prevent the particles from sliding past one another.   **3.** As a liquid absorbs heat, its

particles gain energy. If they absorb enough energy, they are able to overcome the intermolecular forces between them. When this occurs, the liquid begins to vaporize and become a gas.   **5.** At the melting point, all the energy that the solid particles absorb goes toward overcoming the intermolecular forces holding them in place. Their kinetic energy does not increase, so the temperature of the solid does not increase.

Some Properties of Solids

Pages 136–137

1. The particles in a liquid have enough energy to overcome some of the forces between them. As a result, they can move past one another. In contrast, the particles in a solid do not have enough energy to overcome the forces between them. These forces hold the particles in a rigid structure. That structure prevents the solid from changing shape easily, so it cannot take the shape of its container.
3. C   **5.** crystalline solids

Solutions

Pages 138–139

1. B   **3.** To make coffee sweet, the sweetener must be dissolved in the coffee. In other words, sweetened coffee is a solution. The more sweetener that is dissolved in the coffee, the sweeter the coffee is. In general, more solute can dissolve in warm solvents than in cold solvents. Therefore, more sweetener can dissolve in hot coffee than in cold coffee, and hot coffee can be made sweeter than cold coffee can.   **5.** solution B

The Dissolving Process

Pages 140–141

1. Stir or heat the solution.   **3.** The solubility of a substance is the amount of the substance that will dissolve in a given amount of solvent at a given temperature. The dissolving rate of a substance is the speed at which the substance mixes with the solvent to form a solution.   **5.** When a solute dissolves in a solvent, the solute particles become evenly mixed with the solvent particles. This occurs because of random motions of the solute and solvent particles and because of interactions between the particles. The more solute particles that are exposed to solvent particles, the faster the solute will dissolve. Heating increases the motions of the particles, which in turn increases the rate at which they mix. Stirring increases the number of solute particles that are exposed to solvent particles, which also increases the rate at which the solvent and solute particles mix.

Molarity and Mole Fraction

Pages 142–145

1. 0.028 *M*   **3.** The mole fraction of water is 0.720. The mole fraction of methanol is 0.157. The mole fraction of ethanol is 0.123.   **5.** The mole fraction of water is 0.800. The mole fraction of methanol is 0.200.   **7.** The molarity of a solution can change as temperature changes because the volume of the solution changes. The mole fraction of a substance in a mixture does not change with temperature because the number of moles of each substance in the mixture does not change with temperature. **9.** 19.0 L

Molality and Mass Percent

Pages 146–147
1. 0.122 m **3.** 1.67%   **5.** mass percent $C_{27}H_{46}O = 16.23\%$; mass percent $CHCl_3 = 83.77\%$ **7.** 0.05026 m
9. 1.77 L acetone

Colligative Properties

Pages 148–151
1. It would be cheaper to use $CaCl_2$ to keep an aqueous solution from freezing.   **3.** The amount of salt used on sidewalks is relatively small, so it can lower the freezing point of water by only a few degrees at most. This concentration of salt is insufficient to lower the freezing point by 30°C. It would require a very large amount of salt to lower the freezing point by that much.   **5.** −1.8°C   **7.** The freezing point of the ethylene glycol solution is −12.5°C. It would require 2.58 kg methanol to produce the same freezing-point depression as 5.00 kg ethylene glycol.   **9.** 0.33

Separating Solutions

Pages 152–153
1. During distillation, a mixture is heated until the various components of the mixture begin to boil. If all the components of the mixture boil at about the same temperature, the vapor that rises into the apparatus and cools will still be a mixture of the various components. If the components boil at very different temperatures, the vapor rising into the apparatus at any given temperature will be more likely to be made primarily of a single component.   **3.** Salt boils at a much higher temperature than water. To make freshwater from seawater, you could boil the seawater in a distillation apparatus. The water will boil and form water vapor, which will rise into the apparatus. The salt will remain behind in the boiling container. You can then condense the water vapor to form freshwater.   **5.** Diesel fuel has the highest boiling point, and gasoline has the lowest.

Properties of Acids and Bases

Pages 154–155
1. Ammonia should feel slippery and turn red litmus paper blue.   **3.** A solution of aspirin in water would probably turn blue litmus paper red. It would not affect red litmus paper.
5. If NaOH is neutralized by HNO_3, the resulting salt would be $NaNO_3$. The cation, Na^+, would come from the parent base, and the anion, NO_3^- would come from the parent acid.

Arrhenius Acids and Bases

Pages 156–157
1. $HClO_4$ and HF are Arrhenius acids. $Ca(OH)_2$ and $Mg(OH)_2$

are Arrhenius bases.   **3.** $2HBr + Cu(OH)_2 \rightarrow CuBr_2 + 2H_2O$ The salt formed is copper(II) bromide, $CuBr_2$.   **5.** H_3PO_4, $HClO_4$, $H_2C_2O_4$

Brønsted-Lowry and Lewis Acids and Bases

Pages 158–159
1.

Acid	Conjugate Base
$H_2PO_4^-$	HPO_4^{2-}
H_2Se	HSe^-
HNO_2	NO_2^-
$HAsO_4^{2-}$	AsO_4^{3-}

3. HClO is a Brønsted-Lowry acid; its conjugate base is ClO^-. TeO_3^- is a Brønsted-Lowry base; its conjugate acid is $HTeO_3$. AsH_3, $H_2PO_4^-$, and H_2O can all act as both acids and bases. The conjugate base of AsH_3 is AsH_2^-; the conjugate acid of AsH_3 is AsH_4^+. The conjugate base of $H_2PO_4^-$ is HPO_4^{2-}; the conjugate acid of $H_2PO_4^-$ is H_3PO_4. The conjugate base of H_2O is OH^-; the conjugate acid of H_2O is H_3O^+.   **5.** BF_3 is the acid, and F^- is the base. The fluoride ion donates an electron pair to the boron trifluoride, completing boron's octet, as shown below:

Measuring Acids and Bases

Pages 160–163
1. 5.4   **3.** 4.0×10^{-4} M to 1.6×10^{-3} M   **5.** 3.16×10^{-4} M
7. 3.2×10^{-4} M   **9.** The greater the hydroxide ion concentration is, the lower the hydronium ion concentration is, the higher the pH is, and the more basic the solution is. Therefore, the solution with the lower concentration of hydroxide ions, 5.6×10^{-8} M, will be the more acidic solution.

Titration

Pages 164–165
1. A sample graph is shown below:
3. $1.49 \times 10^{-2}\,M$ NaOH   **5.** If the initial volume of the

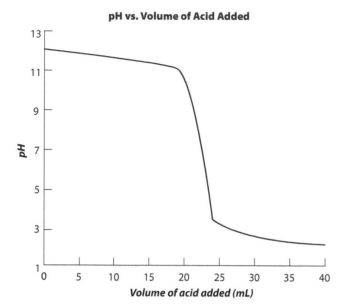

pH vs. Volume of Acid Added

unknown solution isn't known, the student will not be able to calculate the concentration of the unknown solution. However, the student could still calculate the number of moles (or the mass) of the acid or base in the unknown solution, provided she accurately records the volume of titrant added.   **7.** If the student records too small a volume of added base, he will calculate that fewer moles of base were added than were actually added. Therefore, he will calculate that the unknown acid solution contained fewer moles of acid than it actually did, and his calculated concentration of the unknown solution will also be too low.
9. 58.4 mL HNO_3

Strengths of Acids and Bases

Pages 166–167
1. methanoic acid, benzoic acid, hypochlorous acid
3. The HNO_3 solution will have the lower pH.
5. $pK_a = 4.7$, $pK_b = 3.4$ **7.** The generic chemical equation for the dissociation of a strong acid (HA) in water is shown below:
$$HA + H_2O \rightarrow H_3O^+ + A^-$$
The equation for K_a for this reaction is shown below:
$$K_a = \frac{[H_3O^+][A^-]}{[HA]}$$
A strong acid dissociates completely in water, so the concentration of HA in solution will be zero. Substituting 0 for [HA] in the K_a equation produces an expression that involves dividing by zero. A number divided by zero is equal to infinity.   **9.** $6 \times 10^{-6}\,M$

The Conservation of Energy

Pages 168–169
1. endothermic   **3.** The law of conservation of energy states that energy cannot be created or destroyed. Therefore, the total amount of energy in the universe must be constant, because the universe is an isolated system (no matter or energy can enter or leave).   **5.** endothermic

Measuring the Flow of Heat

Pages 170–171
1. The oil is warmer than the plastic, so heat will flow from the oil into the plastic. As the plastic absorbs the heat, its molecules will begin to move more quickly. As the oil loses heat, its molecules will begin to move more slowly.   **3.** C
5. Evaporation is an endothermic process, which means that it absorbs heat. The alcohol absorbs heat from the student's skin as it evaporates. As the student's skin loses heat, it feels cooler.

Specific Heat

Pages 172–173
1. 3.76×10^2 J   **3.** 68 J   **5.** the silver   **7.** 17°C   **9.** The amount of heat lost by the warmer substance in a specific heat calculation will equal the amount of heat gained by the other substance only if heat can move only between the two substances. If the system were not perfectly insulated, some of the heat from the warmer substance could escape into the surroundings. This would result in inaccurate calculations.

Changes in Enthalpy

Pages 174–175
1. A   **3.** negative   **5.** $\Delta H = 285.8$ kJ

Writing Thermochemical Equations

Pages 176–177
1. $Fe_{(s)} + 3HCl_{(aq)} \rightarrow \frac{3}{2} H_{2\,(g)} + FeCl_{3\,(aq)}$ $\Delta H = -87.9$ kJ
3. 117.4 kJ   **5.** 34.5 kJ   **7.** 12.0 kJ   **9.** The ΔH for the reaction is positive, so the reaction is endothermic. Therefore, it must absorb energy from its surroundings to proceed. A warm room contains much more energy than a supercooled freezer. In the freezer, there would be little energy for the reactants to absorb, so the reaction would be much less spontaneous.

Heat During Changes in State

Pages 178–179
1. −8.5 kJ   **3.** It takes much more heat to boil a given number of moles of methanol than to melt it.   **5.** It takes much more energy to boil 2 mol of methanol than to melt 2 mol of solid oxygen.   **7.** 37.2 kJ   **9.** 19.4 mol

Hess's Law

Pages 180–183

1. -792 kJ   **3.** -383 kJ   **5.** $-1,180$ kJ   **7.** 39.7 kJ
9. -195.4 kJ

Reaction Rates and Energy of Activation

Pages 184–185

1. endothermic   **3.** When a system absorbs heat, the particles in the system move more quickly. This increases the frequency and velocity of collisions between particles. According to collision theory, increasing the frequency and velocity of collisions between particles increases the rate of a chemical reaction.   **5.** The rate of reaction depends on how often the reactant particles collide with enough energy to react. If the concentrations of the solutions are lower, there are fewer particles in solution. As a result, they are less likely to collide. When concentration increases, there are more particles in solution, and they are more likely to collide and react.

Factors Affecting Reaction Rates

Pages 186–187

1. The cookies in the 305°F oven will probably bake more slowly than they would in a 350°F oven. If the student did not bake the cookies for a longer time than recommended in the recipe, they would probably be underdone.   **3.** Decreasing the surface area of the solid reactant would probably reduce the rate of the reaction. Decreasing the pressure would probably also decrease the rate of reaction.   **5.** In a pile of flour, only the particles at the outside of the pile can collide with oxygen molecules in the air. In other words, a pile of flour essentially has a fairly low surface area. When the flour particles are suspended in the air, more of the particles can collide with oxygen molecules, so the reaction proceeds much more rapidly. In effect, suspending the flour in the air increases the surface area of the flour.

Collision Theory

Pages 188–189

1. Both reactants are gases. Therefore, as the pressure increases, the volume of the gases will decrease, and the gas molecules will get closer together. The closer together they are, the more likely they are to collide with sufficient energy and in the correct orientation to react and form HF. Therefore, increasing the pressure increases the reaction rate.   **3.** The rate at which the magnesium and the acid react depends on how often the acid ions collide with the magnesium atoms. If the acid solution is hot, the particles in it (including the ions) are moving quickly. This increases the number of collisions that occur. As a result, the reaction rate is higher when hot acid is used than when cold acid is used.   **5.** The glow stick will glow until all of the hydrogen peroxide and organic compound have reacted with each other. For the hydrogen peroxide and the organic

compound to react, their molecules must collide with sufficient energy and in the right orientation for the reaction to occur. Putting the glow stick in the freezer will lower the temperature of the reactants, causing their molecules to move more slowly. As a result, they will collide less often, and fewer of the collisions will have enough energy to react. The lower collision rate causes the chemical reaction to proceed more slowly and makes the glow stick last longer.

Equilibrium

Pages 190–193

1. reactants   **3.** 53; Because K is greater than 1, the products are favored at equilibrium.   **5.** 34.1
7. $[Cl^-] = [Ag^+] = 1.3 \times 10^{-5}$ mol/L   **9.** 0.021 mol/L

Le Chatelier's Principle

Pages 194–197

1. The concentrations of SO_2 and O_2 in the system will increase, and the concentration of SO_3 will decrease.   **3.** The concentration of N_2O_4 in the system will increase, and the concentration of NO_2 will decrease.   **5.** remove heat, remove CO_2 or H_2, or add CO or H_2O **7.** There are equal numbers of moles of gas on each side of the equation. Therefore, increasing pressure on the system will not affect the equilibrium.   **9.** The concentrations of NaOH and HCl in the system will decrease, and the concentrations of NaCl and H_2O will increase.

Spontaneous Reactions

Pages 198–199

1. spontaneous   **3.** positive   **5.** Reaction 1 has a highly negative ΔG value, so it is spontaneous. Reaction 2 has a slightly positive ΔG value, so it is nonspontaneous.

Entropy and Free Energy

Pages 200–201

1. Entropy is a measure of the amount of randomness or disorder in a system. Enthalpy is a measure of the amount of internal energy or heat in a system. Free energy is a measure of the amount of usable energy released or absorbed by a chemical reaction.   **3.** The first reaction is nonspontaneous, and the second reaction is spontaneous.
5. spontaneous   **7.** The ΔS value for the equation is probably negative.   **9.** The ΔG value for this situation is equal to a positive number minus another positive number. Therefore, ΔG will be positive at low temperatures, when T is small and the $T\Delta S$ term is also small. Under these conditions, ΔH is larger than $T\Delta S$, so their difference is a positive number. In contrast, ΔG will be negative at high temperatures, when T is large and the $T\Delta S$ term is also large. Under these conditions, ΔH is smaller than $T\Delta S$, so their difference is a negative number.

Electrochemical Processes

Pages 202–203

1. In a voltaic cell, chemical energy is converted into electrical energy. The reactions that occur in a voltaic cell are spontaneous. In an electrolytic cell, electrical energy is converted into chemical energy. The reactions that occur in an electrolytic cell are nonspontaneous. In other words, energy must be added to an electrolytic cell to cause the reactions to proceed. **3.** When the battery is used to start the car, chemical reactions produce electricity. At that time, the battery is acting as a voltaic cell because it is changing chemical energy into electricity. When electricity generated by the engine is used to regenerate the chemicals in the battery, the battery is acting as an electrolytic cell because it is transforming electrical energy into chemical energy. **5.** The oxidation half-reaction is $Cd \rightarrow Cd^{2+} + 2e^-$. The reduction half-reaction is $Fe^{3+} + e^- \rightarrow Fe^{2+}$.

Voltaic Cells

Pages 204–205

1. C **3.** Cd^{2+} **5.** $Ag^+ + e^- \rightarrow Ag$

Dry Cells

Pages 206–207

1. A **3.** cathode
5. cathode: $2NiO(OH) + 2H_2O + 2e^- \rightarrow 2Ni(OH)_2 + 2OH^-$
anode: $Cd + 2OH^- \rightarrow Cd(OH)_2 + 2e^-$

Electrolytic Cells

Pages 208–209

1. When a cellular phone battery is providing power (electricity) to the phone, it is acting as a voltaic cell because it is converting chemical energy into electrical energy. When the cellular phone is plugged into a wall outlet and the battery is being recharged, the battery is acting as an electrolytic cell because it is converting electrical energy into chemical energy. **3.** When a voltage is applied, electrons flow from the anode to the cathode. The solid gold in the anode is oxidized. It loses electrons and forms Au^{3+} ions. At the cathode, Au^{3+} ions gain electrons and are reduced to form gold metal. The gold then plates out of solution onto the aluminum glasses frame. **5.** The oxidation state of Al in Al_2O_3 is +3. The oxidation state of C in CO_2 is +4. The oxidation states of elemental Al and C are 0. Therefore, Al gains electrons and is reduced, and C loses electrons and is oxidized. If electrons were allowed to flow spontaneously, the reaction would proceed in the opposite direction. Al would lose electrons and become oxidized, and C would gain electrons and become reduced.

Hydrocarbons and Other Organic Chemicals

Pages 210–215

1.

$$H-\overset{\overset{\displaystyle H}{|}}{\underset{\underset{\displaystyle H}{|}}{C}}-\overset{\overset{\displaystyle H}{|}}{\underset{\underset{\displaystyle H}{|}}{C}}-\overset{\overset{\displaystyle H}{|}}{C}=\overset{\overset{\displaystyle H}{|}}{C}-\overset{\overset{\displaystyle H}{|}}{\underset{\underset{\displaystyle H}{|}}{C}}-\overset{\overset{\displaystyle H}{|}}{\underset{\underset{\displaystyle H}{|}}{C}}-\overset{\overset{\displaystyle H}{|}}{\underset{\underset{\displaystyle H}{|}}{C}}-H$$

3. Chemists classify organic compounds on the basis of the arrangements of the atoms in them. **5.** The two-carbon carboxylic acid has the structure shown below:

$$H-\overset{\overset{\displaystyle H}{|}}{\underset{\underset{\displaystyle H}{|}}{C}}-\overset{\overset{\displaystyle O}{\|}}{C}-OH$$

The two-carbon alcohol has the structure shown below:

$$H-\overset{\overset{\displaystyle H}{|}}{\underset{\underset{\displaystyle H}{|}}{C}}-\overset{\overset{\displaystyle H}{|}}{\underset{\underset{\displaystyle H}{|}}{C}}-OH$$

The two-carbon amine has the structure shown below:

$$H-\overset{\overset{\displaystyle H}{|}}{\underset{\underset{\displaystyle H}{|}}{C}}-\overset{\overset{\displaystyle H}{|}}{\underset{\underset{\displaystyle H}{|}}{C}}-NH_2$$

7.

$$H-\overset{\overset{\displaystyle H}{|}}{\underset{\underset{\displaystyle H}{|}}{C}}-\overset{\overset{\displaystyle H}{|}}{C}=\overset{\overset{\displaystyle H}{|}}{C}-\overset{\overset{\displaystyle H}{|}}{\underset{\underset{\displaystyle H}{|}}{C}}-H \qquad H-\overset{\overset{\displaystyle H}{|}}{C}=\overset{\overset{\displaystyle H}{|}}{C}-\overset{\overset{\displaystyle H}{|}}{\underset{\underset{\displaystyle H}{|}}{C}}-\overset{\overset{\displaystyle H}{|}}{\underset{\underset{\displaystyle H}{|}}{C}}-H$$

9.

$$H-C\equiv C-\overset{\overset{\displaystyle H}{|}}{C}=\overset{\overset{\displaystyle H}{|}}{C}-\overset{\overset{\displaystyle H}{|}}{\underset{\underset{\displaystyle H}{|}}{C}}-H$$

Polymers

Pages 216–217

1. A monomer is a relatively small molecule that can join together with other monomers to form a polymer. A polymer forms when many monomers bond together in a chain or network. **3.** A polymer forms when many monomers bond together to form a chain.

5.

$$-\overset{\overset{\displaystyle H}{|}}{\underset{\underset{\displaystyle H}{|}}{C}}-\overset{\overset{\displaystyle Cl}{|}}{\underset{\underset{\displaystyle Cl}{|}}{C}}-\overset{\overset{\displaystyle H}{|}}{\underset{\underset{\displaystyle H}{|}}{C}}-\overset{\overset{\displaystyle Cl}{|}}{\underset{\underset{\displaystyle Cl}{|}}{C}}-\overset{\overset{\displaystyle H}{|}}{\underset{\underset{\displaystyle H}{|}}{C}}-\overset{\overset{\displaystyle Cl}{|}}{\underset{\underset{\displaystyle Cl}{|}}{C}}-\overset{\overset{\displaystyle H}{|}}{\underset{\underset{\displaystyle H}{|}}{C}}-$$

Carbohydrates and Fats

Pages 218–221

1. Cellulose is a polysaccharide.   **3.** $C_{12}H_{22}O_{11}$

5.

$$R-O-\overset{\displaystyle O}{\overset{\|}{C}}-R$$

Proteins and Nucleic Acids

Pages 222–225

1. A   **3.** Proteins are long chains of amino acids bonded together by peptide bonds.   **5.** Possible answer: Both proteins and nucleic acids are polymers, so they are both made up of many similar subunits joined together. One difference between them is that the subunits in nucleic acids are larger than those in proteins. Another difference is that proteins are made up of amino acids, whereas nucleic acids are made up of nucleotides.

Forces Within the Nucleus

Pages 226–227

1. B   **3.** quark, neutron, nucleus, atom   **5.** The strong nuclear force is very strong, but it acts only over very short distances. The electrostatic force is much weaker, but it has an unlimited range. When the protons move outside the range of the strong nuclear force, electrostatic repulsion immediately takes effect and the two parts of the split nucleus quickly accelerate in opposite directions to very high speeds.

Radioactivity and Half-Life

Pages 228–231

1. gamma radiation, beta radiation, alpha radiation
3. one-sixteenth

5. Alpha radiation is made up of alpha particles, or helium nuclei. Alpha particles are positively charged. Therefore, they are attracted to negatively charged objects, such as the negatively charged plate in the experiment. Similarly, beta radiation is made up of negatively charged beta particles (electrons), which are attracted to the positively charged plate. Gamma radiation is made up of gamma rays. Gamma rays have no charge, so they are not affected by an electric field.   **7.** 90.6 years   **9.** Alpha radiation has very low penetrating ability. Therefore, handling an alpha emitter will generally not cause cell damage, because the alpha particles cannot penetrate far enough into the skin to damage the skin cells. However, if an alpha emitter is ingested or inhaled, it can come into very close contact with body cells. The alpha particles can penetrate far enough into these cells to damage them. Gamma rays have high penetrating ability. They can easily penetrate skin and cause cellular damage, even if they are not ingested or inhaled.

Transmutation of Elements

Pages 232–233

1. $^{235}_{92}U \rightarrow \, ^{4}_{2}He + \, ^{231}_{90}Th$ **3.** $^{239}_{93}Np \rightarrow \, ^{239}_{94}Pu + \, ^{0}_{-1}e$

5. $^{14}_{7}N + \, ^{4}_{2}He \rightarrow \, ^{18}_{9}F$

Nuclear Fission and Fusion

Pages 234–235

1. fusion   **3.** 3.8000×10^{-3} g   **5.** The law of conservation of mass does not apply to nuclear reactions.

Periodic Table

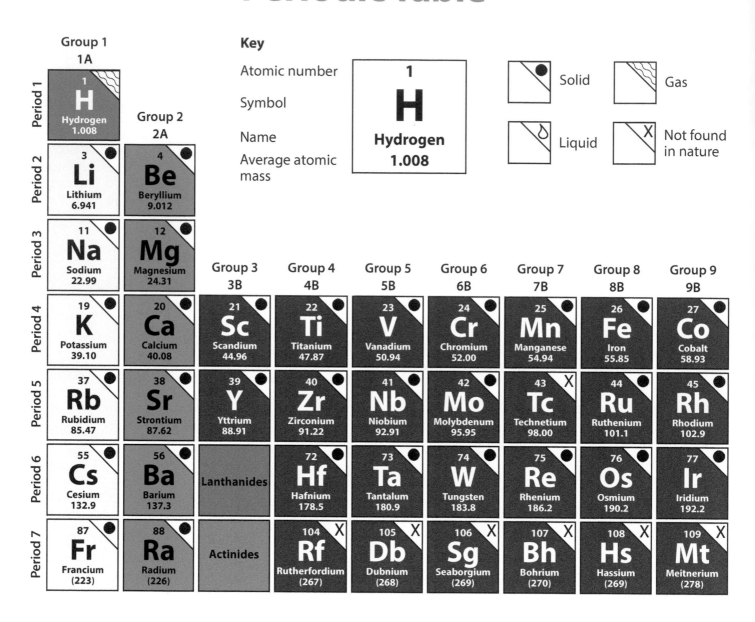

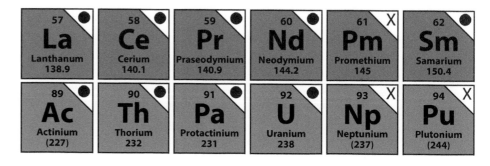

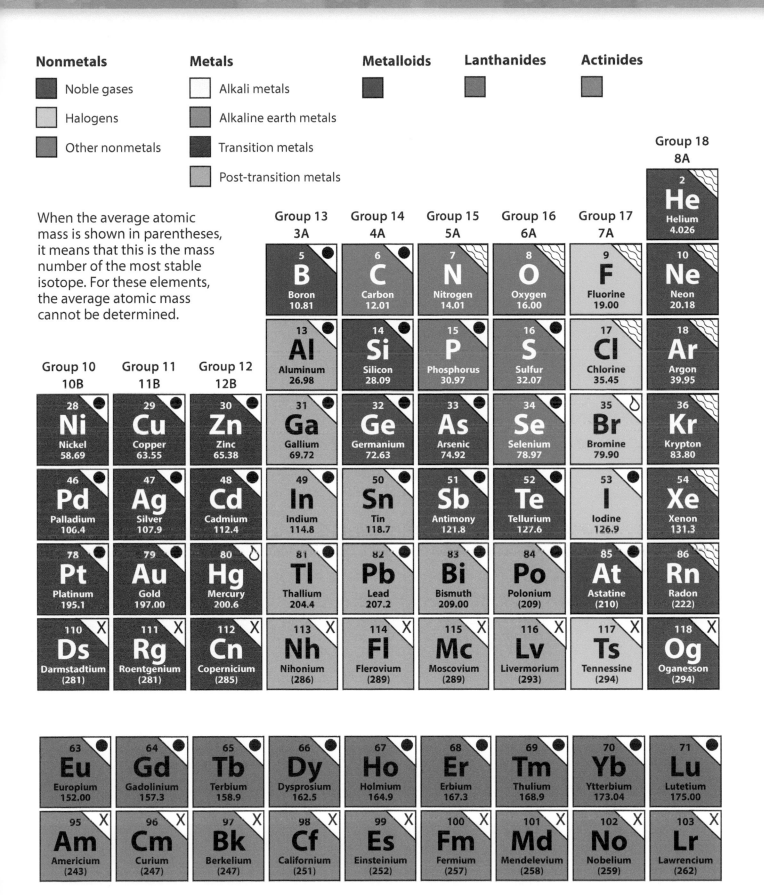

Nonmetals
- Noble gases
- Halogens
- Other nonmetals

Metals
- Alkali metals
- Alkaline earth metals
- Transition metals
- Post-transition metals

Metalloids

Lanthanides

Actinides

When the average atomic mass is shown in parentheses, it means that this is the mass number of the most stable isotope. For these elements, the average atomic mass cannot be determined.

Group 18
8A

2
He
Helium
4.026

Group 13
3A

Group 14
4A

Group 15
5A

Group 16
6A

Group 17
7A

5
B
Boron
10.81

6
C
Carbon
12.01

7
N
Nitrogen
14.01

8
O
Oxygen
16.00

9
F
Fluorine
19.00

10
Ne
Neon
20.18

13
Al
Aluminum
26.98

14
Si
Silicon
28.09

15
P
Phosphorus
30.97

16
S
Sulfur
32.07

17
Cl
Chlorine
35.45

18
Ar
Argon
39.95

Group 10
10B

Group 11
11B

Group 12
12B

28
Ni
Nickel
58.69

29
Cu
Copper
63.55

30
Zn
Zinc
65.38

31
Ga
Gallium
69.72

32
Ge
Germanium
72.63

33
As
Arsenic
74.92

34
Se
Selenium
78.97

35
Br
Bromine
79.90

36
Kr
Krypton
83.80

46
Pd
Palladium
106.4

47
Ag
Silver
107.9

48
Cd
Cadmium
112.4

49
In
Indium
114.8

50
Sn
Tin
118.7

51
Sb
Antimony
121.8

52
Te
Tellurium
127.6

53
I
Iodine
126.9

54
Xe
Xenon
131.3

78
Pt
Platinum
195.1

79
Au
Gold
197.00

80
Hg
Mercury
200.6

81
Tl
Thallium
204.4

82
Pb
Lead
207.2

83
Bi
Bismuth
209.00

84
Po
Polonium
(209)

85
At
Astatine
(210)

86
Rn
Radon
(222)

110 X
Ds
Darmstadtium
(281)

111 X
Rg
Roentgenium
(281)

112 X
Cn
Copernicium
(285)

113 X
Nh
Nihonium
(286)

114 X
Fl
Flerovium
(289)

115 X
Mc
Moscovium
(289)

116 X
Lv
Livermorium
(293)

117 X
Ts
Tennessine
(294)

118 X
Og
Oganesson
(294)

63
Eu
Europium
152.00

64
Gd
Gadolinium
157.3

65
Tb
Terbium
158.9

66
Dy
Dysprosium
162.5

67
Ho
Holmium
164.9

68
Er
Erbium
167.3

69
Tm
Thulium
168.9

70
Yb
Ytterbium
173.04

71
Lu
Lutetium
175.00

95 X
Am
Americium
(243)

96 X
Cm
Curium
(247)

97 X
Bk
Berkelium
(247)

98 X
Cf
Californium
(251)

99 X
Es
Einsteinium
(252)

100 X
Fm
Fermium
(257)

101 X
Md
Mendelevium
(258)

102 X
No
Nobelium
(259)

103 X
Lr
Lawrencium
(262)